Other Simple Annuities

16. $S = R\, s_{\overline{n}|i}\,(1+i)$

Accumulated value of an annuity due

17. $A = R\, a_{\overline{n}|i}\,(1+i)$

Discounted value of an annuity due

18. $A = R\, a_{\overline{n}|i}\,(1+i)^{-k}$

Discounted value of a deferred annuity

19. $A = \dfrac{R}{i}$

Discounted value of an ordinary perpetuity

General Annuities

20. $R = \dfrac{W}{s_{\overline{m/p}|i}}$

Replacement formula for converting an ordinary general annuity to an equivalent ordinary simple annuity

21. $W = R\, s_{\overline{m/p}|i}$

Replacement formula for the replacement of a simple payment R by a general payment W

Amortization and Sinking Funds

22. $P = A(1+i)^k - Rs_{\overline{k}|i}$

Outstanding principal by the retrospective method

23. $P = R\, a_{\overline{n-k}|i}$

Outstanding principal by the prospective method

Bonds

24. $P = Fr\, a_{\overline{n}|i} + C(1+i)^{-n}$

Purchase price of a bond

25. $P = C + (Fr-Ci)a_{\overline{n}|i}$

Alternate purchase-price formula

26. $P-C = (Fr-Ci)a_{\overline{n}|i}$

Bond premium

27. $C-P = (Ci-Fr)a_{\overline{n}|i}$

Bond discount

28. $Q = P_0 + f(P_1-P_0)$

Market price of a bond between bond interest dates

29. $I = f \times Fr$

Accrued bond interest

MATHEMATICS OF FINANCE
SECOND EDITION

MATHEMATICS OF FINANCE

SECOND EDITION

Petr Zima
Conestoga College

Robert L. Brown
University of Waterloo

McGraw-Hill Ryerson Limited
Toronto Montreal New York St. Louis San Francisco Auckland Bogotá
Guatemala Hamburg Johannesburg Lisbon London Madrid Mexico
New Delhi Panama Paris San Juan São Paulo Singapore Sydney Tokyo

MATHEMATICS OF FINANCE,
Second Edition

ISBN: 0-07-548490-0

3 4 5 6 7 8 9 0 D 9 8 7 6 5 4

Printed and bound in Canada by John Deyell Company

Care has been taken to trace ownership of copyright material contained in this text. The publishers will gladly take any information that will enable them to rectify any reference or credit in subsequent editions.

Canadian Cataloguing in Publication Data

Zima, Petr, date
   Mathematics of finance

Includes index.
ISBN 0-07-548490-0

I. Business mathematics.   I. Brown, Robert L., date
II. Title.

HF5691.Z55 1982   513'.93   C82-094993-0

PREFACE

Knowledge in the field of the mathematics of finance continues to be of utmost importance to the well qualified high school, community college, or university student. Recent high and rapidly changing rates of interest have only reinforced that fact.

In the world of finance, it is extremely important that one has an up-to-date text written in a manner that will be easily understood by both instructor and student.

Our new text has been written with these needs in mind. In particular, it has been written assuming that the student will be using a pocket calculator with a full range of functions including a logarithmic function and a power function. With this in mind, and because interest rates can change so rapidly and so significantly, we have excluded the interest rate tables included in more traditional texts. Through experience in our own classrooms, we have found that this deletion is advantageous to the student who must solve complex problems.

This book is designed to be used by students in the last year of high school, by business and business administration students at the community college level, and by business administration and economics students taking introductory courses at the university level. We have assumed some mathematical background in the students using this text. A wide mathematical background, however, is not a prerequisite. In particular, we have not included introductory chapters on basic algebraic techniques. But we have included four appendices with exercises that deal in detail with the topics of exponents and logarithms, progressions, linear interpolation and continuous compounding. We have tried to use as many examples as possible and have included both basic problems in PART A of the Exercises which will help students with the learning of basic concepts, together with advanced problems in PART B of the Exercises which will sharpen high-level skills. At the end of each chapter we included Review Exercises.

The numeric examples in the text have been SI metricated. That is, numbers are in their standard international form as now required by the Ministry of Education in several provinces.

We are indebted to the many people whose constructive criticism resulted in improvements in the original text. Despite a careful scrutiny, it is inevitable that flaws will remain. For these, the authors accept full responsibility and welcome any suggestions. We would like to thank Lynda Hohner for the fine work she performed in typing this manuscript.

We feel that this textbook will answer a growing need for an authentic and up-to-date Canadian text on the applications of the Mathematics of Finance.

PETR ZIMA
ROBERT L. BROWN

Contents:

Appendix 3 Linear Interpolation

Appendix 4 Continuous Compounding
Compound Interest at Nominal Rate j Compounded Continuously. Ordinary Annuity of p Payments per Year at j_∞. Exercises.

TABLES

Answers to Even-Numbered Problems.

INDEX

Simple Interest and Simple Discount

1.1 Simple Interest

Suppose that an investor lends money to a debtor. The debtor must pay back the money originally borrowed, and also the fee charged for the use of the money, called **interest**. From the investor's point of view, interest is income from invested capital. The capital originally invested in an interest transaction is called **the principal**. The sum of the principal and the interest due is called the **amount** or **accumulated value**. Any interest transaction can be described by the **rate of interest**, which is the ratio of the interest earned in one time unit to the principal.

In early times, the principal lent and the interest paid might be tangible goods (e.g. grain). Now, they are most commonly in the form of money. The practice of charging interest is as old as the earliest written records of mankind. Four thousand years ago, the laws of Babylon referred to interest payments on debts.

At **simple interest**, the interest is computed on the original principal during the whole time, or term of the loan, at the stated annual rate of interest.

We shall use the following notation:

P = the principal, or the present value of S, or the discounted value of S, or the proceeds.

I = simple interest.

S = the amount, or the accumulated value of P, or the maturity value of P.

r = rate of interest per year.

t = time in years.

Simple interest is calculated by means of the formula

$$I = Prt \qquad (1)$$

From the definition of the amount S we have

$$S = P + I$$

By substituting for $I = Prt$ we obtain S in terms of P, r, and t

$$S = P + Prt$$

$$S = P(1 + rt) \qquad (2)$$

The factor $(1 + rt)$ in formula (2) is called an **accumulation factor at simple interest** and the process of calculating S from P by formula (2) is called **accumulation at simple interest**. From formula (2) we can express P in terms of S, r, and t and obtain

$$P = \frac{S}{1 + rt} = S(1 + rt)^{-1} \qquad (3)$$

When we calculate P from S, we call P the present value of S or the discounted value of S. The factor $(1 + rt)^{-1}$ in formula (3) is called a **discount factor at simple interest** and the process of calculating P from S is called **discounting at simple interest**, or simple discount at an interest rate.

The time t must be in years. When the time is given in months, then

$$t = \frac{\text{number of months}}{12}$$

When the time is given in days, there are two different varieties of simple interest in use:

1. Exact interest, where $t = \dfrac{\text{number of days}}{365}$

i.e., the year is taken as 365 days (leap year or not).

2. Ordinary interest, where $t = \dfrac{\text{number of days}}{360}$

i.e., the year is taken as 360 days.

The general practice in Canada is to use exact interest, whereas the general practice in the United States and in international business transactions is to use ordinary interest. In this textbook exact interest is used all the time unless specified otherwise.

Example 1   Find the exact and ordinary simple interest on a 90-day loan of $500 at $8\frac{1}{2}\%$.

Solution   We have $P = 500$, $r = 0.085$, time = 90 days

$$\text{Exact interest} = 500 \times 0.085 \times \frac{90}{365} = \$10.48$$

$$\text{Ordinary interest} = 500 \times 0.085 \times \frac{90}{360} = \$10.63$$

Notice that ordinary interest is always greater than the exact interest and thus it brings increased revenue to the lender.

Example 2   A couple borrows $10 000. The annual interest rate is $10\frac{1}{2}$%, payable monthly, and the monthly payment is $200. How much of the first payment goes to interest and how much to principal?

Solution   We have $P = 10\ 000$, $r = 0.105$, $t = \frac{1}{12}$, and

$$I = 10\ 000 \times 0.105 \times \tfrac{1}{12} = \$87.50$$

The interest for the first month is $87.50 and $112.50 is applied to principal reduction.

Example 3   A loan shark made a loan of $100 to be repaid with $120 at the end of one month. What was the annual interest rate?

Solution   We have $P = 100$, $I = 20$, $t = \frac{1}{12}$, and

$$r = \frac{I}{Pt} = \frac{20}{100 \times \frac{1}{12}} = 240\%$$

Example 4   Sixty days after borrowing money a person pays back exactly $200. How much was borrowed if the $200 payment includes the principal and simple interest at 9%?

Solution   We have $S = 200$, $r = 0.09$, and $t = \frac{60}{365}$. Substituting in formula (3) gives

$$P = \frac{200}{1 + 0.09\left(\frac{60}{365}\right)} = \$197.08$$

Example 5   How long will it take $3000 to earn $60 interest at 6%?

Solution   We have $P = 3000$, $I = 60$, $r = 0.06$, and

$$t = \frac{I}{Pr} = \frac{60}{3000 \times 0.06} = \frac{1}{3} = 4 \text{ months}$$

Example 6   *Cash discounts on purchase of merchandise.* To encourage prompt payments of invoices many manufacturers and wholesalers offer cash discounts for payments in advance of the final due date. The following typical credit terms may be printed on sales invoices:

2/10, n/30—Goods billed on this basis are subject to a cash discount of 2% if paid within ten days. Otherwise, the full amount must be paid not later than thirty days from the date of the invoice.

A buyer who takes advantage of cash discounts in effect lends money to the seller and receives as interest the cash discount. Interest rates earned in this manner are usually very high. The following example illustrates the use of a cash discount.

Example: A merchant receives an invoice for a motor boat for $4000 with terms 4/30, n/100. What is the highest simple interest rate at which he can afford to borrow money in order to take advantage of the discount?

Solution   Suppose that the merchant will take advantage of the cash discount of 4% of 4000 = $160 by paying the bill within 30 days from the date of invoice. He needs to borrow 4000 − 160 = $3840 for 70 days. The interest he should be willing to pay on borrowed money should not exceed the cash discount $160.

We have $P = 3840$, $I = 160$, $t = \frac{70}{365}$, and we calculate

$$r = \frac{I}{Pt} = \frac{160}{3840 \times \frac{70}{365}} = 21.73\%$$

The highest simple interest rate at which the merchant can afford to borrow money is 21.73%. If he can borrow money, say at rate 15%, he should do so and realize a profit equal to the difference between the cash discount of $160 and the interest he must pay on a 70-day loan of $3840 at rate 15%. Interest at 15% on $3840 for 70 days $= 3840 \times 0.15 \times \frac{70}{365} = 110.47$. Thus, his profit on the transaction would be $160 - 110.47 = \$49.53$.

Exercise 1.1

1. Find the accumulated value of $500 at 11% ordinary simple interest over 60 days.
2. At what simple rate of interest will $1000 accumulate to $1420 in $2\frac{1}{2}$ years?
3. How long will it take $500 to accumulate to $560 at 12% simple interest?
4. Find the ordinary and exact simple interest on $5000 for 90 days at $10\frac{1}{2}\%$.
5. A student lends his friend $10 for one month. At the end of the month he asks for repayment of the $10 plus purchase of a chocolate bar worth 50¢. What ordinary simple interest rate is implied?
6. What principal will accumulate to $5100 in 6 months if the rate is 9%?
7. What principal will accumulate to $580 in 120 days at 18% exact simple interest?
8. Find the accumulated value of $1000 over 65 days at $11\frac{1}{2}\%$ using both ordinary and exact simple interest.
9. Find the interest earned on $600 over 118 days at 16% using both ordinary and exact simple interest.
10. A man borrows $1000 for 220 days at 17%. What amount must he repay?
11. Find the discounted value of $500 over 82 days at 9% using both ordinary and exact simple interest.
12. Find the discounted value of $100 due in 3 months if the rate is 11%.
13. A bank pays 10% per annum on savings accounts. Interest is credited quarterly on March 31, June 30, September 30, and December 31 based on the minimum quarterly balance. If a person opens an account with a deposit of $200 on January 1 and withdraws $100 on August 8, how much interest is earned in the first year?
14. Mr. X has a Special Savings Account which pays interest at 12% per annum. Interest is calculated by the bank on the minimum monthly balance and is paid into the account on December 31. Given the following transactions for the account opened January 1, find the interest earned in the first year.

Date	Deposits	Withdrawals	Balance
January 1	$100		$100
February 3	$200		$300
April 14		$150	$150
May 18	$300		$450
July 7		$200	$250
September 15		$150	$100
November 3	$100		$200

15. A cash discount of 2% is given if a bill is paid 20 days in advance of its due date. At what interest rate could you afford to borrow money to take advantage of this discount?

16. A merchant receives an invoice for $1000 with terms 3/10, $n/60$. If he pays on the 10th day what rate of interest does he earn?

17. A merchant receives an invoice for $2000 with terms 2/20, $n/60$. What is the highest simple interest rate at which he can afford to borrow money in order to take advantage of the discount?

18. The ABC general store receives an invoice for goods totalling $500. The terms were 3/10, $n/30$. If the store were to borrow the money to pay the bill in 10 days what is the highest interest rate at which the store can afford to borrow?

1.2 The Time between Dates

There are two ways to calculate the number of days between calendar dates.

The most common method is to calculate the exact number of days including all days except the first. The time computed in this way is called the **exact time**. A simple way to determine the exact number of days is to use Table I (see page 247). Table I is essentially a calendar, which gives the serial numbers of the days in the year. The exact time is obtained as a difference between serial numbers of the given dates. In leap years, the serial number of the day is increased by 1 for all dates after February 28.

Another method is based on the assumption that all full months contain 30 days. The time computed this way is called the **approximate time**.

Example 1   Find the exact and approximate time between March 15 and September 3.

Solution   From Table I, March 15 is the 74th day of the year and September 3 is the 246th day of the year. The exact time is $246 - 74 = 172$ days.

For the approximate time we arrange the data in the table shown below:

Date	Month	Day	Month	Day
September 3	9	3	8	33
March 15			3	15
Difference			5	18

The approximate time is 5 months and 18 days, or 168 days.

When the time is given indirectly as the time between dates, we can use either exact or approximate time and compute either exact or ordinary simple interest. Thus there are four distinct ways to compute simple interest between dates, using

1. Exact time and exact interest.

2. Exact time and ordinary interest.

3. Approximate time and exact interest.

4. Approximate time and ordinary interest.

The general practice in Canada is to use Method 1, i.e., exact time and exact interest, in all simple interest calculations. In this book we use Method 1 unless otherwise specified.

Method 2 is also known as the **Banker's Rule** and is used widely in business practice in the United States and in international business transactions. Methods 3 and 4 are used very rarely.

Example 2 On November 3, 1978 a man borrowed $500 at 9%. The debt is repaid on February 8, 1979. Find the simple interest using the four methods.

Solution First we calculate exact and approximate time. From Table I, February 8 is the 39th day of the year and November 3 is the 307th day of the year.

February 8, 1979:	39 + 365 = 404th day, counting from January 1, 1978
November 3, 1978:	307th day, counting from January 1, 1978
Exact time between dates	97 days

For the approximate time we arrange the data in the table shown below, on the basis of months starting from January 1, 1978.

Date	Month	Day
February 8, 1979	14	8
November 3, 1978	11	3
Difference	3	5

The approximate time is 3 months and 5 days, or 95 days.

Exact time and exact interest $\qquad I = 500 \times 0.09 \times \dfrac{97}{365} = \$11.96$

Exact time and ordinary interest $\qquad I = 500 \times 0.09 \times \dfrac{97}{360} = \$12.13$

Approximate time and exact interest $\qquad I = 500 \times 0.09 \times \dfrac{95}{365} = \$11.71$

Approximate time and ordinary interest $\quad I = 500 \times 0.09 \times \dfrac{95}{360} = \$11.88$

Notice the differences in simple interest depending on the method used. This brings out the fact that in computing simple interest, as in all problems in the mathematics of finance both parties to the transaction should understand what method is to be used. The most favorable method for the creditor is the Banker's Rule (exact time and ordinary interest), as it usually yields the maximum interest. (This would not be true, for example, for the time interval February 4 to March 2 of any year, where the approximate time is greater than the exact time.)

Exercise 1.2

1. Find the exact and approximate time from April 18 to November 3.
2. Find the exact and approximate time from October 2 to June 15.
3. On April 7, 1978, Mr. X borrows $1000 at 8%. He repays the debt on November 22, 1978. Find the simple interest using the four methods.
4. A sum of $2000 is invested from May 18, 1982 to April 8, 1983 at 16% simple interest. Find the amount of interest earned using the four methods.
5. On January 1, Mr. A borrows $1000 on a demand loan from his bank. Interest is paid at the end of each quarter (March 31, June 30, September 30, December 31) and at the time of the last payment. Interest is calculated at the rate of 12% on the balance of the loan outstanding. Mr. A repaid the loan with the following payments:

March 1	$100
April 17	$300
July 12	$200
August 20	$100
October 18	$300
	$1000

Calculate the interest payments required and the total interest paid. (Follow normal Canadian practice.)
6. Find the total interest paid in problem 5 using the Banker's Rule.

1.3 Equations of Value

All financial decisions must take into account the basic idea that *money has time value*. In a financial transaction involving money due on different dates, every sum of money should have an attached date, the date on which it falls due. That is, the mathematics of finance deals with *dated values*. This is one of the most important facts in the mathematics of finance.

Illustration: At a simple interest rate of 8%, $100 due in 1 year is considered to be equivalent to $108 due in 2 years since $100 would accumulate to $108 in 1 year. In the same way

$$100(1 + 0.08)^{-1} = \$92.59$$

would be considered an equivalent sum at present.

In general, we compare dated values by the following **definition of equivalence**:

$X due on a given date is equivalent at a given simple interest rate r to $Y due t years later if

$$Y = X(1 + rt) \quad \text{or} \quad X = \frac{Y}{1 + rt} = Y(1 + rt)^{-1}$$

The following time diagram illustrates dated values equivalent to a given dated value X.

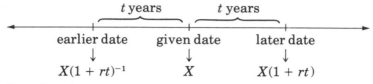

Note   Based on the time diagram above we can state the following simple rules:

When we move money forward, we accumulate, i.e., multiply the sum by an accumulation factor $(1 + rt)$

When we move money backward, we discount, i.e., multiply the sum by a discount factor $(1 + rt)^{-1}$

Example 1   A debt of $1000 is due at the end of 9 months. Find an equivalent debt at a simple interest rate of 9% at the end of 4 months and at the end of 1 year.
Solution   Let us arrange the data on a time diagram below.

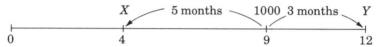

According to the definition of equivalence

$$X = 1000\left[1 + (0.09)\left(\tfrac{5}{12}\right)\right]^{-1} = \$963.86$$
$$Y = 1000\left[1 + (0.09)\left(\tfrac{3}{12}\right)\right] = \$1022.50$$

The sum of a set of dated values, due on different dates, has no meaning. We have to replace all the dated values by equivalent dated values, due on the same date. The sum of the equivalent values is called the **dated value of the set**.

Example 2   A person owes $300 due in 3 months and $500 due in 8 months. What single payment (a) now; (b) in 6 months; (c) in 1 year, will liquidate these obligations if money is worth 8%?
Solution

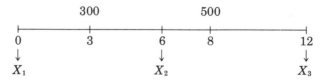

We calculate equivalent dated values of both obligations at the three different times and arrange in the table below.

Obligations	Now	In 6 months	In 1 year
First	294.12	306.00	318.00
Second	474.68	493.42	513.33
Sum	$X_1 = 768.80$	$X_2 = 799.42$	$X_3 = 831.33$

One of the most important problems in the mathematics of finance is the replacing of a given set of payments by an equivalent set.

We say that two sets of payments are equivalent at a given simple interest rate if the dated values of the sets, on any common date, are equal. An equation stating that the dated values, on a common date, of two sets of payments are equal is called an **equation of value** or an **equation of equivalence**. The date used is called the **focal date** or the **comparison date**.

A very effective way to solve many problems in mathematics of finance is to use the equation of value. The procedure is carried out in the following steps.

Step 1   Make a good time diagram, showing the dated values of obligations on one side of the time line and the dated values of payments on the other side. A good time diagram is of great help in the analysis and solution of problems.

Step 2   Select a focal date and bring all the dated values to the focal date using the specified interest rate.

Step 3   Set up an equation of value at the focal date.

Step 4   Solve the equation of value using methods of algebra.

In simple interest problems the answer will vary slightly with the location of the focal date. It is therefore important that the parties involved in the financial transaction agree on the location of the focal date.

In compound interest (Chapter 2) any date may be used as a focal date; that is, the answer is independent of the location of the focal date.

Example 3   A debtor owes $500 due in 3 months and $200 due in 6 months. If his creditor accepts $300 now, how much will be required to liquidate the two obligations at the end of 1 year, provided they agree to use an interest rate of 10% and a focal date at the end of 1 year.

Solution   We arrange all the dated values on a time diagram.

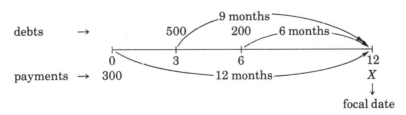

Equation of value at the end of 12 months:
   dated value of the payments = dated value of the debts
$$X + 300\left[1 + (0.10)(\tfrac{12}{12})\right] = 500\left[1 + (0.10)(\tfrac{9}{12})\right] + 200\left[1 + (0.10)(\tfrac{6}{12})\right]$$
$$X + 330.00 = 537.50 + 210.00$$
$$X = \$417.50$$

The payment of $417.50 will be required at the end of 1 year to liquidate both obligations.

Example 4   A person borrows $1000 at 11%. He is to repay the debt with 3 equal payments, the first at the end of 3 months, the second at the end of 6 months and the third at the end of 9 months. Find the size of the payments. Put the focal date (*a*) at the present; (*b*) at the end of 9 months.

Solution a   Arrange all the dated values on a time diagram.

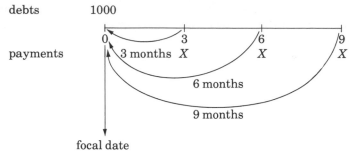

Equation of value at the present:

$$X\left[1 + (0.11)(\tfrac{3}{12})\right]^{-1} + X\left[1 + (0.11)(\tfrac{6}{12})\right]^{-1} + X\left[1 + (0.11)(\tfrac{9}{12})\right]^{-1} = 1000.00$$
$$0.973\ 236\ 01X + 0.947\ 867\ 3X + 0.923\ 787\ 53X = 1000.00$$
$$2.844\ 890\ 8X = 1000.00$$
$$X = \$351.51$$

Solution b   Equation of value at the end of 9 months:

$$X\left[1 + (0.11)(\tfrac{6}{12})\right] + X\left[1 + (0.11)(\tfrac{3}{12})\right] + X = 1000\left[1 + (0.11)(\tfrac{9}{12})\right]$$
$$1.055X + 1.0275X + X = 1082.50$$
$$3.0825X = 1082.50$$
$$X = \$351.18$$

Notice the slight difference in the answer for the different focal dates.

Exercise 1.3

1. A woman owes $100 due in six months and $150 due in 1 year. She and the lender agree that she can pay off both debts today using a simple interest rate of 16% and putting the focal date now. How much will be paid in cash today?
2. A person borrows $1000 to be repaid with two equal instalments, one in six months, the other at the end of 1 year. What will be the size of these payments if the interest rate is 8% and the focal date is 1 year hence? What if the focal date is today?
3. A man borrows $5000 on January 1, 1982. He pays $2000 on April 30, 1982 and $2000 on August 31, 1982. The last payment is to be on January 1, 1983. If interest is at 17% and the focal date is January 1, 1983 find the size of the final payment.
4. A person owes $200 due in 3 months and $800 due in 9 months. What single payment 6 months hence will pay off both debts if interest is at 8% and the focal date is 6 months hence?
5. Mrs. Adams has two options available in repaying a loan. She can pay $200 at the end of 5 months and $300 at the end of 10 months, or she can pay $X at the end of 3 months and $2X at the end of 6 months. Find X if interest is at 12% and the focal date is 6 months hence and the options are equivalent. What is the answer if the focal date is 3 months hence and the options are equivalent?
6. Mr. A will pay Mr. B $200 at the end of 5 years and $800 at the end of 10 years if Mr. B will give him $300 today plus an additional sum of money ($X) at the end of 2 years. Find X if interest is at 13% and the comparison date is today. Find $X if the comparison date is 2 years hence (i.e., at the time $X is paid).

7. A person owes $500 due in 4 months and $700 due in 9 months. What single payment
   a) now;
   b) in 6 months;
   c) in 1 year, will liquidate these obligations if money is worth 11%?
8. Mr. Smith borrows $2000 at 14%. He is to repay the debt with 4 equal payments, one at the end of each 3 month period for 1 year. Find the size of the payments given a focal date:
   a) at the present;
   b) at the end of 1 year.
9. A person borrows $800 at 16%. He agrees to pay off the debt with payments of size X, $2X$, and $4X$ in 3 months, 6 months and 9 months respectively. Find X using all four transaction dates as possible focal dates.

1.4 Partial Payments

Financial obligations are sometimes liquidated by a series of partial payments during the term of obligation. Then it is necessary to determine the balance due on the final due date. There are two common ways to allow interest credit on short-term transactions.

Method 1 (also known as **Merchant's Rule**) The entire debt and each partial payment earns interest to the final settlement date. The balance due on the final due date is simply the difference between the accumulated value of the debt and the accumulated value of the partial payments.

Example 1 On February 4, 1979 a person borrowed $3000 at 11%. He paid $1000 on April 21, 1979; $600 on May 12, 1979 and $700 on June 11, 1979. What is the balance due on August 15, 1979 using Merchant's Rule?
Solution We arrange all dated values on a time diagram.

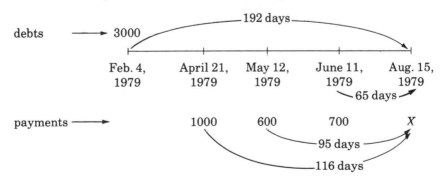

Simple interest is computed at 11% on the original debt of $3000 for 192 days, on the first partial payment of $1000 for 116 days, on the second partial payment of $600 for 95 days, and on the third partial payment of $700 for 65 days.

Calculations are given below.

Original debt	3000.00	1st partial payment	1000.00
Interest for 192 days	173.59	Interest for 116 days	34.96
		2nd partial payment	600.00
Accumulated value	$3173.59	Interest for 95 days	17.18
of the debt		3rd partial payment	700.00
		Interest for 65 days	13.71
		Accumulated value of the partial payments	$2365.85

Balance due on August 15, 1979: 3173.59 − 2365.85 = $807.74

Alternate solution   We can write an equation of value with August 15, 1979 as the focal date.

On August 15, 1979: value of the payments = value of the debts

$$X + 1000\left[1 + (0.11)(\tfrac{116}{365})\right] + 600\left[1 + (0.11)(\tfrac{95}{365})\right]$$

$$+ 700\left[1 + (0.11)(\tfrac{65}{365})\right] = 3000\left[1 + (0.11)(\tfrac{192}{365})\right]$$

$$X + 1034.96 + 617.18 + 713.71 = 3173.59$$

$$X = \$807.74$$

Method 2 (also known as **United States Rule**) The interest on the unpaid balance of the debt is computed each time a partial payment is made. If the payment is greater than the interest due, the difference is used to reduce the debt. If the payment is less than the interest due, it is held without interest until other partial payments are made whose sum exceeds the interest due at the time of the last of these partial payments. (This point is illustrated in problem 4 of the exercise that follows.) The balance due on the final date is the outstanding balance after the last partial payment carried to the final due date.

Example 2   Solve Example 1 using the United States Rule.

Solution   We arrange all dated values on a time diagram.

debts	→3000	76 days		21 days	30 days		65 days	
		Feb. 4, 1979		April 21, 1979	May 12, 1979	June 11, 1979		Aug. 15, 1979
payments →				1000	600	700		X

Instead of having one comparison date we have 4 comparison dates. Each time a payment is made, the preceding balance is accumulated at simple interest rate of 11% to this point and a new balance is obtained.

The calculations are given below.

Original debt	3000.00
Interest for 76 days	68.71
Amount due on April 21, 1979	3068.71
First partial payment	1000.00
Balance due on April 21, 1979	2068.71
Interest for 21 days	13.09
Amount due on May 12, 1979	2081.80
Second partial payment	600.00
Balance due on May 12, 1979	1481.80
Interest for 30 days	13.40
Amount due on June 11, 1979	1495.20
Third partial payment	700.00
Balance due on June 11, 1979	795.20
Interest for 65 days	15.58
Balance due on August 15, 1979	$810.78

The above calculations also may be carried out in a shorter form, as shown below.

Balance due on April 21, 1979 $3000[1 + (.11)(\frac{76}{365})] - 1000 = \$2068.71$

Balance due on May 12, 1979 $2068.71[1 + (.11)(\frac{21}{365})] - 600 = \$1481.80$

Balance due on July 11, 1979 $1481.80[1 + (.11)(\frac{30}{365})] - 700 = \$795.20$

Balance due on August 15, 1979 $795.20[1 + (.11)(\frac{65}{365})]$ $- \$810.78$

Note that the methods result in two different concluding payments. It is important that the two parties to a business transaction agree on the method to be used.

Exercise 1.4

1. A loan of $1000 is due in one year with interest at $14\frac{1}{4}$%. The debtor pays $200 in 3 months and $400 in 7 months. Find the balance due in one year using the Merchant's Rule and the United States Rule.

2. On June 1, 1978 a man borrows $2000 at 12%. He pays $800 on August 17, 1978, $400 on November 20, 1978, and $500 on February 2, 1979. What is the balance due on April 18, 1979 by the Merchant's Rule? By the United States Rule?

3. A debt of $5000 is due in six months with interest at 10%. Partial payments of $3000 and $1000 are made in 2 and 4 months respectively. What is the balance due on the final statement date by the Merchant's Rule? By the United States Rule?

4. A woman borrows $1000 on January 1, 1982 at 16%. She pays $350 on April 12, 1982, $20 on August 10, 1982, and $400 on October 3, 1982. What is the balance due on January 1, 1983 using the Merchant's Rule? The United States Rule?

1.5 Simple Discount

Simple discount at an interest rate. In Section 1.1 we called the process of finding the discounted value P of S discounting at simple interest or simple discount at an interest rate. The difference $D = S - P$ is called the simple discount on S at an interest rate or the **true discount** on S.

Note   For a given interest rate r, the difference $S - P$ has two interpretations.

   1. the interest I on P which when added to P gives S.

   2. the true discount D on S which when subtracted from S gives P.

Example 1   Discount $800 at an interest rate of 10% for 8 months. What is the true discount?

Solution   We have $S = 800$, $r = 10\%$, $t = \frac{8}{12}$ and calculate

$$P = \frac{S}{1 + rt} = \frac{800}{1 + (0.10)\left(\frac{8}{12}\right)} = \$750$$

The true discount

$$D = S - P = 800 - 750 = \$50$$

Simple discount at a discount rate. The **discount rate** d for a year is the ratio of the discount D for the year to the amount S on which the discount is given. The simple discount D on an amount S, also called **bank discount**, for t years at the discount rate d is calculated by means of the formula:

$$D = Sdt \tag{4}$$

and the discounted value P of S, or the proceeds P, is given by

$$P = S - D$$

By substituting for $D = Sdt$ we obtain P in terms of S, d, and t

$$P = S - Sdt$$

$$P = S(1 - dt) \tag{5}$$

The charge for some short-term loans may be based on the final amount rather than on the present value. The lender calculates the bank discount D on the final amount S that must be paid on the due date, deducts it from S and the borrower receives the proceeds P. For this reason bank discount is sometimes called **interest in advance**.

   From formula (5) we can express S in terms of P, d, and t and obtain

$$S = \frac{P}{1 - dt} \tag{6}$$

Formula (6) is used to calculate the maturity value of a loan for specified proceeds.

Example 2   A person borrows $500 for 6 months from a lender who charges a $9\frac{1}{2}\%$ discount rate. (*a*) What is the discount, and how much money does the borrower receive? (*b*) What size loan should the borrower ask for if he wants to receive $500 cash?

Solution a   We have $S = 500$, $d = 9\frac{1}{2}\%$, $t = \frac{1}{2}$ and calculate

discount $D = Sdt = 500 \times 0.095 \times \frac{1}{2} = \$23.75$
proceeds $P = S - D = 500 - 23.75 = \$476.25$

We could calculate the proceeds by formula (5)

$$P = S(1 - dt) = 500\left[1 - (0.095)(\tfrac{1}{2})\right] = \$476.25$$

Solution b   We have $P = 500$, $d = 9\frac{1}{2}\%$, $t = \frac{1}{2}$ and calculate the maturity value of the loan

$$S = \frac{P}{1 - dt} = \frac{500}{1 - (0.095)(\tfrac{1}{2})} = \$524.93$$

The borrower should ask for a loan of $524.93 to receive proceeds of $500.00.

Example 3   Calculate the present value of $1000 due in 1 year: (*a*) at a simple interest rate of 10%; (*b*) at a simple discount rate of 10%.
Solution a   We have $S = 1000$, $r = 10\%$, and $t = 1$ and calculate

$$P = \frac{S}{1 + rt} = \frac{1000}{1 + (0.1)(1)} = \$909.09$$

Solution b   We have $S = 1000$, $d = 10\%$, and $t = 1$ and calculate

$$P = S(1 - dt) = 1000\left[1 - (0.1)(1)\right] - 1000(0.9) = \$900.00$$

Note the difference of $9.09 between the present value at a simple interest rate and the present value at a simple discount rate. We can conclude that a given bank discount rate results in a larger money return to a lender than the same simple interest rate.

It is desirable to determine the simple interest rate which is equivalent to a given discount rate. A discount rate d and interest rate r are equivalent if the two rates result in the same present value P for an amount S due in the future, i.e., when we equate the right-hand sides of formulas (3) and (5)

$$S(1 - dt) = \frac{S}{1 + rt}$$

Dividing both sides by S, and solving for r

$$1 - dt = \frac{1}{1 + rt}$$

$$1 + rt = \frac{1}{1 - dt}$$

$$rt = \frac{1 - 1 + dt}{1 - dt}$$

$$r = \frac{d}{1 - dt} \tag{7}$$

Similarly by solving the equation

$$S(1 - dt) = \frac{S}{1 + rt}$$

for d we can find the discount rate d corresponding to a given interest rate r

$$d = \frac{r}{1 + rt} \qquad (8)$$

Example 4   A bank discounts a sum which is due in 1 year at a discount rate of 9%. What is the equivalent interest rate?

Solution   We have $d = 9\%$, $t = 1$, and using formula (7) calculate

$$r = \frac{d}{1 - dt} = \frac{0.09}{1 - (0.09)(1)} = 9.89\%$$

Thus a lender that charges 9% interest in advance is in fact using a true interest rate of 9.89%.

Note   The interest in advance or bank discount has been popular with lenders in the United States on many short-term loans. From 1968, when the Congress passed the "Truth in Lending Act," a creditor has to state the true simple interest rate that is being charged.

Exercise 1.5

1. A person borrows $1000 from a bank for six months. If the bank uses a discount rate of 10% what is the discount and how much money does the borrower get?
2. Mr. X needs $2000 cash for 9 months. If he borrows from a bank that charges a 12% discount rate, what size loan should he ask for?
3. $S = 2000$, $d = 8\%$, time = 7 months. Find D and P.
4. A note with a maturity value of $700 is sold at a discount rate of 13%, 45 days before maturity. Find the discount and the proceeds.
5. Find the present value of $1000 due in 9 months at a simple interest rate of 12%. At a bank discount rate of 12%.
6. Find the present value of $500 due in 6 months at a simple interest rate of 10%. At a bank discount rate of 10%.
7. A bank discounts a $100 note due in one year using a bank discount rate of 10%. What interest rate are they getting?
8. A bank charges a discount rate of 12% for discounting a note for $800 due in 9 months. What interest rate are they getting?
9. To earn an interest rate of 10% on a 6 month loan, what discount rate should a lender charge?
10. If a sum of money is due in two months, what rate of discount is equivalent to an interest rate of 18%?
11. A note maturing for $1000 on September 20 is sold for $970 on May 4. What discount rate was used? What interest rate will the purchaser realize on this investment?

1.6 Promissory Notes

A **promissory note** is a written promise by a debtor, called the **maker** of the note, to pay to, or to the order of, the creditor, called the **payee** of the note, a sum of money, with or without interest, on a specified date.

The following is an example of an interest-bearing note.

$2000.00	Toronto, September 1, 1982

Sixty days after date, I promise to pay to the order of Mr. A

$$\text{Two thousand and } \frac{00}{100} \text{ dollars}$$

for value received with interest at 11% per annum.

(Signed) *Mr. B.*

The **face value** of the note is $2000.00. The **due date** is 60 days after September 1, 1982, that is October 31, 1982.

In Canada, *three days of grace** are added to the sixty days to arrive at the **legal due date**, or the "**maturity date**," that is November 3, 1982. The **term** of the note is 63 days. By a **maturity value** of a note we shall understand the value of the note at the maturity date. In our example, the maturity value of the note is the accumulated value of $2000 for 63 days at 11%, i.e. $2000[1 + (0.11)(\frac{63}{365})] = \$2037.97$.

If Mr. B chooses to pay on October 31, he will pay interest for 60 days, not 63 days. However, no legal action can be taken against him until the expiry of the three days of grace. Thus, Mr. B would be within his legal rights to repay as late as November 3, and in that case he would pay interest for 63 days.

A promissory note may be sold one or several times before its maturity. Each buyer discounts the maturity value of the note for the time from the date of sale to the maturity date at his discount rate and the seller receives the proceeds of the sale. The buyer may specify the interest rate he wants to realize on the investment, then the proceeds are determined by formula (3) from Section 1.1.

The procedure for discounting of promissory notes can be summarized in 2 steps:

Step 1   Get the maturity value, S, of the note.

The maturity value of a noninterest-bearing note is the face value of the note. The maturity value of an interest-bearing note is the accumulated value of the face value at interest rate r for the term of the note.

Three days of grace. In Canada, "three days of grace" are allowed for the payment of an obligation. This means that the payment becomes due on the third day after the due date of the note.

If interest is being charged, the three days of grace must be added to the time stated in the note, to compute it. If the third day of grace falls on a holiday, payment will become due the next succeeding day that is itself not a holiday.

If the time is stated in months, these must be calendar months and not months of 30 days. For example, 2 months after July 5 is September 5. Thus the legal due date is September 8, and the number of days to be used in calculating the interest (if any) will be 65 days.

In the month in which the payment falls due, there may be no corresponding date to that from which the time is computed. In such a case, the last day of the month is taken as the corresponding date. For example, two months after December 31 is February 28 (or February 29 in leap years), and March 3 would be the legal due date.

Step 2 Get the proceeds, P, by discounting the maturity value, S, at a specified rate from the maturity date back to the date of sale.

Example 1 The note described in the beginning of this section is sold by Mr. A on October 1, 1982 to a bank which discounts notes at $9\frac{1}{2}$% bank discount rate.

   a) How much money would Mr. A receive for the note?
   b) What rate of interest will the bank realize on its investment, if it holds the note till maturity?
   c) What rate of interest will Mr. A realize on his investment, when he sells the note on October 1, 1982?

Solution a   We arrange the dated values on a time diagram below.

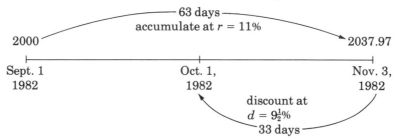

Maturity value of the note is $S = 2000\left[1 + (0.11)\left(\frac{63}{365}\right)\right] = \$2037.97$

Proceeds on October 1, 1982 are $P = 2037.97\left[1 - (0.095)\left(\frac{33}{365}\right)\right] = \$2020.47$.

Solution b   The bank will realize a profit of $17.50 on their investment of $2020.47 for 33 days. Thus we have $P = 2020.47$, $I = 17.50$, and $t = \frac{33}{365}$ and calculate

$$r = \frac{I}{Pt} = \frac{17.50}{2020.47 \times \frac{33}{365}} = 9.58\%$$

An alternate solution is to calculate the equivalent rate r for a given discount rate d, using $d = 0.095$, $t = \frac{33}{365}$, and formula (7)

$$r = \frac{d}{1 - dt} = \frac{0.095}{1 - (0.095)\left(\frac{33}{365}\right)} = 9.58\%$$

Solution c   Mr. A will realize a profit of $20.47 on his investment of $2000 for the 30 days he held the note. The rate of interest Mr. A will realize is

$$r = \frac{I}{Pt} = \frac{20.47}{2000 \times \frac{30}{365}} = 12.45\%$$

Example 2 On April 15 a debtor signs a note for $800 due in 2 months with interest at 12%. On May 10, the holder of the note sells it to a bank which discounts notes at a simple interest rate of 13%. How much is received for the note?

Solution

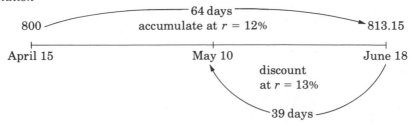

Maturity value of the note is $S = 800\left[1 + (0.12)\left(\frac{64}{365}\right)\right] = \$816.83$

Proceeds on May 10 are $P = 816.83\left[1 + (.13)\left(\frac{39}{365}\right)\right]^{-1} = \$805.64$

Example 3   On April 21, a retailer buys goods amounting to $5000. If he pays cash he will get a 4% cash discount. To take advantage of this cash discount, he signs a 90-day noninterest-bearing note at his bank which discounts notes at a discount rate of 9%. What should be the face value of this note to give him the exact amount needed to pay cash for the goods?

Solution   The cash discount 4% of $5000 is $200. The retailer needs $4800 in cash. He will sign a noninterest-bearing note with maturity value S calculated by formula (6), given $P = 4800$, $d = 9\%$, and $t = \frac{93}{365}$. Thus

$$S = \frac{P}{1 - dt} = \frac{4800}{1 - (0.09)\left(\frac{93}{365}\right)} = \$4912.65$$

The face value of the noninterest-bearing note should be $4912.65.

Exercise 1.6

1. An investor lends $5000 and receives a promissory note promising repayment of the loan in 90 days with 12% simple interest. This note is immediately sold to a bank which charges 10% bank discount. How much does the bank pay for the note? What is the investor's profit? What interest rate will the bank realize on this investment when the note matures?

2. A 60-day note promises to pay $2000 plus interest at 21%. It is discounted at 19% bank discount 30 days before maturity. Find the proceeds of the sale.

3. A 90-day note for $800 bears interest at 10% and is sold 60 days before maturity to a bank that uses a 12% simple interest rate. What are the proceeds? What is the equivalent bank discount rate?

4. Mr. A owes Mr. B $1000. Mr. B agrees to accept as payment a noninterest-bearing note for 90 days which can be discounted immediately at a local bank which charges a bank discount rate of 10%. What should be the face value of the note so that Mr. B will receive $1000 as proceeds?

5. Mr. A has a note for $500 dated October 17, 1983. The note is due in 120 days with interest at 19%. If Mr. A discounts the note on January 15, 1984, at a bank charging a discount rate of 20%, what will be the proceeds? What rate of interest will the bank realize on its investment, if it holds the note until maturity?

6. A storekeeper buys goods costing $800. He asks his creditor to accept a 60-day noninterest-bearing note, which, if his creditor discounts immediately at 18% discount rate, will result in proceeds of $800. For what amount should he make the note?

7. A merchant buys goods worth $2000 and signs a 90-day noninterest-bearing promissory note. Find the proceeds if the supplier sells the note to a bank that uses a 13% discount rate. How much profit did the supplier make if the goods cost $1500?

8. On August 16 a retailer buys goods worth $2000. If he pays cash he will get a 3% cash discount. To take advantage of this he signs a 60-day noninterest-bearing note at a bank that discounts notes at 16% discount rate. What should be the face value of this note to give the retailer the exact amount needed to pay cash for the goods.

9. A company borrowed $50 000 on May 1, 1984 and signed a promissory note bearing interest at 11% for 3 months. On the maturity date, the company paid the interest in full and gave a second note for 3 months without interest and for such an amount that when it was discounted at 12% discount rate on the day it was signed, the proceeds were just sufficient to pay the debt. Find the amount of interest paid on the first note, and the face value of the second note.

10. A wholesale appliance dealer accepted a $15 000 promissory note from a retail store. It was dated May 18, bearing 15% interest and the duration was 6 months. Partial payments of $4000 and $7000 were made on July 7 and September 2 respectively. Using the Merchant's Rule, determine the amount due at the maturity date.

11. Mr. A has a note for $1500 dated June 8, 1984. The note is due in 120 days with interest at 12%.
   a) If Mr. A discounts the note on August 1, 1984 at a bank charging an interest rate of 15%, what will the proceeds be?
   b) What rate of interest will Mr. A realize on his investment?
   c) What rate of interest will the bank realize if the note is paid off in full in exactly 120 days?

1.7 Review Exercises

1. How long will it take $1000
   a) to earn $100 at 15% simple interest?
   b) to accumulate to $1200 at $13\frac{1}{2}$% simple interest?

2. Find the accumulated and the discounted value of $1000 over 55 days at 15% using both ordinary and exact simple interest.

3. A retailer receives an invoice for $8000 for a shipment of furniture with terms 3/10, n/40.
   a) What is the highest simple interest rate at which he can afford to borrow money in order to take advantage of the cash discount?
   b) If the retailer can borrow at simple interest rate 21%, find his profit resulting from the cash discount, when he pays the invoice within 10 days.

4. A cash discount of 5% is given if a bill is paid 30 days in advance of its due date. What is the highest simple interest rate at which you can afford to borrow money in order to take advantage of the cash discount?

5. Paul borrows $4000 at 18% simple interest rate. He is to repay the loan by paying $1000 at the end of 3 months and two equal payments at the end of 6 months and 9 months. Find the size of the equal payments and
   a) use the end of 6 months as a focal date.
   b) use the present as a focal date.

6. Melisa borrows $1000 on May 8, 1982 at $18\frac{1}{2}$% simple interest rate. She pays $500 on July 17, 1982 and $400 on September 29, 1982. What is the balance due on October 31, 1982 using the Merchant's Rule and the United States Rule?

7. Robert borrows $1000 for 8 months from a lender who charges a 16% discount rate.
   a) How much money does Robert receive?
   b) What size loan should Robert ask for in order to receive $1000 cash?
   c) What is the equivalent simple interest rate he is paying on the loan?

8. Consider the following promissory note:

$1500.00   Vancouver, May 11, 1983
Ninety days after date, I promise to pay to the order of J.D. Green
Fifteen hundred and $\dfrac{00}{100}$ dollars
for value received with interest at 18% per annum.
(Signed) *J. B. Smith*

Mr. Green sells the note on July 2, 1983 to a bank that discounts notes at 19% bank discount.
   a) How much money does Mr. Green receive?
   b) What rate of interest does Mr. Green realize on his investment?
   c) What rate of interest does the bank realize on its investments, if it holds the note till maturity?
   d) What rate of interest does the bank realize if Mr. Smith pays off the loan as due in exactly 90 days?

9. A 180 day promissory note for $2000 bears 14% simple interest. After 60 days it is sold to a bank which charges a discount rate of 14%.
   a) Find the price paid by the bank for the note.
   b) What simple interest rate did the original owner of the note actually earn?
   c) If the note is actually paid on the *due* date, what discount rate will the bank have realized?

10. A note for $800 is due in 90 days with simple interest at $18\frac{1}{4}$%. On the maturity date, the maker of the note paid the interest in full and gave a second note for 60 days without interest and for such an amount that when it was discounted at 17% discount rate on the day it was signed, the proceeds were just sufficient to pay the debt.
   Find the interest paid on the first note, and the face value of the second note.

2

Compound Interest

2.1 Fundamental Compound Interest Formula

If the interest due is added to the principal at the end of each interest period and thereafter earns interest, the interest is said to be **compounded**. The sum of the original principal and total interest is called the **compound amount** or **accumulated value**. The difference between the accumulated value and the original principal is called the **compound interest**. The time between two successive interest computations is called the **interest period** or **conversion period**. This time unit need not be a year. Most of you will be already familiar with situations where interest is "payable quarterly," or "compounded semi-annually," or "convertible monthly." These rates are referred to as "nominal" rates of interest and are handled as shown in Example 1.

Example 1 Find the compound interest earned on $1000 for 2 years at 10% compounded semi-annually and compare it with the simple interest earned on $1000 for 2 years at 10% per annum.

Solution Since the conversion period is 6 months, interest is earned at the rate of 5% per period, and there are 4 interest periods in 2 years.

At the end of	Compound interest	Accumulated value
the 1st interest period	$1000 \times 0.05 = 50$	$1050.00
the 2nd interest period	$1050 \times 0.05 = 52.50$	$1102.50
the 3rd interest period	$1102.50 \times 0.05 = 55.13$	$1157.63
the 4th interest period	$1157.63 \times 0.05 = 57.88$	$1215.51

The compound interest earned on $1000 for 2 years at 10% compounded semi-annually is $215.51, whereas the simple interest on $1000 for 2 years at 10% is $I = 1000 \times 0.10 \times 2 = \$200$.

In the following we shall develop quicker methods for calculating the compound interest.

The following notation will be used:

P = the original principal, or the present value of S, or the discounted value of S.

S = the compound amount of P, or the accumulated value of P.

n = the number of interest (or conversion) periods involved.

m = the number of interest periods per year, or the frequency of compounding.

j_m = the nominal (yearly) interest rate which is compounded (payable, convertible) m times per year.

i = the interest rate per conversion period.

Note   The rate i equals j_m/m and is always used in the compound interest calculation. For example, $j_{12} = 9\%$ means that a yearly rate of 9% is converted (compounded, payable) 12 times per year and that $i = \frac{9}{12}\% = \frac{3}{4}\%$ is the interest rate per month.

Let P represent the principal at the beginning of the first interest period and i the interest rate per conversion period. We shall calculate the accumulated values at the ends of successive interest periods for n periods.

At the end of the 1st period:

the interest due $\qquad\qquad$ Pi

the accumulated value $\qquad$ $P + Pi = P(1 + i)$

At the end of the 2nd period:

the interest due $\qquad\qquad$ $[P(1 + i)]i$

the accumulated value $\qquad$ $P(1 + i) + [P(1 + i)]i$
$$= P(1 + i)(1 + i) = P(1 + i)^2$$

At the end of the 3rd period:

the interest due $\qquad\qquad$ $[P(1 + i)^2]i$

the accumulated value $\qquad$ $P(1 + i)^2 + [P(1 + i)^2]i$
$$= P(1 + i)^2(1 + i) = P(1 + i)^3$$

Continuing in this manner for n periods the accumulated value S at the end of n periods is given by the **fundamental compound interest formula**

$$S = P(1 + i)^n \qquad\qquad\qquad (9)$$

The factor $(1 + i)^n$ is called the **accumulation factor** or the **accumulated**

value of $1. * The process of calculating S from P is called **accumulation**. To obtain the accumulated value S of P for n periods at rate i, we multiply P by the corresponding accumulation factor $(1 + i)^n$.

Example 2   Accumulate $100 at $j_{12} = 12\%$ for (a) 5 years; (b) 25 years.

Solution a   We have $P = 100$, $i = .01$, $n = 60$, and calculate

$$S = 100(1.01)^{60} = \$181.67.$$

The compound interest on $100 at $j_{12} = 12\%$ for 5 years is $81.67.

Solution b   We have $P = 100$, $i = .01$, $n = 300$, and calculate

$$S = 100(1.01)^{300} = \$1978.85.$$

The compound interest on $100 at $j_{12} = 12\%$ for 25 years is $1878.85, which is more than 18 times the original investment of $100. If the investment had been at 1% simple interest per month, the interest earned would have been only $300. The solution to Example 2 (b) illustrates the power of compound interest at a high rate of interest for a long period of time.

The table and graph below show the effect of time and rate on the growth of money at compound interest.

Growth of $100 at compound interest rate j_{12}

Years	6%	8%	10%	12%
5	134.89	148.98	164.53	181.67
10	181.94	221.96	270.70	330.04
15	245.41	330.69	445.39	599.58
20	331.02	492.68	732.81	1 089.26
25	446.50	734.02	1 205.69	1 978.85
30	602.26	1 093.57	1 983.74	3 594.96
35	812.36	1 629.26	3 263.87	6 530.96
40	1 095.75	2 427.34	5 370.07	11 864.77
45	1 478.00	3 616.36	8 835.42	21 554.69
50	1 993.60	5 387.82	14 536.99	39 158.34

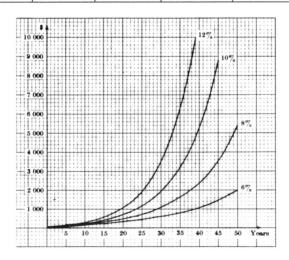

---

*It is assumed that students will be using pocket calculators equipped with the functions y^x and log x, to solve the problems in the Mathematics of Finance. In the examples in this textbook, we have used all digits of the factors provided by a pocket calculator and rounded off to the nearest cent only in the final answer.

Example 3   A person deposits $1000 into a savings account that earns interest at 12.25% compounded daily. How much interest will be earned: a) during the first year? b) during the second year?

Solution a   We have $P = 1000$, $i = \dfrac{.1225}{365}$, $n = 365$ and

calculate the accumulated value at the end of 1 year

$$S = 1000\left(1 + \frac{.1225}{365}\right)^{365} = \$1130.30$$

The compound interest earned during the first year is $130.30.

Solution b   We calculate the accumulated value at the end of 2 years

$$S = 1000\left(1 + \frac{.1225}{365}\right)^{730} = \$1277.57$$

The compound interest earned during the second year is

$1277.57 - 1130.30 = \$147.27$

Most Canadian financial institutions offer to their clients savings accounts on which the interest is calculated daily (not compounded daily) on either the minimum or final daily balance and added to the account semi-annually or monthly.

Example 4   Jennifer has a savings account which pays interest at $15\frac{1}{2}\%$ per annum calculated daily. The interest is calculated on the final daily balance and is paid into the account on June 30 and December 31. Given the following transactions for her account opened February 8, find the interest earned in the first year.

Date	Deposits	Withdrawals	Balance
February 8	$1500		$1500
March 5		$100	$1400
June 17	$300		$1700
August 20		$700	$1000

Solution   Let us arrange the data on a time diagram below.

Days		25	104	13	51	133
	0	39	64	168	181	232	365
	Jan.1	Feb.8	March 5	June 17	June 30	Aug.20	Dec.31
Balances		1500	1400	1700	$1700+I_1$	$1000+I_1$	$1000+I_1+I_2$

Interest from Feb. 8 to March 5 $= 1500 \times 0.155 \times \frac{25}{365} = \$15.92$
Interest from March 5 to June 17 $= 1400 \times 0.155 \times \frac{104}{365} = 61.83$
Interest from June 17 to June 30 $= 1700 \times 0.155 \times \frac{13}{365} = 9.38$

Interest from Feb. 8 to June 30 $\longrightarrow$ $I_1 = 87.13$

Interest from June 30 to Aug.20 $= 1787.13 \times 0.155 \times \frac{51}{365} = 38.70$
Interest from Aug. 20 to Dec.31 $= 1087.13 \times 0.155 \times \frac{133}{365} = 61.40$

Interest from June 30 to Dec. 31 $\longrightarrow$ $I_2 = 100.10$

Total interest earned in the first year is $I_1 + I_2 = \$187.23$.

Exercise 2.1

Part A

In questions 1 to 8 make use of the following table. In each case find the accumulated value and the compound interest earned.

No.	Principal	Nominal Rate	Conversion Frequency	Time
1.	$100	$15\frac{1}{2}$%	Annually	5 years
2.	$500	$11\frac{1}{4}$%	Monthly	2 years
3.	$220	8.8%	Quarterly	3 years
4.	$1000	9%	Semi-annually	6 years
5.	$50	12%	Monthly	4 years
6.	$800	$7\frac{3}{4}$%	Annually	10 years
7.	$300	8%	Weekly	3 years
8.	$1000	10%	Daily	2 years

9. Accumulate $500 for one year at (a) $j_{12} = 8\%$, (b) $j_{12} = 12\%$, (c) $j_{12} = 16\%$.
10. How much money will be required on December 31st, 1986 to repay a loan of $2000 made December 31st, 1983 if $j_4 = 12\%$?
11. Find the accumulated value of $100 over 5 years at 16% nominal rate compounded: (a) annually; (b) semi-annually; (c) quarterly; (d) monthly; (e) daily.
12. Parents put $1000 into a savings account at the birth of their daughter. If the account earns interest at 12% compounded monthly, how much money will be in the account when their daughter is 18 years old?
13. In 1492, Queen Isabella sponsored Christopher Columbus' journey by giving him $10 000. If she had placed this money in a bank account at $j_1 = 3\%$ (interest rates weren't as high in 1492 as today), how much money would be in the account in 1992?
14. John has a savings account which pays interest at $13\frac{3}{4}$% per annum.
    The interest is calculated daily on the minimum daily balance and is paid into the account at the end of each month.
    Given the following transactions for his account opened on March 15, find the interest earned by the end of July.

Date	Deposit	Withdrawal
March 15	800	
April 30	300	
July 7		200

Part B

1. Melinda has a savings account that earns interest at 12% per annum. She opened her account with $1000 on December 31. How much interest will she earn during the first year if
   a) the interest is compounded daily;
   b) the interest is calculated daily and paid into the account on June 30 and December 31;
   c) the interest is calculated daily and paid into the account at the end of each month?
2. Prove the fundamental compound interest formula $S = P(1+i)^n$ using mathematical induction.

3. Set up a table and plot the graph showing the growth of $100 at compound interest rate $j_{365} = 8\%, 12\%, 16\%$ and $time = 5, 10, 15, 20$ and 25 years.
4. Find the compound interest earned on an investment of $10 000 for 10 years at nominal rate 12% compounded with frequencies $m = 1, 2, 4, 12, 52$ and 365.

2.2 Equivalent Rates

The yearly nominal rate is meaningless until we specify the frequency of conversion m. The table below illustrates the effect of frequency of conversion on the amount to which $10 000 will accumulate in 10 years at a nominal rate of 8% compounded with frequencies $m = 1, 2, 4, 12$, and 365.

Frequency of conversion	Rate per period	Number of periods	Amount
$m = 1$	$i = 8\%$	10	$21 589.25
$m = 2$	$i = 4\%$	20	$21 911.23
$m = 4$	$i = 2\%$	40	$22 080.40
$m = 12$	$i = \frac{2}{3}\%$	120	$22 196.40
$m = 365$	$i = \frac{8}{365}\%$	3650	$22 253.41

At the same nominal rate the accumulated value depends on the frequency of conversion; it increases with the increased frequency of conversion.

For a given nominal rate j_m compounded m times per year, we define the corresponding **effective rate** to be that rate j which, if compounded annually, will produce the same amount of interest per year. To find the yearly effective rate j corresponding to a given nominal rate j_m we compare the accumulated values of $1 at the end of 1 year. At the rate j, $1 will accumulate at the end of 1 year to $1 + j$. At the rate $i = j_m/m$, $1 will accumulate at the end of 1 year to $(1 + i)^m$.

Thus,

$$1 + j = (1 + i)^m$$

$$j = (1 + i)^m - 1 \tag{10}$$

Example 1   Find the effective rate j corresponding to (a) $j_2 = 10\%$, (b) $j_{12} = 18\%$, (c) $j_{365} = 13\frac{1}{4}\%$.

Solution a $1 at rate j for 1 year will accumulate to $1+j$

$1 at rate $j_2 = 10\%$ for 1 year will accumulate to $(1.05)^2$

Comparing the accumulated values we obtain

$1 + j = (1.05)^2 = 1.1025$ and $j = 0.1025 = 10.25\%$.

Solution b   We have $i = 1\frac{1}{2}\% = .015$ and applying equation (10)

$j = (1.015)^{12} - 1 = 0.195\ 618\ 16 \doteq 19.56\%$.

Solution c   Applying equation (10) we have

$j = \left(1 + \frac{.1325}{365}\right)^{365} - 1 = .141\ 651\ 39 \doteq 14.17\%$.

Two compound interest rates are said to be *equivalent* if they yield the same accumulated values at the end of one year, and hence at the end of any number of years.

Example 2   Find the rate j_4 equivalent to (a) $j_{12} = 12\%$; (b) $j_2 = 10\%$.

Solution   We shall compare the accumulated values of $1 at the end of 1 year.
Solution a $1 at the rate j_4 will accumulate at the end of 1 year to $(1 + i)^4$.
$1 at the rate $j_{12} = 12\%$ will accumulate at the end of 1 year to $(1.01)^{12}$.
Thus

$$(1 + i)^4 = (1.01)^{12}$$
$$1 + i = (1.01)^3$$
$$i = (1.01)^3 - 1$$
$$i = 0.030\ 301$$

and

$$j_4 = 4i = 0.121204 \doteq 12.12\%$$

Solution b $1 at the rate j_4 will accumulate at the end of 1 year to $(1 + i)^4$.
$1 at the rate $j_2 = 10\%$ will accumulate at the end of 1 year to $(1.05)^2$.
Thus

$$(1 + i)^4 = (1.05)^2$$
$$1 + i = (1.05)^{\frac{1}{2}}$$
$$i = (1.05)^{\frac{1}{2}} - 1$$
$$i = 0.024\ 695\ 08$$

and

$$j_4 = 4i = 0.0987803 \doteq 9.88\%$$

Example 3   What simple interest rate is equivalent to $j_2 = 9\%$ if money is invested for 3 years?

Solution   Let r be the unknown simple interest rate. $1 invested at rate r will accumulate at the end of 3 years to $1 + 3r$. $1 invested at $j_2 = 9\%$ will accumulate at the end of 3 years to $(1.045)^6$.
Thus

$$1 + 3r = (1.045)^6$$
$$1 + 3r = 1.302\ 260\ 1$$
$$r = 0.100\ 753\ 38$$
$$r \doteq 10.08\%$$

Exercise 2.2

Part A

Find the annual effective rate (two decimals) equivalent to the following rates:

1. $j_2 = 7\%$
2. $j_4 = 16\%$
3. $j_4 = 8\%$
4. $j_{365} = 12\%$
5. $j_{12} = 18\%$

Find the nominal rate (two decimals) equivalent to the given yearly effective rate:

6. $j = 6\%$ find j_2
7. $j = 9\%$ find j_4

8. $j = 10\%$ find j_{12}
9. $j = 17\%$ find j_{365}
10. $j = 8\%$ find j_{52}

Find the nominal rate (two decimals) equivalent to the given nominal rate:

11. $j_2 = 8\%$ find j_4
12. $j_4 = 6\%$ find j_2
13. $j_{12} = 18\%$ find j_4
14. $j_6 = 10\%$ find j_{12}
15. $j_4 = 8\%$ find j_2
16. $j_{52} = 11\%$ find j_2.
17. $j_2 = 18\frac{1}{4}\%$ find j_{12}.
18. $j_4 = 12.79\%$ find j_{365}.
19. What simple interest rate is equivalent to $j_{12} = 13\frac{1}{2}\%$ if money is invested for 2 years?
20. What simple interest rate is equivalent to $j_{365} = 12\%$ if money is invested for 3 years?
21. If the interest on the outstanding balance of a credit card account is charged at $1\frac{3}{4}\%$ per month, what is the effective rate of interest?
22. A trust company offers guaranteed investment certificates paying $j_2 = 15.5\%$ and $j_1 = 16\%$. Which option yields the higher effective rate of interest?
23. Which rate gives the best and the worst rate of return on your investment?

   a) $j_{12} = 15\%, j_2 = 15\frac{1}{2}\%, j_{365} = 14.9\%$
   b) $j_{12} = 16\%, j_2 = 16\frac{1}{2}\%, j_{365} = 15.9\%$

Part B

1. Find out what is the current best and worst interest rate available on 5 year guaranteed investment certificates by checking three different financial institutions. Calculate the difference in compound interest earned using the best and the worst rate available if you buy a $2000, 5-year certificate.
2. Find the effective rate of interest on the major credit cards and charge-accounts in major department stores.
3. For a given nominal rate $j_2 = 2i$ develop equations for equivalent nominal rates j_1, j_4, j_{12} and j_{365}.
4. For a given nominal rate $j_{12} = 12i$ develop equations for equivalent nominal rates $j_1, j_2, j_4, j_{52}, j_{365}$.
5. Twenty thousand dollars is invested for 5 years at a nominal rate of 16%. Find the accumulated value of the investment if the rate is compounded with frequencies $m = 1,2,4,12$ and 365 using
   a) the fundamental compound interest formula.
   b) equivalent effective rates.
   c) equivalent rates compounded monthly.
      Compare your answers in a) b) and c).
6. A sum of money is left invested for 3 years. In the first year it earns interest at $j_{12} = 15\%$. In the second year, the rate of interest earned is $j_4 = 10\%$ and in the third year the rate of interest changes to $j_{365} = 12\%$. Find the level rate of interest, j_1, that would give the same accumulated value at the end of three years.

7. A bank pays 12% per annum on its savings accounts. At the end of every three years, a 2% bonus is paid on the balance at that time. Find the effective rate of interest, j_1, earned by an investor if the deposit is withdrawn:
   a) in 2 years,
   b) in 3 years,
   c) in 4 years.

8. j_2 and $j_1 = j_2 + .0025$ are equivalent rates of interest. Find j_2.

9. An insurance company says you can pay for your life insurance by paying $100 at the beginning of each year or $51.50 at the beginning of each half-year. They say the rate of interest underlying this calculation is $j_2 = 3\%$. What is the true value of j_2?

2.3 Discounted Value at Compound Interest

In business transactions it is frequently necessary to determine what principal P now will accumulate at a given interest rate to a specified amount S at a specified future date. From fundamental formula (9) we can obtain

$$P = \frac{S}{(1 + i)^n} = S(1 + i)^{-n} \tag{11}$$

P is called the **discounted value** of S, or **present value** of S, or **proceeds**. The process of finding P from S is called **discounting**. The difference $S - P$ is called **compound discount** on S. It is *compound discount at an interest rate* and it is practically always used in compound discount problems. Compound discount at a discount rate will not be considered in this text.

The factor $(1 + i)^{-1}$ in (11) is called the **discount factor** or the **discounted value of $1**.

To obtain a discounted value P of S for n periods at rate i, we multiply S by the corresponding discount factor $(1+i)^{-n}$. Values of $(1+i)^{-n}$ will be calculated by using the function y^x of your calculator.

Example 1 Find the discounted value of $100\ 000 due in (a) 10 years; (b) 25 years, if money is worth $j_{12} = 12\%$.
Solution a We have $S = 100\ 000$, $i = .01$, $n = 120$ and calculate $P = 100\ 000(1.01)^{-120} = \$30\ 299.48$.
Solution b We have $S = 100\ 000$, $i = .01$, $n = 300$ and calculate $P = 100\ 000(1.01)^{-300} = \$5053.45$.

Example 2 Let us suppose you can buy a lot for $18\ 000 cash or for payments of $10\ 000 now, $5000 in 1 year and $5000 in 2 years. If money is worth $j_{12} = 16\%$, which option is better for you?
Solution We arrange the data on a time diagram below. Notice that time is in terms of interest conversion periods.

option 1:   18 000

```
  ├───────────────────────┼───────────────────────┤
  0                        12                       24
                      (1 year)                  (2 years)
```

option 2:   10 000   5000   5000

Discounted value of option 1 is $18 000.

Discounted value of option 2 is $10\ 000 + 5000\left(1+\dfrac{.16}{12}\right)^{-12} + 5000\left(1+\dfrac{.16}{12}\right)^{-24}$

$= 10\ 000 + 4265.23 + 3638.43$

$= \$17\ 903.66$

You should take option 2 and save $18\ 000 - 17\ 903.66 = \$96.34$ at present.

A different rate of interest could lead to a different decision. If money were worth $j_{12} = 12\%$, the discounted value of option 2 would be

$10\ 000 + 5000(1.01)^{-12} + 5000(1.01)^{-24} = 10\ 000 + 4437.25 + 3937.83$

$\qquad\qquad\qquad\qquad\qquad\qquad\qquad = \$18\ 375.08$

and you should take option 1 and save $375.08.

Example 3   A note for $2 000 dated September 1, 1983 is due with compound interest at $j_{12} = 16\%$, 3 years after date.* On December 1, 1984 the holder of the note has it discounted by a lender who charges $j_4 - 17\frac{1}{4}\%$.
Find the proceeds and the compound discount.

Solution   We arrange the data on a time diagram below.

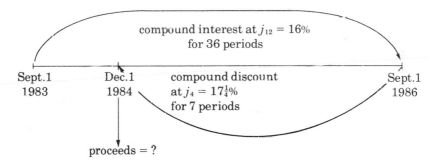

The maturity value of the note is $S = 2000\left(1+\dfrac{.16}{12}\right)^{36} = \$3221.91.$

The proceeds are $P = 3221.91\left(1+\dfrac{.1725}{4}\right)^{-7} = \$2397.50.$

The compound discount equals $3221.91 - 2397.50 = \$824.41.$

Exercise 2.3
Part A:
Find the discounted value in each of the following situations.

---

*Long-term promissory notes (with a term longer than one year) are usually subject to compound interest. There is no requirement to add three days of grace in determining the legal due date (maturity date) of a long-term promissory note.

No.	Amount	Nominal Rate	Conversion	Time
1.	$100	16%	quarterly	3 years
2.	$50	$8\frac{1}{2}$%	monthly	2 years
3.	$2000	11.8%	yearly	10 years
4.	$500	20%	semi-annually	5 years
5.	$800	12%	daily	3 years

6. What amount of money invested today will grow to $1000 at the end of 5 years if $j_4 = 18\%$?

7. How much would have to be deposited today in an investment fund paying $j_{12} = 10.4\%$ to have $2000 in three years time?

8. What is the discounted value of $2500 due in 10 years if $j_2 = 9.6\%$?

9. On her 20th birthday a girl receives $1000 as a result of a deposit her parents made on the day she was born. How large was that deposit if it earned interest at $j_2 = 6\%$?

10. An obligation of $2000 is due December 31, 1987. What is the value of this obligation on June 30, 1983 at $j_4 = 13\frac{1}{4}\%$?

11. A note dated October 1, 1983 calls for the payment of $800 in 7 years. On October 1, 1985 it is sold at a price that will yield the investor $j_4 = 16\%$. How much is paid for the note?

12. A note for $250 dated August 1, 1983 is due with compound interest at $j_{12} = 15\frac{1}{4}\%$ 4 years after date. On November 1, 1984 the holder of the note has it discounted by a lender who charges $j_4 = 13\frac{1}{2}\%$.
What are the proceeds?

13. A note for $1000 dated January 1, 1985 is due with compound interest at 13% compounded semi-annually 5 years after date. On July 1, 1986 the holder of the note has it discounted by a lender who charges $14\frac{1}{2}\%$ compounded quarterly. Find the proceeds.

14. A man can buy a piece of land for $17 000 cash or payments of $12 000 down and $10 000 in 5 years. If he can earn $j_{365} = 16\%$, which plan is better?

15. Find the total current value on July 1, 1983 of payments of $1000 on July 1, 1973 and $600 on July 1, 1990 if $j_2 = 9\%$.

16. If money is worth 15% effective, find the present value of a debt of $3000 with interest at $16\frac{1}{2}\%$ compounded semi-annually due in 5 years.

Part B

1. A person can buy a lot for $13 000 cash outright or $6000 down, $6000 in 2 years and $6000 in 5 years. Which option is better if money can be invested at
   a) $j_{12} = 18\%$,
   b) $j_4 = 12\%$ for the first 3 years and $j_4 = 14\%$ for the next 2 years?

2. A note for $2500 dated January 1, 1984 is due with interest at $j_{12} = 15\%$ 40 months later. On May 1, 1984 the holder of the note has it discounted by Financial Consultants Inc. at $j_4 = 16\frac{1}{4}\%$. The same day the note is sold by Financial Consultants Inc. to a bank that discounts notes at 16% effective. What is the profit made by Financial Consultants Inc.?

3. Find the compound discount if $1000 due in 5 years with interest at $14\frac{1}{2}\%$ effective is discounted at nominal rate 16% compounded with frequencies $m = 1,2,4,12,52$ and 365.

4. The management of a company must decide between two proposals. The following information is available:

	Investment	Net Cash Inflow at the End of		
Proposal	Now	Year 1	Year 2	Year 3
A	80 000	95 400	39 000	12 000
B	100 000	35 000	58 000	80 000

Advise management regarding the proposal that should be selected, assuming that on projects of this type the company can earn 14% effective.

2.4 Accumulated and Discounted Value for a Fractional Period of Time

Formulas (9) and (11) were developed under the assumption that n is an integer. Theoretically, formulas (9) and (11) can be used when n is a fraction. When we calculate the accumulated or the discounted value using formulas (9) or (11) for the fractional part of an interest conversion period we call it the **exact** or **theoretical method** of accumulating or discounting.

Example 1   Find the accumulated and the discounted value of $1500 for 16 months at $j_4 = 18\%$, using the exact method.

Solution   To calculate the exact accumulated value S of $1500, we use formula (9), substituting for $P = 1500$, $i = \frac{.18}{4} = 0.045$, $n = 5\frac{1}{3}$.

We obtain $S = 1500(1.045)^{5\ 1/3} = \$1896.90$

To calculate the exact discounted value P of $1500, we use formula (11), substituting for $S = 1500$, $i = 0.045$, $n = 5\frac{1}{3}$.

We obtain $P = 1500(1.045)^{-5\ 1/3} = \$1186.14$

In practice, the exact method of accumulating or discounting at a compound interest rate is rarely used. Instead, we use compound interest for the full number of conversion periods and simple interest for the fractional part of a conversion period. This method is called an **approximate** or **practical** method of accumulating or discounting and is illustrated in the following example. The use of simple interest for the fraction of a period is equivalent to linear interpolation as will be shown in problem 2 of Part B of Exercise 2.4. Linear interpolation is explained, in detail, in Appendix 3.

Example 2   Find the accumulated and the discounted value of $1500 for 16 months at $j_4 = 18\%$, using the approximate method, and compare the results with those of Example 1.

Solution   To calculate the approximate accumulated value S of $1500 for 16 months at $j_4 = 18\%$ we first accumulate $1500 for 5 periods at $j_4 = 18\%$ ($i = 0.045$) and then accumulate this value for additional 1 month at a simple interest rate of 18%. (See diagram.)

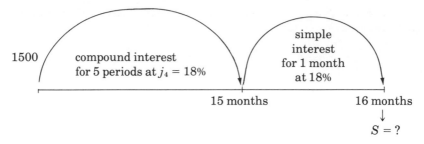

$$S = ?$$

Numerically, we can combine the two accumulations and obtain

$$S = 1500(1.045)^5\left[1+(.18)\left(\tfrac{1}{12}\right)\right] = \$1897.31$$

Note that in the simple interest accumulation we multiply by an accumulation factor $(1+rt)$ where r is a yearly rate and t is time in years.

To calculate the approximate discounted value P of $1500 for 16 months at $j_4 = 18\%$ we first discount $1500 for 6 periods at $j_4 = 18\%$ (in general we discount for the smallest number of whole periods containing the given time) and then accumulate this value for 2 months at a simple interest rate of 18%. (See diagram.)

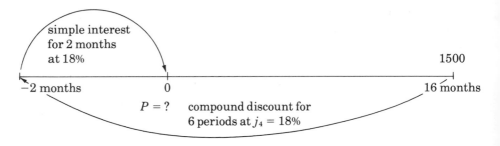

Numerically, we can combine the compound discount and simple interest calculations and obtain

$$P = 1500(1.045)^{-6}\left[1+(.18)\left(\tfrac{2}{12}\right)\right] = \$1186.40$$

Comparing the results of Example 2 with those of Example 1 we can conclude that the approximate accumulated and discounted values are slightly greater than the exact accumulated and discounted values.

The proof that the approximate accumulated and discounted values are always greater than the exact accumulated and discounted values is left as an exercise. See problem 1 of Part B of Exercise 2.4.

Unless stated otherwise, it will be understood that the practical method is to be used throughout this textbook.

Example 3   A note for $3000 without interest is due on August 18, 1985. On June 11, 1984, the holder of the note has it discounted by a lender who charges $j_{12} = 12\%$. What are the proceeds?

Solution   The legal due date is August 18, 1985. We arrange the data on the diagram below.

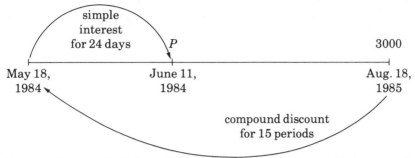

First we discount $3000 for 15 periods at rate $i = 1\%$ and then accumulate this value for 24 days at a simple interest rate 12%. Numerically

$$P - 3000(1.01)^{-15}\left[1 + (0.12)\left(\tfrac{24}{365}\right)\right] = \$2604.44$$

The proceeds are $2604.44.

Exercise 2.4
Part A
For each of problems 1 to 4 find the answer first using the exact method and then the practical method. Compare your answers in each case.

1. Find the accumulated value of $100 over 5 years 7 months if $j_2 = 13\tfrac{1}{2}\%$.
2. Find the accumulated value of $800 over 4 years 7 months if $j_4 = 20\%$.
3. Find the discounted value of $5000 due in 8 years 10 months if interest is at rate $j_2 = 12.73\%$.
4. Find the discounted value of $280 due in 3 years 7 months if interest is at rate $j_1 = 10\%$.
5. A note of face value $2000 is due without interest on October 20, 1988. On April 28, 1983, the holder of the note has it discounted at a bank that charges $j_4 = 12\%$. What are the proceeds?
6. On July 7, 1983, Mrs. Smith borrowed $1200 at $j_{12} = 12\%$. How much would she have to repay on September 18, 1986?
7. On April 7, 1984, a debt of $4000 was incurred at a rate $j_2 = 18\%$. What amount will be required to settle the debt on September 19, 1989?
8. A noninterest-bearing note for $850 is due December 8, 1986. On August 7, 1983, the holder of the note has it discounted by a lender who charges $j_2 = 15\tfrac{1}{4}\%$. What are the proceeds?

Part B
1. a) Assuming that $0 < i < 1$, prove that
    (i) $(1+i)^t < 1 + it$ if $0 < t < 1$
    (ii) $(1+i)^t > 1 + it$ if $t > 1$
    [Hint: Use the binomial theorem.]
    b) Give a geometric illustration of the relationships in (a) by graphing $(1+i)^t$ and $1 + it$.

c) Show that the approximate accumulated and discounted values are greater than the exact accumulated and discounted values when fractional parts of interest periods are involved.

2. A common method for finding an unknown value between two known values is called linear interpolation. It is based on the following formula:

$$f(n + k) = (1 - k)f(n) + kf(n + 1)   0 < k < 1$$

e.g.

$$f(2\tfrac{2}{3}) = \tfrac{1}{3}f(2) + \tfrac{2}{3}f(3)$$

Applying this to the compound interest formula where $f(n) = (1 + i)^n$ we get:

$$(1 + i)^{n+k} = (1 - k)(1 + i)^n + k(1 + i)^{n+1}   0 < k < 1$$

Prove that using linear interpolation is equivalent to assuming simple interest in the final fractional period, i.e., prove:

$$(1 - k)(1 + i)^n + k(1 + i)^{n+1} = (1 + i)^n(1 + ki)$$

Students not familiar with linear interpolation should read Appendix 3.

3. A note for $1200 dated August 24, 1983 is due with interest at $j_{12} = 14\tfrac{3}{4}\%$ in 2 years. On June 18, 1984 the holder of the note has it discounted by a lender who charges $16\tfrac{1}{4}\%$ compounded quarterly. Find the proceeds and the compound discount.

4. A promissory note for $2000 dated April 5, 1984 is due on October 4, 1988 with interest at $j_1 = 12\%$. On June 7, 1985 the holder of the note has it discounted at a bank who charges $j_4 = 14\%$. Find the proceeds and the compound discount.

2.5 Finding the Rate and the Time

When S, P and n are given, we can substitute the given values into the fundamental compound interest formula $S = P(1+i)^n$ and solve it for the unknown interest rate i. We shall discuss two methods of solutions. Both methods give the exact value of i.

a) We can solve the exponential equation

$$P(1+i)^n = S$$

directly for i, using the power key of our calculator.
    We have

$$P(1+i)^n = S$$
$$(1+i)^n = \frac{S}{P}$$
$$1+i = \left(\frac{S}{P}\right)^{1/n}$$
$$i = \left(\frac{S}{P}\right)^{1/n} - 1$$

b) Logarithms may be used to solve the exponential equation $P(1+i)^n = S$ for the unknown rate i. An explanation of common logarithms together with applications to compound interest problems will be found in

Appendix 1. In this textbook we assume that students have pocket calculators with a built-in common logarithmic function log x and its inverse function 10^x. This eliminates the use of logarithmic tables.

Example 1   At what nominal rate j_{12} will money triple itself in 12 years?

Solution   We can use any sum of money as the principal. Let $P = x$, then $S = 3x$, and $n = 144$.

Substituting in $S = P(1+i)^n$ we obtain an equation for the unknown interest rate i per month

$$3x = x(1+i)^{144}$$
$$(1+i)^{144} = 3$$

Solving the exponential equation $(1+i)^{144} = 3$ directly for i and then using a pocket calculator we have

$$(1+i)^{144} = 3$$
$$1+i = 3^{1/144}$$
$$i = 3^{1/144} - 1$$
$$i = .007\ 658\ 43$$
$$j_{12} = 12i = .091\ 901\ 14$$
$$j_{12} \doteq 9.19\%$$

Solving the exponential equation $(1+i)^{144} = 3$ using logarithms we have

$$144\ \log(1+i) = \log 3$$
$$144\ \log(1+i) = .477\ 121\ 25$$
$$\log(1+i) - .003\ 313\ 34$$
$$1+i = 1.007\ 658\ 43$$
$$i = .007\ 658\ 43$$

and

$$j_{12} = .091\ 901\ 14$$
$$j_{12} \doteq 9.19\%.$$

When S, P and i are given, we can substitute the given values into the fundamental compound amount formula $S = P(1+i)^n$ and solve it for the unknown n using one of the following methods:

a) Logarithms may be used to solve the exponential equation $P(1+i)^n = S$ for the unknown exponent n. If the theoretical method of accumulation is used, i.e., compound interest is allowed for the fractional part of the conversion period, a logarithmic solution gives the correct value of n.

b) Method of interpolation. Linear interpolation is explained in Appendix 3. If the practical method of accumulation is used, i.e., simple interest is allowed for the fractional part of the conversion period, interpolation gives the correct value of n. The actual accuracy of the solution depends on the number of decimal places in the accumulation factors used in the interpolation. In our examples we shall round off the factors to 4 decimal places, since additional places do not significantly increase the accuracy.

Example 2   How long will it take $500 to accumulate to $850 at $j_{12} = 12\%$? Assume that

a) the theoretical method of accumulation is in effect;
b) the practical method of accumulation is in effect.

Solution Let n represent the number of months, then we have

$$500(1+1\%)^n = 850$$
$$(1.01)^n = \frac{850}{500}$$
$$(1.01)^n = 1.7$$

a) If compound interest is allowed for the fractional part of the interest conversion period, we can solve the equation $(1.01)^n = 1.7$ by logarithms. We have

$$n \log 1.01 = \log 1.7$$
$$n = \frac{\log 1.7}{\log 1.01}$$
$$n = 53.3277 \text{ months}$$

Using approximate time (1 month = 30 days)

$$n \doteq 4 \text{ years 5 months 10 days}$$

b) If simple interest is allowed for the fractional part of the interest conversion period, then we find n by interpolation. Arranging the data in an interpolation table we have,

	$(1.01)^n$	n	
	1.6945	53	
.0169 { .0055 {	1.7000	n	} d } 1
	1.7114	54	

$$\frac{d}{1} = \frac{.0055}{.0169}$$
$$d \doteq .33$$

and $n = 53.33$ months.

Using approximate time (1 month = 30 days) we can find .33 months $\sim$ 10 days and $n \doteq 4$ years 5 months and 10 days.

Alternate Solution b

The accumulated value of $500 for 53 periods at $j_{12} = 12\%$ is $500 (1.01)^{53} = \$847.23$. Now we calculate how long it will take $847.23 to accumulate $2.77 simple interest at rate 12%.

$$t = \frac{I}{Pr} = \frac{2.77}{847.23 \times .12} = .027\ 245\ 65 \text{ years}$$

Using approximate time (1 year = 360 days) we obtain

$$t = 9.808\ 434\ 5 \text{ days} \sim 10 \text{ days}$$

Thus the time is 4 years 5 months and 10 days.

Note: In this example both methods, theoretical and practical, give the same answer, when the time is expressed in days. The actual difference in time between the two solutions is less than $\frac{7}{100}$ of a day.

If no interest is allowed for part of the interest period it would take 54 months or $4\frac{1}{2}$ years to accumulate at least $850.

Exercise 2.5
Part A
In problems 1 to 4 find the nominal rate of interest using both methods.

1. $P = \$2000$; $S = \$3000$; Time = 3 years 9 months.
   Find j_4.
2. $P = \$100$; $S = \$150$; Time = 4 years 7 months.
   Find j_{12}.
3. $P = \$200$; $S = \$600$; Time = 15 years.
   Find j_1.
4. $P = \$1000$; $S = \$1581.72$; Time = 3 years 6 months.
   Find j_2.

In problems 5 to 8 find the time, assuming that both the theoretical and the practical methods are used to accumulate P to S.

5. $P = \$2000$; $S = \$2800$; $j_4 = 10\%$.
6. $P = \$100$; $S = \$130$; $j_2 = 9\%$.
7. $P = \$500$; $S = \$800$; $j_{12} = 12\%$.
8. $P = \$1800$; $S = \$2200$; $j_4 = 8\%$.
9. An investment fund advertises that it will guarantee to double your money in 10 years. What rate of interest j_1 is implied?
10. If an investment grows 50% in 4 years what rate of interest j_4 is being earned?
11. From 1977 to 1982, the earnings per share of common stock of a company increased from $4.71 to $9.38. What was the compounded annual rate of increase to the nearest .1%?
12. If an investment grows from $4000 to $6000 in 3 years, what was the rate of growth j_{365}?

In problems 13 to 15 use logarithms to find the time.

13. How long will it take to double your deposit in a savings account that accumulates at
    a) $j_1 = 19.56\%$?
    b) $j_{365} = 15\%$?
14. How long will it take for $800 to grow to $1500 in a fund earning interest at rate 9.8% compounded semi-annually?
15. How long will it take to increase your investment by 50% at rate $14\frac{1}{4}\%$ compounded daily?

Part B

Use exact methods in all problems of Part B.

1. At a given rate of interest j_2, money will double in value in 8 years. If you invest $1000 at this rate of interest, how much money will you have
   a) in 5 years?
   b) in 10 years?
2. If money doubles at a certain rate of interest compounded daily in 6 years, how long will it take for the same amount of money to triple in value?
3. Draw a graph showing the time needed to double your money at rate j_1 for the rates 2%, 4%, 6%,... 20%.
4. Five hundred dollars was deposited on January 1, 1980 in an account paying 12% compounded semi-annually. On January 1, 1983, $400 was deposited in another account paying $15\frac{2}{3}\%$ effective per annum. Find the time when the two accounts will be of equal value if the exact method is used for fractions of an interest period.
5. Determine how long $1 must be left to accumulate at $j_{12} = 18\%$ for it to amount

to twice the accumulated value of another $1 deposited at the same time at $j_2 = 10\%$.

6. Money doubles in t years at rate of interest j_1. At what rate of interest j_1 will money double in $\frac{t}{2}$ years? Why isn't your answer $2j_1$?

2.6 Equations of Value

In Chapter 1, Section 1.3 we dealt with equations of value at a simple interest rate. We suggest that the student read over Section 1.3 before studying this section, since most of the principles and procedures from Section 1.3 will apply here as well.

In general, we compare dated values by the following **definition of equivalence**:

$X due on a given date is equivalent at a given compound interest rate i to $Y due n periods later, if

$$Y = X(1 + i)^n \text{ or } X = Y(1 + i)^{-n}$$

The following diagram illustrates dated values equivalent to a given dated value X.

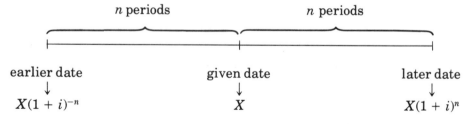

Note   Based on the time diagram above we can state the following simple rules:

When we move money forward, we accumulate, i.e., we multiply the sum by an accumulation factor $(1 + i)^n$.

When we move money backward, we discount, i.e., we multiply the sum by a discount factor $(1 + i)^{-n}$.

The following property of equivalent dated values holds at compound interest:

At a given compound interest rate, if X is equivalent to Y, and Y is equivalent to Z, then X is equivalent to Z.

To prove this property we arrange our data on a time diagram.

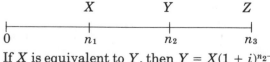

If X is equivalent to Y, then $Y = X(1 + i)^{n_2 - n_1}$

If Y is equivalent to Z, then $Z = Y(1 + i)^{n_3 - n_2}$

Eliminating Y from the second equation we obtain

$$Z = X(1 + i)^{n_2-n_1}(1 + i)^{n_3-n_2} = X(1 + i)^{n_3-n_1}$$

Thus Z is equivalent to X.*

Note The above property, also called transitivity does not hold at a simple interest rate. As a result, the solutions to the problems by equations of value at simple interest do depend on the selection of the focal date.

Example 1 An obligation of $500 falls due at the end of 3 years. Find an equivalent debt at the end of (a) 3 months; (b) 3 years 9 months, at $j_4 = 12\%$.

Solution We arrange the data on a time diagram below.

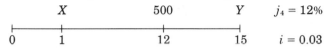

By definition of equivalence

$$X = 500(1.03)^{-11} = \$361.21$$
$$Y = 500(1.03)^{3} = \$546.36$$

Note that X and Y are equivalent by verifying

$$Y = X(1.03)^{14} \text{ or } 546.36 = 361.21(1.03)^{14}$$

The sum of a set of dated values, due on different dates, has no meaning. We have to replace all the dated values by equivalent dated values, due on the same date. The sum of the equivalent values is called the **dated value of the set**.

At compound interest the following property is true: *The various dated values of the same set are equivalent.* The proof is left as an exercise. See problem 1 of Part B of Exercise 2.6.

Example 2 A person owes $200 due in 6 months and $300 due in 15 months. What single payment (a) now, (b) in 12 months will liquidate these obligations if money is worth $j_{12} = 15\%$?

Solution We arrange the data on the diagram below. Let X be the single payment now and Y be the single payment in 12 months.

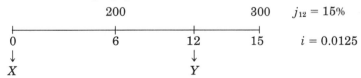

We calculate the equivalent dated values X and Y

$$X = 200(1.0125)^{-6} + 300(1.0125)^{-15} = 185.63 + 249.00 = \$434.63$$
$$Y = 200(1.0125)^{6} + 300(1.0125)^{-3} = 215.48 + 289.03 = \$504.51$$

We can verify the property of equivalence of X and Y by showing that

$$Y = X(1.0125)^{12} = 434.63(1.0125)^{12} = \$504.50$$

or $X = Y(1.0125)^{-12} = 504.51(1.0125)^{-12} = \$434.64$

The 1 cent error is due to rounding off in calculating X and Y.

---

*In mathematics, an equivalence relation must satisfy the property of transitivity. Thus, strictly speaking, the equivalence of dated values at a simple interest rate is not an equivalence relation. The equivalence of dated values at a compound interest rate is an equivalence relation.

As stated in Section 1.3, one of the most important problems in the mathematics of finance is the replacing of a given set of payments by an equivalent set. Two sets of payments are equivalent at a given compound interest rate if the dated values of the sets, on any common date, are equal. An equation stating that the dated values, on a common date, of two sets of payments are equal is called an **equation of value** or an **equation of equivalence**. The date used is called the **focal date** or the **comparison date**.

The procedure, described in Section 1.3, for solving problems in mathematics of finance by equations of value, applies the same way when compound interest is used. The answers however will not depend on the location of the focal date.

The following examples illustrate the use of equations of value in the mathematics of finance.

Example 3   A debt of $1000 with interest at $j_4 = 10\%$ will be repaid by a payment of $200 at the end of 3 months and 3 equal payments at the ends of 6, 9, and 12 months. What will these payments be?

Solution   We arrange all the dated values on a time diagram.

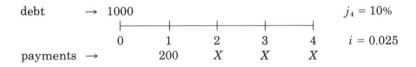

debt   → 1000 $j_4 = 10\%$

               0   1   2   3   4 $i = 0.025$

payments →   200   X   X   X

Any date can be selected as a focal date. We show the calculation using the end of 12 months and the present.

Equation of value at the end of 12 months:

$$\text{dated value of the payments} = \text{dated value of the debts}$$
$$200(1.025)^3 + X(1.025)^2 + X(1.025)^1 + X = 1000(1.025)^4$$
$$215.38 + 1.050\ 625X + 1.025X + X = 1103.81$$
$$3.075\ 625X = 888.43$$
$$X = \$288.86$$

Equation of value at the present:

$$200(1.025)^{-1} + X(1.025)^{-2} + X(1.025)^{-3} + X(1.025)^{-4} = 1000.00$$
$$195.12 + 0.951\ 814\ 4X + 0.928\ 599\ 41X + 0.905\ 950\ 64X = 1000.00$$
$$2.786\ 364\ 5X = 804.88$$
$$X = \$288.86$$

Example 4   A man leaves an estate of $50\ 000 which is invested at $j_{12} = 9\%$.

At the time of his death, he has two children aged 13 and 18. Each child is to receive an equal amount from the estate when they reach age 21. How much does each child get?

Solution   The older child will get X in 3 years; the younger child will get X in 8 years. We arrange the dated values on a time diagram.

$j_{12} = 9\%$
$i = 0.0075$

Equation of value at present:

the dated value of the payments = the value of the estate
$$X(1.0075)^{-36} + X(1.0075)^{-96} = 50\ 000$$
$$.764\ 148\ 95X + .488\ 061\ 70X = 50\ 000$$
$$1.252\ 210\ 65X = 50\ 000$$
$$X = \$39\ 929.39$$

Each child will receive $39 929.39.
The following calculation checks the correctness of the answer.

Amount in fund at the end of 3 years = $50\ 000(1.0075)^{36}$	= $65 432.27
Payment to the older child	= $39 929.39
Balance in the fund	= $25 502.88
Amount in fund after 5 more years = $25\ 502.88(1.0075)^{60}$	= $39 929.38

The one cent difference is due to rounding.

Exercise 2.6
Part A

1. If money is worth $j_4 = 16\%$, find the sum of money due at the end of 15 years equivalent to $1000 due at the end of 6 years.
2. What sum of money, due at the end of 5 years is equivalent to $1800 due at the end of 12 years if money is worth $j_2 = 11\frac{3}{4}\%$?
3. An obligation of $2500 falls due at the end of 7 years. Find an equivalent debt at the end of (a) 3 years; (b) 10 years, if $j_{12} = 10\%$.
4. One thousand dollars is due at the end of 2 years and $1500 at the end of 4 years. If money is worth $j_4 = 8\%$ find an equivalent single amount at the end of 3 years.
5. Eight hundred dollars is due at the end of 4 years and $700 at the end of 8 years. If money is worth $j_{12} = 12\%$ find an equivalent single amount at (a) the end of 2 years; (b) the end of 6 years; (c) the end of 10 years. Show your answers are equivalent.
6. A debt of $2000 is due at the end of 8 years. If $1000 is paid at the end of 3 years, what single payment at the end of 7 years would liquidate the debt if money is worth $j_2 = 12\%$?
7. A person borrows $4000 at $j_4 = 12\%$. He promises to pay $1000 at the end of one year, $2000 at the end of 2 years and the balance at the end of 3 years. What will the final payment be?
8. A consumer buys goods worth $1500. He pays $300 down and will pay $500 at the end of 6 months. If the store charges $j_{12} = 18\%$ on the unpaid balance, what final payment will be necessary at the end of one year?

9. A woman's bank account showed the following deposits and withdrawals:

	Deposits	Withdrawals
January 1, 1983	$200	
July 1, 1983	$150	
January 1, 1984		$250
July 1, 1984	$100	

If the account earns $j_2 = 16\%$, find the balance in the account on January 1, 1985.

10. Instead of paying $400 at the end of 5 years and $300 at the end of 10 years, a man agrees to pay X at the end of 3 years and $2X$ at the end of 6 years. Find X if $j_1 = 10\%$.

11. A man stipulates in his will that $50 000 from his estate is to be placed in a fund from which his three children are to each receive an equal amount when they reach age 21. When the man dies, the children are ages 19, 15, and 13. If this fund earns interest at $j_2 = 12\%$, how much does each receive?

12. A piece of land can be purchased by paying $50 000 cash or $20 000 down and two equal payments of $20 000 at the end of two years and four years respectively. To pay cash, the buyer would have to withdraw money from an investment earning interest at rate $j_2 = 8\%$. Which option is better and by how much?

Part B

1. a) Prove the following property in the case of a set of two dated values: The various dated values of the same set are equivalent at compound interest.
   b) Show, algebraically, why this is not true for simple interest.

2. If money is worth 14% per annum effective, what single sum of money payable at the end of 2 years will equitably replace $1000 due today plus a $2000 debt due at the end of 4 years with interest at $12\frac{1}{2}\%$ per annum compounded semi-annually.

3. On January 1, 1983 Mr. Smith borrowed $5000 to be repaid in a lump sum payment with interest at $j_4 = 13\%$ on January 1, 1989. It is now January 1, 1985. Mr. Smith would like to pay $500 today and complete the liquidation with equal payments on January 1, 1987 and January 1, 1989. If money is now worth $j_4 = 12\%$, what will these payments be?

2.7 Other Applications of Compound Interest Theory

We know that the more money you invest at some given interest rate, i, the more dollars of interest you will earn. Further, once you earn a dollar's worth of interest, it becomes a part of the invested money and earns interest itself. The latter characteristic is referred to as multiplicative or geometric growth and is what differentiates compound interest from simple interest.

Any time we have geometric growth we can use the theory of compound interest.

Example 1   A tree, measured in 1983, contains an estimated 150 cubic metres of wood. If the tree grows at a rate of 3% per annum, how much wood would it produce in 1993?

Solution   This is just geometric growth, so we can use compound interest theory. Thus, in 1993

$$\text{Amount of wood} = 150(1.03)^{10}$$
$$\doteq 202 \text{ cubic metres}$$

Example 2   The population of Canada in 1971 was 21.6 million people. In 1981 it was 24.4 million people.
a) What was the annual growth rate from 1971 to 1981?
b) At this rate of growth, when will the population reach 30 million people?

Solution
a) This is the same as finding the unknown rate of interest in a compound interest question. Hence,

$$21.6(1+i)^{10} = 24.4$$
$$(1+i)^{10} = \frac{24.4}{21.6}$$
$$1+i = \left(\frac{24.4}{21.6}\right)^{\frac{1}{10}}$$
$$1+i = 1.012\ 263\ 6$$
$$i \doteq 1.23\%$$

b) This is the same as finding unknown time in a compound interest question. Therefore

$$24.4(1.0123)^t = 30$$
$$(1.0123)^t = \frac{30}{24.4}$$
$$t \log(1.0123) = \log\frac{30}{24.4}$$
$$t \doteq 16.90 \text{ years.}$$

Therefore our population will reach 30 million sometime late in 1997 assuming the same rate of growth.

One very valuable use of compound interest theory is the analysis of rates of inflation as the next example shows.

Example 3   In 1970, the Canadian Consumer Price Index was set at 100. In 1978, the index was 175.15. That means that if goods cost an average of $100 in 1970, they cost $175.15 in 1978.
a) Over that 8 year period what was the average annual compound percentage rate of change?
b) If that rate of inflation was to continue, how long would it take before the purchasing power of a 1970 Canadian dollar was only 50¢?

Solution:
a) Find i such that

$$100(1+i)^8 = 175.15$$
$$(1+i)^8 = 1.7515$$
$$i = (1.7515)^{1/8} - 1$$
$$i \doteq 7.26\%$$

b) Find t such that
$$(1.0726)^t = 2$$
$$t \log(1.0726) = \log 2$$
$$t \doteq 9.89 \text{ years}$$

A rough rule of thumb used by many professionals says that at a rate of interest $j\%$, compounded yearly, the value of money will double in $\frac{70}{j}$ years. That is at 5%, money will double in value in 14 years; at 10% in 7 years. Similarly, if inflation runs at 5% for 14 years, the purchasing power of money will be cut in half. The same would be true of an inflation rate at 10% for 7 years. This is called the "Rule of 70."

Exercise 2.7
Part A
1. A city increased in population 4% a year during the period 1970 to 1980. If the population was 40 000 in 1970, what is the estimated population in 1990, assuming the rate of growth remains the same?
2. The population of Happy Town on December 31, 1982 was 15 000. The town is growing at a rate of 2% per annum. What would be the increase in population in the calendar year 1990?
3. If the population of a city goes from 100 000 to 160 000 in 8 years, what is the annual rate of increase?
4. If the cost of living rises 8% a year, how long will it take for the purchasing power of $1 to fall to 60¢?
5. The cost of living rises 8.7% a year for 5 years. Over that period of time, what would be the increase in value of a $60 000 house due to inflation only?
6. A university graduate starts his new job on his 22nd birthday at an annual salary of $20 000. If his salary goes up 10% a year (on his birthday) how much will he be making when he retires one day before his 65th birthday?

Part B
1. a) Investigate the accuracy of the "Rule of 70" by determining the exact time to double the value of money for the following rates of interest:
    $j_4 = 8\%, j_{12} = 12\%, j_{365} = 15\%$.
    b) Find an algebraic expression for the length of time it takes for money to double in value at rate i per period.
2. a) The number of fruit-flies in a certain lab increases at the compound rate of 4% every 40 minutes. If there are 100 000 flies at 1 p.m. today, what will be the increase in the number of flies between 7 a.m. and 11 a.m. tomorrow?
    b) At what time will there be 200 000 flies in the lab?
3. The population of Ecuador grows at 3% per annum and will double in size in x years. The population of Canada grows at $1\frac{1}{2}\%$ per annum and will double in size in y years. Find the ratio y/x.
4. The population of a county was 200 000 in 1970, and 250 000 in 1980. Estimate the change in population of the county between 1990 and 1995.

2.8   Review Exercises

1. Find the total value on June 1, 1984 of $1000 due on December 1, 1979 and $800 due on December 1, 1989 at $j_2 = 11.38\%$.

2. A person deposits $1500 into a mutual fund. If the fund earns 9.8% a year compounded daily for 10 years what will be the accumulated value of the initial deposit?

3. On the birth of their first grandchild, the Smiths bought a $100 savings bond which paid interest at $j_1 = 8\%$. How much money did their grandchild receive upon cashing this bond on her 20th birthday?

4. In the 1970 census the U.S.A. population was estimated at 203 million people. If this population grew at a rate of 3% per annum, what would be the population of the U.S.A. in the year 2000?

5. The XYZ company has had an increase in sales of 4% per annum. If sales in 1978 are $680 000, what would be the estimated sales for 1983?

6. Find the amount of interest earned between 5 and 10 years after the date of an investment of $100 if interest is paid semi-annually at $j_2 = 16\%$?

7. John buys goods worth $1500. He wants to pay $500 at the end of 3 months, $600 at the end of 6 months, and $300 at the end of 9 months. If the store charges $j_{12} = 21\%$ on the unpaid balance, what downpayment will be necessary?

8. A trust company offers guaranteed investment certificates paying $j_2 = 16\frac{3}{4}\%$, $j_4 = 16\frac{1}{4}\%$, or $j_{12} = 16\frac{1}{8}\%$. Rate the options from best to worst.

9. A note with face value $3000 is due without interest on November 21, 1987. On April 3, 1983 the holder of the note has it discounted at a bank charging $j_4 = 14\%$. What are the proceeds?

10. How long will it take $1000 to accumulate to $2500 at $j_{365} = 14\%$?

11. An investment fund advertises that it will triple your money in 10 years. What rate of interest j_4 is implied?

12. A loan of $10 000, taken on January 1, 1982 is to be repaid on January 1, 1988. The debtor would like to pay $2000 on January 1, 1985 and make equal payments on January 1, 1987 and January 1, 1988. What will the size of these payments be if interest is assumed to be at $j_{12} = 15\frac{1}{4}\%$?

13. By what date will $1000 deposited on November 20, 1983 at $j_{365} = 12\frac{1}{2}\%$ be worth at least $1250?

14. To pay off a loan of $5000 at $j_{12} = 15\%$, Mr. Smith agrees to make three payments in two, five and ten months respectively. The second payment is to be double the first, and the third payment is to be triple the first. What is the size of each payment?

15. At what nominal rate compounded daily will your investment double in 5 years?

16. Paul has deposited $1000 in a savings account paying interest at 10% per annum and now finds that his deposits have accumulated to $1610.51. If he had been able to invest the $1000 over the same period in a guaranteed investment certificate paying interest at $j_1 = 13\frac{1}{4}\%$ and had deposited this interest in his savings account, to what sum would his $1000 now have accumulated?

3

Ordinary Simple Annuities

3.1 Definitions

An **annuity** is a sequence of periodic payments, usually equal, made at equal intervals of time. Premiums on insurance, mortgage payments, interest payments on bonds, payments of rent, payments on instalment purchases, and dividends are just a few examples of annuities.

The time between successive payments of an annuity is called the **payment interval**. The time from the beginning of the first payment interval to the end of the last payment interval is called the **term** of an annuity. When the term of an annuity is fixed, i.e., the dates of the first and the last payments are fixed, the annuity is called an **annuity certain**. When the term of the annuity depends on some uncertain event, the annuity is called a **contingent annuity**. Bond interest payments form an annuity certain; life-insurance premiums form a contingent annuity (they cease with the death of the insured). Unless otherwise specified the word annuity will refer to an annuity certain.

When the payments are made at the ends of the payment intervals, the annuity is called an **ordinary annuity**. When the payments are made at the beginning of the payment intervals, the annuity is called an **annuity due**.

When the payment interval and interest conversion period coincide, the annuity is called a **simple annuity**, otherwise it is a **general annuity**.

We define the **accumulated value** of an annuity as the equivalent dated value of the set of payments due at the end of the term. Similarly, the **discounted value** of an annuity is defined as the equivalent dated value of the set of payments due at the beginning of the term.

We shall use the following notation:

R = the payment of the annuity.

n = the number of interest conversion periods during the term of an annuity (in the case of a simple annuity, n equals the total number of payments).

i = interest rate per conversion period.

S = the accumulated value, or the amount of an annuity.

A = the discounted value, or the present value of an annuity.

In this chapter, we shall deal only with ordinary simple annuities, that is, annuities whose payments are made at the ends of the interest conversion periods.

3.2 Accumulated Value of an Ordinary Simple Annuity

The accumulated value S of an ordinary simple annuity is defined as the equivalent dated value of the set of payments due at the end of the term, i.e., on the date of the last payment. Below we display an ordinary simple annuity on a time diagram with the interest period as the unit of measure.

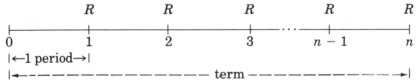

We can calculate the accumulated value S by repeated application of the compound interest formula as shown in the next example.

Example 1   Find the accumulated value of an ordinary simple annuity consisting of 4 quarterly payments of $250 each if money is worth 12% per annum compounded quarterly.

Solution   We arrange the data on a time diagram below.

```
        250           250           250           250
 +-------+-------------+-------------+-------------+
 0       1             2             3             4
                                                   |
                                                   v
                                               S = ?
```

To obtain S, we write an equation of value using the end of the term as the focal date. This gives

$$S = 250 + 250(1.03)^1 + 250(1.03)^2 + 250(1.03)^3$$
$$= 250 + 257.50 + 265.23 + 273.18 = \$1045.91$$

Now we develop a formula for the accumulated value, S, of an ordinary simple annuity using the sum of a geometric progression. Geometric progressions are dealt with in Appendix 2.

Let us consider an ordinary simply annuity of n payments of $1 each as shown on a time diagram below.

Let us denote the accumulated value of this annuity $s_{\overline{n}|i}$, read "s angle n at i." To obtain $s_{\overline{n}|i}$ we write an equation of value at the end of the term, accumulating each $1 payment to the date of the last payment.

$$s_{\overline{n}|i} = 1 + 1(1 + i)^1 + 1(1 + i)^2 + 1(1 + i)^3 + \ldots + 1(1 + i)^{n-1}$$

The expression on the right is a geometric progression of n terms whose first term is $t_1 = 1$ and whose common ratio is $r = (1 + i) > 1$. Then, applying the formula for the sum of a geometric progression, we obtain

$$s_{\overline{n}|i} = t_1 \frac{r^n - 1}{r - 1} = 1\frac{(1 + i)^n - 1}{(1 + i) - 1} = \frac{(1 + i)^n - 1}{i}$$

The factor $s_{\overline{n}|i} = \dfrac{(1 + i)^n - 1}{i}$ is called an **accumulation factor for n payments**, or the **accumulated value of $1 per period**.

To obtain the accumulated value, S, of an ordinary simple annuity of n payments of R each, we simply multiply R by $s_{\overline{n}|i}$. Thus the basic formula for the accumulated value S of an ordinary simple annuity is

$$S = Rs_{\overline{n}|i} = R\frac{(1 + i)^n - 1}{i} \qquad (12)$$

Using (12) in Example 1 above we calculate

$$S = 250\, s_{\overline{4}|.03} = 250\frac{(1.03)^4 - 1}{.03} = \$1045.91$$

Traditionally, textbooks in Mathematics of Finance provided Compound Interest Tables which gave values of the factors

$$(1 + i)^n, (1 + i)^{-n}, s_{\overline{n}|i} = \frac{(1 + i)^n - 1}{i} \text{ and } a_{\overline{n}|i} = \frac{1 - (1 + i)^{-n}}{i}.$$

(The last factor will be introduced in Section 3.3). The tables listed the values of $s_{\overline{n}|i}$ for specific values of the interest rate i and for specific values of the number of payments n. If i was not listed in the tables, the problem could not be solved using the tables. If n was not listed in the table, the annuity had to be divided into several annuities so that the number of payments in each annuity would be within the range of the table, and the equation of value could be used to calculate $s_{\overline{n}|i}$.

In this textbook we eliminated the compound interest tables and we calculate the factors $s_{\overline{n}|i} = \dfrac{(1 + i)^n - 1}{i}$ directly on a calculator and use all the digits of the display of the calculator to achieve the highest possible accuracy in our results.

For historical purposes we show an example of a Compound Interest Table for $i = 1\%$ and n from 1 to 100. We also illustrate the tabular method in comparison with the calculator method in Example 2.

COMPOUND INTEREST TABLE

$i = 1\%$

n	$(1+i)^n$	$s_{\overline{n}|i}$	$a_{\overline{n}|i}$
$\tfrac{1}{12}$	1.0008 2954	0.0829 5381	0.0828 8506
$\tfrac{1}{6}$	1.0016 5976	0.1659 7644	0.1657 0141
$\tfrac{1}{4}$	1.0024 9068	0.2490 6793	0.2484 4912
$\tfrac{1}{3}$	1.0033 2228	0.3322 2835	0.3311 2825
$\tfrac{5}{12}$	1.0041 5458	0.4154 5776	0.4137 3885
$\tfrac{1}{2}$	1.0049 8756	0.4987 5621	0.4962 8098
1	1.0100 0000	1.0000 0000	0.9900 9901
2	1.0201 0000	2.0100 0000	1.9703 9506
3	1.0303 0100	3.0301 0000	2.9409 8521
4	1.0406 0401	4.0604 0100	3.9019 6555
5	1.0510 1005	5.1010 0501	4.8534 3124
6	1.0615 2015	6.1520 1506	5.7954 7647
7	1.0721 3535	7.2135 3521	6.7281 9453
8	1.0828 5671	8.2856 7056	7.6516 7775
9	1.0936 8527	9.3685 2727	8.5660 1758
10	1.1046 2213	10.4622 1254	9.4713 0453
11	1.1156 6835	11.5668 3467	10.3676 2825
12	1.1268 2503	12.6825 0301	11.2550 7747
13	1.1380 9328	13.8093 2804	12.1337 4007
14	1.1494 7421	14.9474 2132	13.0037 0304
15	1.1609 6896	16.0968 9554	13.8650 5252
16	1.1725 7864	17.2578 6449	14.7178 7378
17	1.1843 0443	18.4304 4314	15.5622 5127
18	1.1961 4748	19.6147 4757	16.3982 6858
19	1.2081 0895	20.8108 9504	17.2260 0850
20	1.2201 9004	22.0190 0399	18.0455 5297
21	1.2323 9194	23.2391 9403	18.8569 8313
22	1.2447 1586	24.4715 8598	19.6603 7934
23	1.2571 6302	25.7163 0183	20.4558 2113
24	1.2697 3465	26.9734 6485	21.2433 8726
25	1.2824 3200	28.2431 9950	22.0231 5570
26	1.2952 5631	29.5256 3150	22.7952 0366
27	1.3082 0888	30.8208 8781	23.5596 0759
28	1.3212 9097	32.1290 9669	24.3164 4316
29	1.3345 0388	33.4503 8766	25.0657 8530
30	1.3478 4892	34.7848 9153	25.8077 0822
31	1.3613 2740	36.1327 4045	26.5422 8537
32	1.3749 4068	37.4940 6785	27.2695 8947
33	1.3886 9009	38.8690 0853	27.9896 9255
34	1.4025 7699	40.2576 9862	28.7026 6589
35	1.4166 0276	41.6602 7560	29.4085 8009
36	1.4307 6878	43.0768 7836	30.1075 0504
37	1.4450 7647	44.5076 4714	30.7995 0994
38	1.4595 2724	45.9527 2361	31.4846 6330
39	1.4741 2251	47.4122 5085	32.1630 3298
40	1.4888 6373	48.8863 7336	32.8346 8611
41	1.5037 5237	50.3752 3709	33.4996 8922
42	1.5187 8989	51.8789 8946	34.1581 0814
43	1.5339 7779	53.3977 7936	34.8100 0806
44	1.5493 1757	54.9317 5715	35.4554 5352
45	1.5648 1075	56.4810 7472	36.0945 0844
46	1.5804 5885	58.0458 8547	36.7272 3608
47	1.5962 6344	59.6263 4432	37.3536 9909
48	1.6122 2608	61.2226 0777	37.9739 5949
49	1.6283 4834	62.8348 3385	38.5880 7871
50	1.6446 3182	64.4631 8218	39.1961 1753

n	$(1+i)^n$	$s_{\overline{n}|i}$	$a_{\overline{n}|i}$
51	1.6610 7814	66.1078 1401	39.7981 3617
52	1.6776 8892	67.7688 9215	40.3941 9423
53	1.6944 6581	69.4465 8107	40.9843 5072
54	1.7114 1047	71.1410 4688	41.5686 6408
55	1.7285 2457	72.8524 5735	42.1471 9216
56	1.7458 0982	74.5809 8192	42.7199 9224
57	1.7632 6792	76.3267 9174	43.2871 2102
58	1.7809 0060	78.0900 5966	43.8486 3468
59	1.7987 0960	79.8709 6025	44.4045 0079
60	1.8166 9670	81.6696 6986	44.9550 3841
61	1.8348 6367	83.4863 6655	45.5000 3803
62	1.8532 1230	85.3212 3022	46.0396 4161
63	1.8717 4443	87.1744 4252	46.5739 0258
64	1.8904 6187	89.0461 8695	47.1028 7385
65	1.9093 6649	90.9366 4882	47.6266 0777
66	1.9284 6015	92.8460 1531	48.1451 5621
67	1.9477 4475	94.7744 7546	48.6585 7050
68	1.9672 2220	96.7222 2021	49.1669 0149
69	1.9868 9442	98.6894 4242	49.6701 9949
70	2.0067 6337	100.6763 3684	50.1685 1435
71	2.0268 3100	102.6831 0021	50.6618 9539
72	2.0470 9931	104.7099 3121	51.1503 9148
73	2.0675 7031	106.7570 3052	51.6340 5097
74	2.0882 4601	108.8246 0083	52.1129 2175
75	2.1091 2847	110.9128 4684	52.5870 5124
76	2.1302 1975	113.0219 7530	53.0564 8638
77	2.1515 2195	115.1521 9506	53.5212 7364
78	2.1730 3717	117.3037 1701	53.9814 5905
79	2.1947 6754	119.4767 5418	54.4370 8817
80	2.2167 1522	121.6715 2172	54.8882 0611
81	2.2388 8237	123.8882 3694	55.3348 5753
82	2.2612 7119	126.1271 1931	55.7770 8666
83	2.2838 8390	128.3883 9050	56.2149 3729
84	2.3067 2274	130.6722 7440	56.6484 5276
85	2.3297 8997	132.9789 9715	57.0776 7600
86	2.3530 8787	135.3087 8712	57.5026 4951
87	2.3766 1875	137.6618 7499	57.9234 1535
88	2.4003 8494	140.0384 9374	58.3400 1520
89	2.4243 8879	142.4388 7868	58.7524 9030
90	2.4486 3267	144.8632 6746	59.1608 8148
91	2.4731 1900	147.3119 0014	59.5652 2919
92	2.4978 5019	149.7850 1914	59.9655 7346
93	2.5228 2869	152.2828 6933	60.3619 5392
94	2.5480 5698	154.8056 9803	60.7544 0982
95	2.5735 3755	157.3537 5501	61.1429 8002
96	2.5992 7293	159.9272 9256	61.5277 0299
97	2.6252 6565	162.5265 6548	61.9086 1682
98	2.6515 1831	165.1518 3114	62.2857 5923
99	2.6780 3349	167.8033 4945	62.6591 6755
100	2.7048 1383	170.4813 8294	63.0288 7877

Example 2 Find the accumulated value of an annuity of $100 at the end of each month at $j_{12} = 12\%$ over 15 years, using a) a calculator only; b) the compound interest table.

Solution a We have $R = 100$, $i = 1\%$, $n = 15 \times 12 = 180$ and calculate

$$S = 100 \, s_{\overline{180}|.01} = 100 \frac{(1.01)^{180} - 1}{.01} = \$49\,958.02$$

Solution b Since the value of $n = 180$ is beyond the table limit, we divide the annuity of 180 payments into two annuities of 90 payments each as shown on the time diagram below (other combinations are possible).

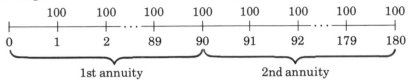

Using 180 as a focal date we obtain the accumulated value of the 1st annuity at 180

$$100 \, s_{\overline{90}|.01}(1.01)^{90}$$

and the accumulated value of the 2nd annuity at 180

$$100 \, s_{\overline{90}|.01}$$

Thus the accumulated value of the annuity of 180 payments is calculated using the compound interest table

$$S = 100 \, s_{\overline{90}|.01}(1.01)^{90} + 100 \, s_{\overline{90}|.01}$$
$$= 100(144.863\,267\,46)(2.448\,632\,67) + 100(144.863\,267\,46) = \$49\,958.02.$$

Example 3 A couple deposits $500 every 3 months into a savings account that pays interest at $j_4 = 11\%$. They made the first deposit on March 1, 1982. How much money will they have in the account just after they make their deposit on September 1, 1986?

Solution We arrange the data on a time diagram below, noting that the ordinary annuity starts one interest period before the 1st payment, i.e., on December 1, 1981.

	500	500	500		500	500
0	1	2	3	...	18	19
Dec. 1	March 1	June 1	Sept. 1		June 1	Sept. 1
1981	1982	1982	1982		1986	1986
						$S = ?$

The time elapsed from December 1, 1981 to September 1, 1986 is exactly 4 years 9 months or 19 quarters of a year. Thus we calculate the accumulated value S of an ordinary simple annuity of 19 payments of $500 each at $j_4 = 11\%$

$$S = 500 \, s_{\overline{19}|.0275} = 500 \frac{(1.0275)^{19} - 1}{.0275} = \$12\,261.51$$

Example 4 Mr. Smith has deposited $1000 at the end of each year into his Registered Retirement Savings Plan for the last ten years. His investments earned $j_1 = 9\%$ for the first four years and $j_1 = 9\frac{1}{2}\%$ for the last six years. What is the value of his RRSP 5 years after his last deposit assuming that his RRSP earns interest at $j_1 = 9\frac{1}{2}\%$ for the 5 year period after the last deposit.

Solution   We arrange data on a time diagram below.

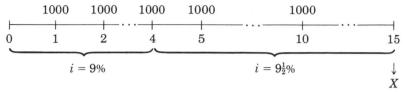

The equation of value at the end of 15 years gives the accumulated value X of all deposits.

$$X = 1000s_{\overline{4}|.09}(1.095)^{11} + 1000s_{\overline{5}|.095}(1.095)^5$$

$$= 1000\frac{(1.09)^4 - 1}{.09}(1.095)^{11} + 1000\frac{(1.095)^6 - 1}{.095}(1.095)^5$$

$$= 12\ 409.91 + 11\ 993.90 = \$24\ 403.81$$

The value of the RRSP 5 years after the last deposit is $24 403.81.

Exercise 3.2
Part A

1. Find the accumulated value of an ordinary simple annuity of $2000 per year for 5 years if money is worth a) $j_1 = 9\%$, b) $j_1 = 12\frac{1}{2}\%$, c) 18.88% effective.
2. Find the accumulated value of an annuity of $500 at the end of each month for 4 years at 9% per annum payable monthly.
3. A woman deposits $100 every 3 months into a savings account that pays interest at $j_4 = 16\%$. If she makes her first deposit on July 1, 1983 how much will she have in her account just after she makes her deposit on January 1, 1986?
4. One hundred dollars at the end of each year for 5 years is equivalent to what single payment at the end of 5 years if interest is at a) $j_1 = 15\frac{3}{4}\%$, b) 11% effective?
5. A man is repaying a debt with payments of $120 a month. If he misses his payments for June, July, August, and September, what payment will be required in October to put him back on schedule if interest is at 18% per annum convertible monthly?
6. Find the accumulated value of an annuity of $50 a month for 25 years if interest is a) 8% per annum compounded monthly, b) at $j_{12} = 16\%$.
7. Find the accumulated value of annual deposits of $100 each immediately after the 10th deposit, if the deposits earned 10% per annum in the first 5 years and 12% per annum in the last 5 years.
8. A man deposits $100 at the end of each year for 5 years and then $200 at the end of each year for 8 years. Find the accumulated value of these deposits if interest is 7% per annum.
9. A woman deposits $500 into an investment fund each January 1 starting in 1979 and continuing to 1988 inclusive. If the fund pays interest at $j_1 = 10\%$, how much will be in her account of January 1, 1993?
10. Mr. Jones has deposited $800 at the end of each year into a RRSP investment fund for the last 10 years. His investments earned $j_1 = 10\%$ for the first 7 years

and j_1 = 9% for the last 3 years. How much money does he have in his account 10 years after his last deposit if interest rates have remained level at j_1 = 9%?

Part B:

1. Jane opens a Savings Account with a deposit of $1000 on January 1, 1982. She then makes monthly deposits for 10 years (first deposit February 1, 1982) of $200. She then makes monthly withdrawals of $300 for 5 years (first withdrawal February 1, 1992). Find the balance in this account just after the last $300 withdrawal (i.e., January 1, 1997) if j_{12} = 12%.
2. Frank has deposited $1000 at the end of each year into his Registered Home Ownership Savings Plan (RHOSP) for the last ten years. His deposits earned interest at j_1 = 9% for the first 3 years, at j_1 = 11% for the next 4 years and at j_1 = 14% for the last 3 years. What is the value of his RHOSP after his last deposit?
3. Prove
   a) $(1 + i)s_{\overline{n}|i} = s_{\overline{n+1}|i} - 1$
   b) $s_{\overline{m+n}|i} = s_{\overline{m}|i} + (1 + i)^m s_{\overline{n}|i} = (1 + i)^n s_{\overline{m}|i} + s_{\overline{n}|i}$
   Illustrate both (a) and (b) using a time diagram.
4. If $s_{\overline{n}|i}$ = 10 and i = 10%, find $s_{\overline{n+2}|i}$, $s_{\overline{2n}|i}$.
5. Beginning June 30, 1982 and every three months until December 31, 1986 Albert deposits $300 to a new savings account. Starting September 30, 1987 he makes quarterly withdrawals of $500. What is Albert's balance after the withdrawal of June 30, 1989 if interest is at j_4 = 14% until March 31, 1985 and j_4 = 12% afterward?
6. It is desired to check a column of values of $s_{\overline{n}|i}$ from n = 20 through n = 40 by verifying their sum by means of an independent formula. Derive an expression for the sum of these values.
7. Show that $s_{\overline{n}|i} = n + \dfrac{n(n - 1)}{1 \cdot 2}i + \dfrac{n(n - 1)(n - 2)}{1 \cdot 2 \cdot 3}i^2 + \cdots$
8. a) Show that $(1 + i)^n = 1 + i\, s_{\overline{n}|i}$.
   b) Verbally interpret this formula.
9. Find an expression for an accumulation factor for n equal payments of $1 assuming simple interest at rate i per payment period.

3.3 Discounted Value of an Ordinary Simple Annuity

The discounted value A of an ordinary simple annuity is defined as the equivalent dated value of the set of payments due at the beginning of the term, i.e., 1 period before the first payment. Below we display an ordinary simple annuity on a time diagram.

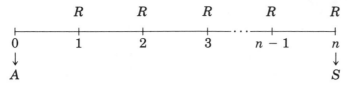

We note that A and S are both dated values of the same set of payments and thus they can be made equivalent to each other using

$$A = S(1 + i)^{-n}$$

Substituting for S from equation (12) we have

$$A = Rs_{\overline{n}|i}(1 + i)^{-n} = R\frac{(1 + i)^n - 1}{i}(1 + i)^{-n}$$

$$= R\frac{1 - (1 + i)^{-n}}{i}$$

If we set

$$a_{\overline{n}|i} = \frac{1 - (1 + i)^{-n}}{i}$$

we obtain

$$A = Ra_{\overline{n}|i} = R\frac{1 - (1 + i)^{-n}}{i} \tag{13}$$

The factor $a_{\overline{n}|i} = \dfrac{1 - (1 + i)^{-n}}{i}$ (read "a angle n at i") is called a **discount factor for n payments,** or **the discounted value of \$1 per period**.

In this textbook we calculate the factors $a_{\overline{n}|i} = \dfrac{1 - (1 + i)^{-n}}{i}$ directly on a calculator and use all the digits of the display of the calculator to achieve the highest possible accuracy in our results.

The basic formula (13) for the discounted value A of an ordinary simple annuity can be also developed using the sum of a geometric progression in a manner similar to that used in Section 3.2 to develop formula (12). This is left as an exercise.

Example 1   How much money is needed now to provide \$500 at the end of each month (first payment 1 month from now) for 15 years if the money earns interest at

a) $j_{12} = 13\frac{1}{4}\%$ for the next 15 years.
b) $j_{12} = 12\%$ for the first 8 years and at $j_{12} = 15\%$ for the next 7 years.

Solution a   We have $R = 500$, $i = \dfrac{.1325}{12}$, $n = 15 \times 12 = 180$ and using (13) we calculate

$$A = 500\, a_{\overline{180}|i} = 500\frac{1 - (1 + i)^{-180}}{i} = \$39\ 009.58$$

Note that the face value of 180 payments of \$500 each is \$90 000 whereas only \$39 009.58 is required at present to furnish these payments.

Solution b   We arrange the data on a time diagram below.

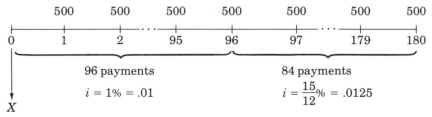

The equation of value at present gives the discounted value X of all payments

$$X = 500a_{\overline{96}|.01} + 500a_{\overline{84}|.0125}(1.01)^{-96}$$

$$= 500\frac{1 - (1.01)^{-96}}{.01} + 500\frac{1 - (1.0125)^{-84}}{.0125}(1.01)^{-96}$$

$$= 30\ 763.85 + 9\ 968.59 = \$40\ 732.44.$$

Example 2   Mr. Jones signed a contract that calls for a down payment of $1500 and for the payment of $200 a month for 10 years. Money is worth 12% per annum compounded monthly.

a) What is the cash value of the contract?
b) If Mr. Jones missed the first 8 payments, what must he pay at the time the 9th payment is due to bring himself up to date?
c) If Mr. Jones missed the first 8 payments, what must he pay at the time the 9th payment is due to discharge his indebtedness completely?
d) If, at the beginning of the 5th year (just after the 48th payment is made), the contract is sold to a buyer at a price which will yield $j_{12} = 15\%$, what does the buyer pay?

Solution a   Let C denote the cash value of the contract. Then C is $1500 plus the discounted value of 120 monthly payments of $200 each

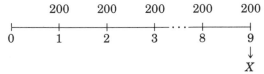

$$C = 1500 + 200a_{\overline{120}|.01} = 1500 + 200\frac{1 - (1.01)^{-120}}{.01}$$

$$= 1500 + 13\ 940.10 = \$15\ 440.10$$

Solution b   Let X denote the required payment. Mr. Jones must pay the accumulated value of the first 9 payments at the time the 9th payment is due.

We calculate

$$X = 200s_{\overline{9}|.01} = 200\frac{(1.01)^9 - 1}{.01} = \$1873.71$$

Solution c   Let Y denote the required payment. Mr. Jones must pay the accumulated value of the first 9 payments plus the discounted value of the last $120 - 9 = 111$ payments at the time the 9th payment is due, in order to discharge his indebtedness completely.

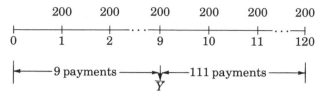

$$Y = 200s_{\overline{9}|.01} + 200a_{\overline{111}|.01}$$
$$= 200\frac{(1.01)^9 - 1}{.01} + 200\,\frac{1 - (1.01)^{-111}}{.01} = 1873.71 + 13\,372.38 = \$15\,246.09$$

Alternatively, we can calculate Y by finding the discounted value of all 120 payments and then accumulating it to the end of the 9th period, i.e.,

$$Y = 200\,a_{\overline{120}|.01}(1.01)^9 = 200\frac{1 - (1.01)^{-120}}{.01}(1.01)^9 = \$15\,246.09$$

Solution d   Let Z be the price of the contract the buyer must pay. Then Z is the discounted value of the remaining $120 - 48 = 72$ payments at $j_{12} = 15\%$. We calculate

$$Z = 200a_{\overline{72}|.0125} = 200\frac{1 - (1.0125)^{-72}}{.0125} = \$9458.49$$

The concept of the discounted value has important applications in *investment decision making*. In making investment decisions such as which asset to acquire or whether to buy or lease, we should compare the net discounted value of the cash flows of the different alternatives. This principle of comparison of the net discounted value of cash flows applies whether the asset is an investment in a machine, real estate, an entire business or an investment in bonds, etc.

Example 3   A company is considering the possibility of acquiring new computer equipment for $400 000 cash. The salvage value is estimated to be $50 000 at the end of the 6-year life of the equipment. Maintenance costs will be $4000 per month, payable at the end of each month. The company could lease the equipment for $12 000 per month, payable at the end of each month. Under the 6-year lease agreement the lessor would pay the maintenance costs. If the company can earn $j_{12} = 18\%$ on its capital, advise the company whether to buy or to lease.

Solution   We consider two alternatives: BUY or LEASE, and calculate the net discounted value of the cash flows for each alternative.

Net Discounted Value (NDV) = Discounted Value of Cash Inflows −
Discounted Value of Cash Outflows

NDV of BUY $= 50\,000(1.015)^{-72} - (400\,000 + 4\,000a_{\overline{72}|.015})$
$= 17\,116.50 - 575\,378.67 = -\$558\,262.17$

NDV of LEASE $= -12\,000a_{\overline{72}|.015} = -\$526\,136.00$

The negative values of NDV represent costs to the company and since NDV of LEASE is less than NDV of BUY, the company should lease the equipment.

Example 4   A mining company is considering whether or not to develop a mining property. It is estimated that an immediate expenditure of $7 000 000 will be needed to bring the property into production. Thereafter, the net cash inflow will be $1 700 000 at the end of each year for the next 10 years. An additional expenditure of $3 200 000 at the end of 11 years will have to be made to restore the property to an attractive condition. On projects of this type the company would expect to earn at least 20% per annum. Advise whether the company should proceed.

Solution　Discounted Value of cash outflows at $j_1 = 20\%$ is

$$7\ 000\ 000 + 3\ 200\ 000(1.20)^{-11} = 7\ 430\ 681.60$$

Discounted value of cash inflows at $j_1 = 20\%$ is

$$1\ 700\ 000 a_{\overline{10}|.20} = 7\ 127\ 202.50$$

The net discounted value of the project at $j_1 = 20\%$ is

$$7\ 127\ 202.50 - 7\ 430\ 681.60 = -303\ 479.10$$

The negative net discounted value of the project means that the project will not yield a 20% return per annum and therefore should be rejected.

If the above calculations are repeated using a desired rate of return of 15%, the net discounted value of the project will be

$$1\ 700\ 000 a_{\overline{10}|.15} - 7\ 000\ 000 - 3\ 200\ 000(1.15)^{-11} = \$844\ 088.35$$

The positive net discounted value of the project means that the project is earning more than 15% per annum.

Exercise 3.3
Part A

1. Find the discounted value of an ordinary simple annuity of $1000 per year for 5 years if money is worth a) $j_1 = 8\%$, b) $j_1 = 16\%$, c) $j_1 = 12.79\%$.
2. Find the discounted value of an annuity of $380 at the end of each month for 3 years at a) $j_{12} = 8\%$, b) $j_{12} = 12\%$, c) $j_{12} = 10.38\%$.
3. Mr. Jones wants to save enough money to send his two children to college. They are three years apart in age so he wants to have a sum of money that will provide $3000 a year for six years. Find that single sum required one year before the first withdrawal if interest is 13% per annum.
4. A woman has an insurance policy whose cash value at age 65 will provide payments of $1500 a year for 15 years, first payment at age 66. If the insurance company pays $j_1 = 9\%$ on its funds, what is the cash value at age 65?
5. A man buys a car by paying $500 down plus $180 a month for 3 years. What was the price of the car if the interest rate on the loan is $j_{12} = 18\%$?
6. An annuity pays $R per month starting February 1, 1982 and ending January 1, 1985 (inclusive). If the value of this annuity on January 1, 1985 is $8000 and $j_{12} = 11\%$, what is its value on January 1, 1982?
7. An heir receives an inheritance of $700 each half year for 15 years, the first payment being made in 6 months. If money is worth $j_2 = 10\%$, what is the cash value of this inheritance?
8. Find the discounted value of annual payments of $1000 each over 10 years if interest is $j_1 = 11\%$ for the first 4 years and $j_1 = 13\%$ for the last 6 years.
9. An annuity pays $2000 at the end of each year for 5 years and then $1000 at the end of each year for the next 8 years. Find the discounted value of these payments if $j_1 = 10\%$.
10. An annuity pays 10 annual payments of $200 each starting January 1, 1986. Find the discounted value of these payments on January 1, 1983 if $j_1 = 11\%$.

11. A contract calls for payments of $250 a month for 10 years. At the beginning of the 5th year (just after the 48th payment is made) the contract is sold to a buyer at a price that will yield $j_{12} = 14\%$. What does the buyer pay?

Part B

1. Derive the formula

$$a_{\overline{n}|i} = \frac{1 - (1 + i)^{-n}}{i}$$

as the sum of a geometric progression.

2. Prove
   a) $(1 + i)a_{\overline{n}|i} = a_{\overline{n-1}|i} + 1$
   b) $\dfrac{1}{s_{\overline{n}|i}} + i = \dfrac{1}{a_{\overline{n}|i}}$
   c) $a_{\overline{m+n}|i} = a_{\overline{m}|i} + (1 + i)^{-m}a_{\overline{n}|i} = (1 + i)^{-n}a_{\overline{m}|i} + a_{\overline{n}|i}$
   Illustrate part (c) on a time diagram.

3. a) Rank n, $a_{\overline{n}|i}$, and $s_{\overline{n}|i}$ in increasing order of magnitude.
   b) Explain your answer in (a) logically.
   c) Under what conditions will equality hold for all n?

4. If $a_{\overline{n}|i} = 10$ and $i = .08$, find $s_{\overline{n}|i}$ and $a_{\overline{2n}|i}$.

5. Explain logically $1 = ia_{\overline{n}|i} + (1 + i)^{-n}$ and illustrate on a time diagram.

6. If $a_{\overline{2n}|i} = 1.6a_{\overline{n}|i}$ and $i = 10\%$, find $s_{\overline{2n}|i}$.

7. If $a_{\overline{n}|i} = 6$ when $i = \dfrac{1}{9}$, find $a_{\overline{n+2}|i}$.

8. Mrs. Smith signed a contract that calls for payments of $150 a month for 5 years. If money is worth $j_{12} - 15\%$:
   a) What is the cash value of the contract?
   b) If Mrs. Smith missed making the first 6 payments, what must she pay at the time of the 7th payment to be fully up to date?
   c) If Mrs. Smith missed the first 6 payments, what must she pay at the time of the 7th payment to fully discharge all indebtedness? (Can you find the answer to (c) directly from the answer to (a)?)
   d) If, at the beginning of the 3rd year (after 24 payments have been made) the contract is sold to a buyer at a price that will yield $j_{12} = 18\%$, what does the buyer pay? Is this value larger or smaller than the discounted value of Mrs. Smith's indebtedness at that time?

9. An annuity pays $200 at the end of each month for 2 years, then $300 at the end of each month for the next year and then $400 at the end of each month for the next 2 years. Find the discounted value of these payments at $j_{12} = 10\%$.

10. Find an expression for a discount factor for n equal payments of $1 assuming simple interest at rate i per payment period.

11. If money doubles itself in n years at rate i, show that $a_{\overline{n}|i}$, $a_{\overline{2n}|i}$, and $s_{\overline{n}|i}$ are in arithmetic progression.

12. Prove that $(1 - ia_{\overline{n}|i})$, 1, $(is_{\overline{n}|i} + 1)$ are in geometric progression.

13. If $X(s_{\overline{2n}|i} + a_{\overline{2n}|i}) = (s_{\overline{3n}|i} + a_{\overline{n}|i})$ what is the value of X?

14. An oil company requires an arctic drilling machine and is deciding whether to purchase it for $1 000 000 cash or to lease it for $240 000, payable at the end of

each half-year. The salvage value is $100 000 at the end of the machine's 6 year life. Maintenance costs are $10 000 each 6 months, but payable by the lessor, if the machine is leased. If the company can earn 16% on its capital, compounded semi-annually, advise the company whether to lease or buy.

15. The Ace Manufacturing Company is considering the purchase of two machines. Machine A costs $200 000 and machine B costs $400 000. The machines are projected to have a life of five years and to yield the following revenues:

End of Year	Cash Revenue Machine A	Machine B
1	none	$90 000
2	$100 000	90 000
3	100 000	90 000
4	100 000	90 000
5	100 000	300 000

The market rate of interest is 14% per annum compounded yearly.
Which machine should the company purchase?

16. The Northeast Mining Company is considering the exploitation of a mining property. If the company goes ahead, the estimated cash flows are as follows:

	Cash Inflow	Cash Outflow
Now	0	$3 000 000
End of year 1	$1 000 000	$2 000 000
End of year 2	$1 000 000	0
End of year 3	$1 000 000	0
End of year 4	$1 000 000	0
End of year 5	$1 000 000	0
End of year 6	$1 000 000	0
End of year 7	$1 000 000	0
End of year 8	$1 000 000	0

The project would be financed out of working capital, on which Northeast expects to earn at least 16% per annum.
Advise whether Northeast should proceed.

3.4 Finding the Periodic Payment

When equations (12) and (13) of Section 3.2 and 3.3 are solved for R, we obtain

$$R = \frac{S}{s_{\overline{n}|i}} = \frac{S}{\frac{(1 + i)^n - 1}{i}} \tag{14}$$

$$R = \frac{A}{a_{\overline{n}|i}} = \frac{A}{\frac{1 - (1 + i)^{-n}}{i}} \tag{15}$$

as the periodic payment of an ordinary simple annuity whose accumulated value S or discounted value A is given.

Example 1   A man wants to accumulate a $200 000 retirement fund. He plans to make the first deposit on March 1, 1984 and his plan calls for the last deposit to be made on September 1, 2005. Find the size of each deposit if
   a) he makes the deposits semi-annually in a fund that pays $12\frac{1}{2}\%$ per annum compounded semi-annually.
   b) he makes the deposits monthly in a fund that pays $12\frac{1}{2}\%$ per annum compounded monthly.

Solution a   Arranging the data on a time diagram below we have $S = 200\ 000$, $i = \dfrac{.125}{2} = .0625$, $n = 44$.

	R	R	R
├─────────┼───────────┼─── ··· ───┤			
0	1	2	44
Sept. 1	March 1	Sept. 1	Sept. 1
1983	1984	1984	2005

$$S = 200\ 000$$

Using (14) we calculate $R = \dfrac{200\ 000}{s\,\overline{44}|.0625} = \dfrac{200\ 000}{\dfrac{(1.0625)^{44} - 1}{.0625}} = \$932.58$

Semi-annual deposits of $932.58 will accumulate at $j_2 = 12\frac{1}{2}\%$ to 200 000 by September 1, 2005.

Solution b   Arranging the data on a time diagram below we have $S = 200\ 000$, $i = \dfrac{.125}{12}$, $n = 259$

	R	R	R
├─────────┼───────────┼─── ··· ───┤			
0	1	2	259
Feb. 1	March 1	April 1	Sept. 1
1984	1984	1984	2005

$$S = 200\ 000$$

Using (14) we calculate $R = \dfrac{200\ 000}{s\,\overline{259}|i} = \dfrac{200\ 000}{\dfrac{(1 + i)^{259} - 1}{i}} = \$152.70$

Monthly deposits of $152.70 will accumulate at $j_{12} = 12\frac{1}{2}\%$ to 200 000 by September 1, 2005.

Example 2   With the death of the insured on September 1, 1982 a life insurance policy pays out $80 000 as a death benefit. The beneficiary is to receive monthly payments, with the first payment on October 1, 1982. Find the size of the monthly payments and the date of the concluding payment, if interest is earned at $j_{12} = 11\%$ and the beneficiary is to receive 120 payments.

Solution   We have $A = 80\ 000$, $i = \dfrac{.11}{12}$, $n = 120$ and

using (15) we calculate $R = \dfrac{80\ 000}{a\,\overline{120}|i} = \dfrac{80\ 000}{\dfrac{1 - (1 + i)^{-120}}{i}} = \$1102.00$

The date of the last payment is September 1, 1992.

Exercise 3.4
Part A

1. What quarterly deposits should be made into a special savings account paying $j_4 = 16\%$ to accumulate $10 000 at the end of 10 years?

2. A car selling for $5800 may be purchased by paying $800 down and the balance in equal monthly payments for 3 years. Find these monthly payments at $j_{12} = 18\%$.

3. It is estimated that a machine will need replacing 10 years from now at a cost of $80 000. How much must be set aside each year to provide that money if the company's savings earn interest at 8% per annum effective?

4. An insurance policy is worth $10 000 at age 65. What monthly annuity will this fund provide for 15 years if the insurance company pays interest at $j_{12} = 10\%$?

5. On the birth of their first child a couple put $1500 in a special savings account paying interest at $j_1 = 11\%$. This fund is used to pay college fees and allows for three withdrawals corresponding to the 18th through 20th birthdays. What size are these withdrawals?

6. A television set worth $780 may be purchased by paying $80 down and the balance in monthly instalments for 2 years. Find these monthly instalments if $j_{12} = 15\%$.

7. A family needs to borrow $5000 for some home renovations. The loan is to be repaid with monthly payments over 5 years. If they go to a finance company the interest rate will be $j_{12} = 24\%$; if they use their credit card, the interest rate will be $j_{12} = 21\%$; and if they go to the bank, the rate will be $j_{12} = 18\%$. Find the respective monthly payments and the total of all payments for each loan.

8. At age 65 Mr. Jones takes his life savings of $120 000 and buys a 15-year annuity certain with monthly payments. Find the size of these payments
   a) at 12% compounded monthly;
   b) at 9% compounded monthly.

9. A person buys a boat with a cash price of $4500. He pays $500 down, and the balance is financed at $j_{12} = 14.79\%$. If he is to make 24 equal monthly payments, what will be the size of each payment?

10. Jackie has made semi-annual deposits of $500 for 5 years into a savings fund paying interest at $j_2 = 13\frac{3}{4}\%$. What semi-annual deposits for the next 2 years will bring the fund up to $10 000?

Part B

1. a) Barbara wants to accumulate $10 000 by the end of 10 years. She starts making quarterly deposits in her bank account which pays $j_4 = 14\%$. Find the size of these deposits.
   b) After 4 years, the bank changes the interest rate to $j_4 = 12\%$. Find the size of the quarterly deposits now required if the $10 000 goal is to be met.

2. A woman wants to accumulate $7000 in a fund at the end of 10 years. She deposits $300 at the end of each year for the first five years and then $300 + x$ at the end of each year for the next five years. Find x if $j_1 = 13\frac{1}{4}\%$.

3. A man aged 30 wishes to accumulate a fund for retirement by depositing $1000 at the end of each year for the next 35 years. Starting on his 66th birthday he will make 15 annual withdrawals of equal amount. Find the amount of each withdrawal if $j_1 = 10\%$ throughout the 50 year period.

4. To prepare for early retirement, a self-employed consultant makes deposits of $5500 into his Registered Retirement Savings Plan each year for 20 years, starting on his 31st birthday. When he is 51 he wishes to draw out 30 equal annual payments. What is the size of each withdrawal at $j_1 = 12\%$ for the first 10 year period, and $j_1 = 11\%$ for the next 40 year period?

5. You want to accumulate $100 000 at the end of 20 years. You deposit $1000 at the end of each of the first 10 years, and $1000 + x$ at the end of each of the second 10 years. Interest is $10\frac{1}{4}\%$ effective.
   a) Find x.
   b) If the last 4 payments of $1000 (at years 7-10) were missed, what would be the value of x?

6. Beginning on June 1, 1990 and continuing until December 1, 1995 a company will need $250 000 semi-annually to retire a series of bonds. What equal semi-annual deposits in a fund paying $j_2 = 10\%$ beginning on June 1, 1985 and continuing until December 1, 1995 are necessary to retire the bonds as they fall due?

7. Mr. Smith has been accumulating a retirement fund at 9% effective which will provide him with an income of $12 000 per year for 20 years, the first payment on his 65th birthday. If he now wishes to reduce the number of retirement payments to 15, what should he receive annually?

3.5 Finding the Term of an Annuity

In some problems the accumulated value S or the discounted value A, the periodic payment R, and the rate i are specified. This leaves the number of payments n to be determined. Formulas (12) and (13) may be solved for n by the use of logarithms. Normally, when given a value of S, or A, or R and a rate i, you will not find an integer time period n for the annuity. Algebraically this means that there is usually no integer n such that $S = Rs_{\overline{n}|i}$ or $A = Ra_{\overline{n}|i}$. It is necessary to make the concluding payment different from R in order to have equivalence. One of the following procedures is followed in practice.

Procedure 1   The last regular payment is increased by a sum which will make the payments equivalent to the accumulated value S or the discounted value A.

Procedure 2   A smaller concluding payment is made one period after the last full payment. Sometimes, when a certain sum of money is to be accumulated, a smaller concluding payment will not be required because the interest after the last full payment will equal or exceed the balance needed (see Example 1).

Unless specified otherwise, we shall use procedure 2 throughout this book. Procedure 2 is more often used in practice.

Example 1   A couple wants to accumulate $10 000 by making payments of $800 at the end of each half year into a savings account that earns interest at $j_2 = 9\%$. Find the number of full payments required and the size of the concluding payment using both procedures 1 and 2.

Solution   We have $S = 10\,000$, $R = 800$, $i = 4\frac{1}{2}\%$, and we want to calculate n. From equation (12) we obtain

$$800 s_{\overline{n}|.045} = 10\,000$$
$$s_{\overline{n}|.045} = 12.5$$
$$\frac{(1.045)^n - 1}{.045} = 12.5$$
$$(1.045)^n - 1 = (12.5)(.045)$$
$$(1.045)^n = 1.5625$$
$$n \log 1.045 = \log 1.5625$$
$$n = 10.138\,998$$

Thus there will be 10 full deposits.

Procedure 1   Let X be the sum which will be added to the last regular payment to make the payments equivalent to the accumulated value $S = 10\,000$. We arrange the data on a time diagram below.

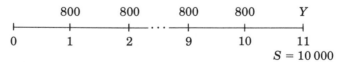

Using 10 as a focal date, we obtain the equation of value for unknown X

$$800 s_{\overline{10}|.045} + X = 10\,000$$
$$X = 10\,000 - 800 s_{\overline{10}|.045}$$
$$X = 10\,000 - 9830.57$$
$$X = \$169.43$$

Thus the 10th deposit will be $969.43.

Procedure 2   Let Y be the size of a smaller concluding payment made a half year after the last full deposit. We arrange the data on a time diagram below.

	800	800	800	800	Y
0	1	2	9	10	11

$S = 10\,000$

Using 11 as the focal date we obtain the equation of value for unknown Y

$$800 s_{\overline{10}|.045}(1.045) + Y = 10\,000$$
$$10\,272.94 + Y = 10\,000$$
$$Y = -\$272.94$$

The negative value of Y indicates that there is no concluding payment required; the interest after the last full payment will exceed the required balance by $272.94. Check: Carrying the accumulated value of 10 payments forward for one-half year will result in the accumulated value $800 s_{\overline{10}|.045}(1.045) = \$10\,272.94$.

Example 2   A man dies and leaves his wife an estate of $50 000. The money is invested at $j_{12} = 12\%$. How many monthly payments of $750 would the widow receive and what would be the size of the concluding payment?

Solution   We have $A = 50\ 000$, $R = 750$, $i = 1\%$. Substituting in equation (13) we obtain

$$750a_{\overline{n}|.01} = 50\ 000$$

$$a_{\overline{n}|.01} = \frac{50\ 000}{750}$$

$$\frac{1 - (1.01)^{-n}}{.01} = \frac{200}{3}$$

$$1 - (1.01)^{-n} = \frac{2}{3}$$

$$(1.01)^{-n} = \frac{1}{3}$$

$$-n \log 1.01 = \log \frac{1}{3}$$

$$n = 110.409\ 63$$

Thus the widow will receive 110 full payments of $750 and 1 smaller concluding payment, say X, 1 month after the last full payment. We arrange the data on a time diagram below.

Using 111 as the focal date, we obtain the equation of value for unknown X

$$750s_{\overline{110}|.01}(1.01) + X = 50\ 000(1.01)^{111}$$
$$150\ 575.63 + X = 150\ 883.76$$
$$X = \$308.13$$

Using 0 as the focal date, we obtain the equation of value

$$750a_{\overline{110}|.01} + X(1.01)^{-111} = 50\ 000$$
$$49\ 897.89 + X(1.01)^{-111} = 50\ 000$$
$$X(1.01)^{-111} = 102.11$$
$$X = 102.11(1.01)^{111}$$
$$X = \$308.13$$

Exercise 3.5

Part A

1. A debt of $4000 bears interest at $j_2 = 12\%$. It is to be repaid by semi-annual payments of $400. Find the number of full payments needed and the final smaller payment.

2. An heiress takes her inheritance of $25 000 and invests it at $j_{12} = 9\%$. How many monthly payments of $250 can she expect to receive and what will be the size of the concluding payment? Use both procedure 1 and procedure 2.

3. A couple wants to accumulate $10 000. If they deposit $250 at the end of each quarter year in an account paying $j_4 = 16\%$, how many deposits must they make and what will be the size of the final deposit? Use both procedure 1 and procedure 2.

4. A firm buys a machine for $30 000. They pay $5000 down and $5000 at the end of each year. If interest is at $j_1 = 10\%$, how many full payments must they make and what will be the size of the concluding payment?

5. A fund of $20 000 is to be accumulated by n annual payments of $2500 plus a final smaller payment made one year after the last regular payment. If the effective rate of interest is $j_1 = 18\%$, find n and the final irregular payment.

6. A loan of $10 000 is to be repaid by monthly payments of $400, the first payment due in one year's time. If $j_{12} = 12\%$, find the number of regular monthly payments needed and the size of the final smaller payment.

7. A fund of $8000 is to be accumulated by semi-annual payments of $2000. If $j_2 = 12\%$, find the number of full deposits required and the final smaller deposit.

8. On July 1, 1983 a woman has $10 000 in an account paying interest at $j_4 = 12\frac{1}{2}\%$. She plans to withdraw $500 every three months with the first withdrawal on October 1, 1983. How many full withdrawals can she make and what will be the size and the date of the concluding withdrawal?

Part B

1. Robert is accumulating a $10 000 fund by depositing $100 at the end of each month, starting September 1, 1982. If the interest rate on the fund is $j_{12} = 12\%$ until May 1, 1985 and then it drops to $j_{12} = 10\frac{1}{2}\%$, find the time and amount of the reduced final deposit.

2. A widow as beneficiary of a $50 000 insurance policy will receive $15 000 immediately and $1800 every three months thereafter. The company pays interest at $j_4 = 9\%$; after 3 years the rate is increased to $j_4 = 11\%$.
   a) How many full payments of $1800 will she receive?
   b) What additional sum paid with the last full payment will exhaust her benefits?
   c) What payment 3 months after the last full payment will exhaust her benefits?

3. On his 25th birthday Richard deposited $2000 in a fund paying 10% effective and continued to make such deposits each year, the last on his 49th birthday. Beginning on his 50th birthday, Richard plans to make equal annual withdrawals of $20 000.
   a) How many such withdrawals can be made?
   b) What additional sum paid with the last withdrawal will exhaust the fund?
   c) What sum paid one year after the last full withdrawal will exhaust the fund?

4. A couple bought land worth $30 000. They paid $5000 down and signed a contract agreeing to repay the balance with interest at 12% effective by annual payments of $5000 as long as necessary and a smaller concluding payment one year later. The contract was sold just after the 4th annual payment to an investor who wants to realize a yield of 13% effective. Find the selling price.

5. A loan of $2000 is to be repaid by annual payments of $400 per annum for the first 5 years and payments of $450 per year thereafter for as long as necessary. Find the total number of payments and the amount of the smaller final payment made one year after the last regular payment. Assume an effective rate of 18%.

3.6 Finding the Interest Rate

A very practical application of equations (12) and (13) is finding the interest rate. In many business transactions the true interest rate is concealed in one way or another. In order to compare different propositions (options, investments), it is necessary to determine the true interest rate of each proposition and make the decisions based on true interest rates.

When R, n and either S or A are given, the interest rate i may be determined approximately by linear interpolation. For most practical purposes linear interpolation gives sufficient accuracy.

Example 1   Find the interest rate j_4 at which deposits of $250 at the end of every 3 months will accumulate to $5000 in 4 years.

Solution   We have $S = 5000$, $R = 250$, $n = 16$ and using (12) we obtain

$$250s_{\overline{16}|i} = 5000$$
$$s_{\overline{16}|i} = 20$$

We want to find the rate $j_4 = 4i$ such that $s_{\overline{16}|i} = \dfrac{(1 + i)^{16} - 1}{i} = 20.$

By successive trials we find two factors $s_{\overline{16}|i}$, one greater than 20 and one less than 20. The corresponding rates $j_4 = 4i$ will provide an upper and lower bound on the unknown rate j_4, which is then approximated by a linear interpolation.*

For $j_4 = 10\%$ we calculte $s_{\overline{16}|i} = 19.3802$
For $j_4 = 11\%$ we calculate $s_{\overline{16}|i} = 19.7640$
For $j_4 = 12\%$ we calculatc $s_{\overline{16}|i} = 20.1569$

Now we have two rates $j_4 = 11\%$ and $j_4 = 12\%$, 1% apart, that provide upper and lower bounds for interpolation.

Arranging our data in an interpolation table we have:

	$s_{\overline{16}|i}$	j_4
19.7640	11%
20.0000	j_4
20.1569	12%

$$\frac{d}{1\%} = \frac{.2360}{.3929}$$

$$d \doteq .60\%$$

and $j_4 = 11.60\%$

We may check the accuracy of this answer by substituting $R = 250$, $n = 16$ and $i = \dfrac{.1160}{4}$ into (12) and calculate the accumulated value

$$S = 250\,\frac{(1 + i)^{16} - 1}{i} = \$4999.65$$

Linear interpolation between two nominal rates, 1% apart, gave us a very good approximation of the unknown rate j_4.

---

*The values of factors $s_{\overline{n}|i}$ and $a_{\overline{n}|i}$ will be rounded off to 4 decimal places, since additional places do not really increase the accuracy. For fixed n, factors $s_{\overline{n}|i}$ increase when i increases, whereas factors $a_{\overline{n}|i}$ decrease when i increases. Closer bounds on the nominal rate j_m generally provide better approximations of the unknown rate j_m by linear interpolation. In this textbook we will interpolate between two nominal rates that are 1% apart.

Example 2   A used car sells for $600 cash or $100 down and $90 a month for 6 months. Find the interest rate j_{12} if the purchaser buys the car on the instalment plan.

Solution   For any instalment plan, the following equation of value must hold to have the cash option equivalent to the instalment option.

cash price = down payment + discounted value of instalments

We have

$$600 = 100 + 90a_{\overline{n}|i}$$

$$a_{\overline{n}|i} = \frac{500}{90}$$

$$a_{\overline{n}|i} = 5.5556$$

For $j_{12} = 26\%$ we calculate $a_{\overline{n}|i} = 5.5701$
For $j_{12} = 27\%$ we calculate $a_{\overline{n}|i} = 5.5545$
Arranging our data in an interpolation table we have:

	$a_{\overline{n}|i}$	j_{12}
	5.5701	26%
	5.5556	j_{12}
	5.5545	27%

$.0156 \left\{ .0145 \left\{ \begin{matrix} \\ \\ \end{matrix} \right. \right.$ $\left. \begin{matrix} \\ \\ \end{matrix} \right\} d \left. \right\} 1\%$

$$\frac{d}{1\%} = \frac{.0145}{.0156}$$

$$d \doteq .93\%$$

$$\text{and } j_{12} = 26.93\%$$

Checking the accuracy of our answer we calculate the discounted value of the instalment plan at $j_{12} = 26.93\%$

$$100 + 90a_{\overline{n}|i} = \$600$$

NOTE Most provinces in Canada have "truth in lending" laws setting down regulations on the disclosure of the rate of interest involved in any financial transaction.

Exercise 3.6

Part A

1. Find the interest rate j_2 at which semi-annual deposits of $500 will accumulate to $6000 in 5 years.
2. What rate of interest, j_1, must be earned for deposits of $500 at the end of each year to accumulate to $12 000 in 10 years?
3. An insurance company will pay $80 000 to a beneficiary or monthly payments of $1000 for 10 years. What rate j_{12} is the insurance company using?
4. A television set sells for $700. Sales tax of 7% is added to that. The T.V. may be purchased for $100 down and monthly payments of $60 for one year. What is the interest rate j_{12}? What is the effective annual interest rate?
5. You borrow $1600 from a licensed small loan company and agree to pay $160 a month for 12 months. What nominal rate j_{12} is the company charging?
6. A store offers to sell a watch for $55 cash or $5 a month for 12 months. What nominal rate j_{12} is the store actually charging on the instalment plan, if the first payment is made immediately?

Part B

The following problems are examples of situations that could arise if there were no government legislation concerning disclosure of interest rate. It is very important to check out all loan clauses fully.

1. The "Fly By Night' Used Car Lot uses the following ad to illustrate their 12% finance plan on a car paid for over 3 years.

Cost of car	4000.00	
12%finance charge	1440.00	(12% of 4000 $\times$ 3 years)
Total cost	5440.00	

   Monthly payment $= \dfrac{5440}{36} = \$151.11$

   What is the true interest rate j_{12} being charged?

2. A dealer sells an article for $600. He will allow a customer to buy it by paying $240 down and the balance by paying $30 a month for a year. If you pay cash for the item he will give you a 10% discount. Find the interest rate j_{12} paid by the purchaser who uses the instalment plan described above.

3. Goods worth $1000 are purchased using the following carrying-charge plan: A down payment of $100 is required after which 18% of the unpaid balance is added on and the amount is then divided into 12 equal monthly instalments. What rate of interest j_{12} does the plan include?

4. A finance company charges 15% "interest in advance" and allows the client to repay the loan in 12 equal monthly payments. The monthly payment is calculated as one twelfth of the total of principal and interest (15% of principal). Find the nominal rate compounded monthly and the effective rate charged.

5. To buy a car costing $6800 you can pay $800 down and the balance in 36 monthly payments of $225 each. You can also borrow the money from a loan company and repay $6800 by making quarterly payments of $530 over 5 years, first payment in 3 months. Compare the effective rates of interest charged and determine which option is better.

6. A T.V. rental company uses the following illustration to prove that renting a T.V. at $25 a month is cheaper than buying.

Cost of T.V.	$600
Sales Tax	42
Total	$642

   Therefore monthly payments over 3 years at 21% are

   $\$29.07 \left(29.07 = \dfrac{642 + (.21)(642)(3)}{36} \right)$

   Redo this illustration properly at $j_{12} = 21\%$ and comment.

3.7 Review Exercises

1. Find the accumulated and the discounted value of an annuity of $500 at the end of each month at $j_{12} = 18\%$ for a) 10 years, b) 20 years.

2. At age 65 Mrs. Smith takes her life savings of $100 000 and buys a 20-year annuity certain with quarterly payments. Find the size of these payments
   a) at 10% compounded quarterly.
   b) at 12% compounded quarterly.

3. A couple needs a loan of $10 000 to buy a boat. One lender will charge $j_{12} = 18\%$, a second lender offers $j_{12} = 19\%$. What will be the monthly savings in interest using the lower rate if the monthly payments are to run for 5 years?

4. Find the accumulated and the discounted value of semi-annual payments of $500 at the end of every half year over 10 years if interest is $j_2 = 10\%$ for the first four years and $j_2 = 12\%$ for the last six years.

5. Charlie wants to accumulate $100 000 by making monthly deposits of $1000 into a fund that accumulates interest at $j_{12} = 15\%$. Find the number of full deposits required and the size of the concluding deposit using both procedures.

6. Lisa borrows $10 000 at $j_4 = 18\%$. How many $800 quarterly payments will she pay and what will be the size of the partial concluding payment, 3 months after the last full $800 payment?

7. On June 1, 1983 Ms. Smith purchased furniture for $2200. She paid $400 down and agreed to pay the balance by monthly payments of $100 plus a smaller final payment, the first payment due on July 1, 1983. If money earns interest at $j_{12} = 18\%$, when is the final payment made and what is the amount of the final payment?

8. A used car sells for $500 cash or $100 down and $80 a month for 6 months. Find the interest rate j_{12} if the purchaser buys the car on the instalment plan.

9. Find j_{12} at which deposits of $200 at the end of each month will accumulate to $10 000 in 3 years.

10. The XYZ Finance Company charges 10% "interest in advance" and allows the client to repay the loan in 12 equal monthly payments. Thus for a loan of $600, they would charge $60 interest and have 12 monthly repayments of $55 each. What is the corresponding rate of interest convertible monthly?

11. A refrigerator is listed at $650. If a customer pays $200 down, the balance plus a carrying charge of $50 can be paid in 12 equal monthly payments. If the customer pays cash, he can get a discount of 15% off the list price. What is the nominal rate converted monthly if the refrigerator is bought on time?

12. Paul wants to accumulate $5000 by depositing $300 every 3 months into an account paying $15\frac{1}{2}\%$ per annum converted quarterly. He makes the first deposit on July 1, 1983. How many full deposits should he make and what will be the size and the date of the concluding deposit?

13. How much a month for 5 years at $j_{12} = 15\%$ would you have to save in order to receive $800 a month for 3 years afterward?

14. A bank account paying $j_{12} = 13\frac{1}{2}\%$ contains $5680 on March 1, 1983. Beginning April 1, 1983 the first of a sequence of monthly withdrawals of $400 is made. What is the date of the last withdrawal? By what date (first of the month) will the balance again exceed $400?

15. Jones agrees to pay Smith $800 at the end of each quarter for 5 years, but is unable to do so until the end of the 15th month when he wins $100 000 in a provincial lottery. Assuming money is worth $j_4 = 15\%$, what single payment at the end of fifteen months liquidates his debt?

16. A deposit of $1000 is made to open an account on March 1, 1980. Monthly deposits of $300 are then made for 5 years, starting April 1, 1980. Starting April 1, 1985 the first of a sequence of 20 monthly withdrawals of $1000 is made. Find the balance in the account on December 1, 1987 assuming $j_{12} = 12\%$.

Other Simple Annuities

4.1 Annuities Due

An **annuity due** is an annuity whose periodic payments are due at the beginning of each payment interval. The term of an annuity due starts at the time of the first payment and ends one payment period after the date of the last payment. The time diagram below shows the simple case (payment interval and interest period coincide) of an annuity due of n payments.

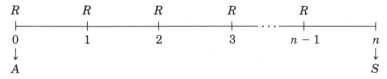

It is easy to recognize an annuity due as a "slipped" ordinary annuity. Thus we can simply write formulas for the accumulated value S and discounted value A of an annuity due, by adjusting equations (12) and (13) from Chapter 3.

Since the accumulated value of annuity was defined as the equivalent dated value of the payments at the end of the term, it means that the accumulated value S of an annuity due is an equivalent value due one period after the last payment.

The accumulated value of the payments at the end of the $(n - 1)$th period is $Rs_{\overline{n}|i}$. We then accumulate $Rs_{\overline{n}|i}$ for 1 interest period, to obtain

$$S = Rs_{\overline{n}|i}(1 + i) \tag{16}*$$

To find A, we recall that the discounted value of an annuity was defined as the equivalent dated value of the payments at the beginning of the term.

The discounted value of the payments 1 period before the 1st payment is $Ra_{\overline{n}|i}$. We then accumulate $Ra_{\overline{n}|i}$ for 1 interest period to obtain

$$A = Ra_{\overline{n}|i}(1 + i) \qquad\qquad (17)\dagger$$

Example 1 Mary Jones deposits \$100 at the beginning of each month for 3 years in an account paying $j_{12} = 12\%$. How much is in her account at the end of 3 years?
Solution We arrange the data on a time diagram below.

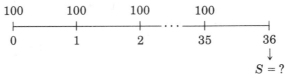

We have $R = 100$, $i = .01$, $n = 36$ and using (16) we calculate

$$S = 100\ s_{\overline{36}|.01}(1.01) = \$4350.76$$

Example 2 The monthly rent for a townhouse is \$520 payable at the beginning of each month. If money is worth $j_{12} = 9\%$

    a) what is the equivalent yearly rental payable in advance,
    b) what is the cash equivalent of 5 years of rent?

Solution a We calculate the discounted value A of an annuity due of 12 payments of \$520 each at $j_{12} = 9\%$ using (17)

$$A = 520\ a_{\overline{12}|.0075}(1.0075) = \$5990.75$$

Solution b We calculate the discounted value A of an annuity due of 60 payments of \$520 each at $j_{12} = 9\%$

$$A = 520\ a_{\overline{60}|.0075}(1.0075) = \$25\ 238.03$$

Example 3 A debt of \$10 000 with interest at $j_4 = 11\%$ is to be paid off by 8 equal quarterly payments, the first due today. Find the quarterly payment.
Solution Arranging the data on a time diagram below:

$$
\begin{array}{cccccc}
R & R & R & & R & \\
\vdash\!\!\!-\!\!\!-\!\!\!-\!\!\!+\!\!\!-\!\!\!-\!\!\!-\!\!\!+\!\!\!-\!\!\!-\!\!\!+\cdots\!\!-\!\!\!+\!\!\!-\!\!\!-\!\!\!-\!\!\dashv \\
0 \quad\ \ 1 \quad\ \ 2 \qquad\ 7 \qquad 8 \\
\$10\ 000
\end{array}
$$

We have $A = 10\ 000$, $i = .0275$, $n = 8$ and calculate R using (17)

$$R\ a_{\overline{8}|.0275}(1.0275) = 10\ 000$$
$$R = \frac{10\ 000}{a_{\overline{8}|.0275}(1.0275)}$$
$$R = \$1371.85$$

---

*Some textbooks use the notation $\ddot{s}_{\overline{n}|i}$ when referring to the accumulated value of an annuity due. Thus

$$S = R\ddot{s}_{\overline{n}|i} = Rs_{\overline{n}|i}(1 + i)$$

†Some textbooks use the notation $\ddot{a}_{\overline{n}|i}$ when referring to the discounted value of an annuity due. Thus

$$A = R\ddot{a}_{\overline{n}|i} = Ra_{\overline{n}|i}(1 + i)$$

Exercise 4.1

Part A

1. Deposits of $500 are made at the beginning of each half-year for 5 years into an account paying $j_2 = 16\%$. How much is in the account
   a) at the end of 5 years,
   b) just before the 6th deposit?
2. A debt of $1000 with interest at $j_{12} = 18\%$ is to be paid off over 18 months by equal monthly payments, the first due today. Find the monthly payment.
3. Find the discounted value and accumulated value of $500 payable semi-annually at the beginning of each half-year over 10 years if interest is 8% per annum payable semi-annually.
4. A couple wants to accumulate $10 000 by December 31, 1990. They make 10 annual deposits starting January 1, 1981. If interest is 12% effective, what annual deposits are needed?
5. The premium on a life insurance policy can be paid either yearly or monthly in advance. If the annual premium is $120 what monthly premium would be equivalent at $j_{12} = 11\%$?
6. A life insurance policy allows the option of paying your premium yearly or monthly in advance. If the monthly premium quoted is $15 what annual premium would be equivalent at $j_{12} = 12\%$?
7. An insurance policy pays a death benefit of $10 000 or payments at the beginning of each month for 10 years. What size would these monthly payments be if $j_{12} = 10\%$?
8. A used car sells for $2550. Brent wishes to pay for it in 18 monthly instalments, the first due on the day of purchase. If 21% compounded monthly is charged, find the size of the monthly payment.
9. A realtor rents office space for $5800 every three months payable in advance. He immediately invests half of each payment in a fund paying 13% compounded quarterly. How much is in the fund at the end of 5 years?
10. A refrigerator is bought for $60 down and $60 a month for 15 months. If interest is charged at $j_{12} = 18\frac{1}{2}\%$, what is the cash price of the refrigerator?

Part B

1. A man aged 40 deposits $1000 at the beginning of each year for 25 years into an RRSP paying interest at 9% effective. Starting on his 65th birthday he makes 15 annual withdrawals from the fund at the beginning of each year. During this period the fund pays interest at 12% effective. Find the amount of each withdrawal starting at age 65.
2. John Doe signed a contract that calls for payments of $500 at the beginning of each 6 months for 10 years. If money is worth $j_2 = 13\%$ find the value of the remaining payments
   a) just after he makes the 4th payment
   b) just before he makes the 6th payment.
   If after making the first 3 payments he failed to make the next 3 payments,
   c) what would he have to pay when the next payment is due to bring himself back on schedule?
3. Using a geometric progression derive the formula for the accumulated value, S, of an annuity due:
$$S = R\, s_{\overline{n}|i}(1 + i)$$

Show that it is equivalent to

$$S = R(s_{\overline{n+1}} - 1)$$

4. Using a geometric progression derive the formula for the discounted value, A, of an annuity due:

$$A = R\, a_{\overline{n}|i}(1 + i)$$

Show that it is equivalent to

$$A = R(a_{\overline{n-1}|i} + 1)$$

5. A mutual fund promises a rate of growth of 10% a year on funds left with it. How much would an investor who makes deposits of $100 at the beginning of each year have on deposit by the time the first deposit has grown by 159%? You may assume that this time is approximately an integral number of years and that the investor is about to make, but has not made, an annual deposit at that time.

4.2 Deferred Annuities

A **deferred annuity** is an annuity whose first payment is due some time later than the end of the first interest period. It is customary to analyze all deferred annuities as ordinary deferred annuities. Thus, an ordinary deferred annuity is an ordinary annuity whose term is deferred for (let's say) k periods. The time diagram below shows the simple case of an ordinary deferred annuity.

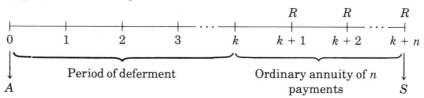

Note that in the above diagram the period of deferment is k periods and the first payment of the ordinary annuity is at time $k + 1$. This is because the term of an ordinary annuity starts one period before its first payment. Thus, when the time of the first payment is given, it is necessary to determine the period of deferment by moving back one interest period.

To find the discounted value, A, of an ordinary deferred annuity we find the discounted value of n payments one period before the first payment and discount this sum for k periods. We obtain

$$A = R\, a_{\overline{n}|i}(1 + i)^{-k} \tag{18*}$$

If you now return to Exercises 3.3, Part A, you will see that we have already handled questions of this nature (Questions 8, 9 and 10 for example). We will look at two further examples:

---

*Some textbooks use the notation $_{k|}a_{\overline{n}|i}$ when referring to a deferred annuity. Thus $A = R_{k|}a_{\overline{n}|i} = R\, a_{\overline{n}|i}(1 + i)^{-k}$.

Example 1   What sum of money should be set aside on a child's birth to provide 8 semi-annual payments of $1500 to cover the expenses for university education if the first payment is to be made on the child's 19th birthday? The fund will earn interest at $j_2 = 12\%$.

Solution   We arrange the data on a time diagram below:

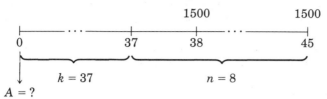

We have $R = 1500$, $i = .06$, $n = 8$, $k = 37$ and using (18) we calculate

$$A = 1500 \, a_{\overline{8}|.06}(1.06)^{-37} = \$1078.58$$

Example 2   A woman wins $100\ 000 in a provincial lottery. She takes only $20\ 000 in cash and invests the balance at $j_{12} = 8\%$ with the understanding that she will receive 180 equal monthly payments with the first one to be made in 4 years. Find the size of the payments.

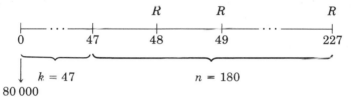

We have $A = 80\ 000$, $i = \dfrac{.08}{12}$, $n = 180$, $k = 47$ and using (18) we obtain an equation for R

$$80\ 000 = R \, a_{\overline{180}|i}(1 + i)^{-47}$$

Solving for R we obtain

$$R = \frac{80\ 000(1 + i)^{47}}{a_{\overline{180}|i}} = \$1044.76$$

Exercise 4.2
Part A

1. Find the discounted value of an ordinary annuity deferred 5 years paying $1000 a year for 10 years if interest is at $j_1 = 8\%$.
2. Find the discounted value of an ordinary annuity deferred 3 years six months which pays $500 semi-annually for 7 years if interest is 17% per annum payable semi-annually.
3. What sum of money must be set aside at a child's birth to provide for 6 semi-annual payments of $1500 to cover the expenses for a college education if the first payment is to be made on the child's 19th birthday and interest is at $j_2 = 8\%$?
4. On Mr. Smith's 55th birthday, the Smiths decide to sell their house and move into an apartment. They realize $80\ 000 on the sale of the house and invest this money in a fund paying $j_1 = 9\%$. On Mr. Smith's 65th birthday they make their

first withdrawal that will exhaust the fund over 15 years (i.e., 15 withdrawals). What is the dollar size of each withdrawal?

5. Mrs. Jones changes employers at age 46. She is given $8500 as her vested benefits in the company's pension plan. She invests this money in an RRSP (Registered Retirement Savings Plan) paying $j_1 = 8\%$ and leaves it there until her ultimate retirement at age 60. She plans on 25 annual withdrawals from this fund, the first withdrawal on her 61st birthday. Find the size of these withdrawals.

6. Find the value on January 1, 1985 of quarterly payments of $100 each over 10 years if the first payment is on January 1, 1987 and interest is 13% per annum compounded quarterly.

7. Find the value on July 1, 1984 of semi-annual payments of $500 each over 6 years if the first payment is on January 1, 1988 and interest is $11\frac{1}{4}\%$ per annum payable semi-annually.

8. The XYZ Furniture Store sells a chesterfield for $950. It can be purchased for $50 down and no payments for 3 months. At the end of the third month you make your first payment and continue until a total of 18 payments are made. Find the size of each payment if interest is at $j_{12} = 18\%$.

9. An 8-year-old child wins $1 000 000 from a lottery. The law requires that this money be set aside in a trust fund until the child reaches age 18. The child's parents decide that the money should be paid out in 20 equal payments with the first payment at age 18. Find these payments if the trust fund pays interest at 10% per annum effective.

Part B

1. Show that formula (18) for the discounted value, A, of an ordinary deferred annuity is equivalent to

$$A = R(a_{\overline{k+n}|i} - a_{\overline{k}|i})$$

2. A parcel of land, valued at $35 000, is sold for $15 000 down. The buyer agrees to pay the balance with interest at $j_{12} = 12\%$ by paying $500 monthly as long as necessary, the first payment due 2 years from now.
   a) Find the number of full payments needed and the size of the concluding payment one month after the last $500 payment.
   b) Find the monthly payment needed to pay off the balance by 36 equal payments, if the first payment is 1 year from now and interest is at $j_{12} = 12\%$.

4.3 Summary of Simple Annuities

The most effective way to solve an annuity problem is to make a time diagram, determine the type of annuity and then apply the proper formula.

The following time diagrams with the attached formulas for accumulated and discounted values provide a summary of simple annuities.

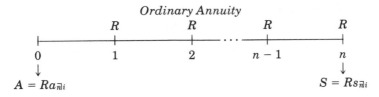

Ordinary Annuity

$A = Ra_{\overline{n}|i}$

$S = Rs_{\overline{n}|i}$

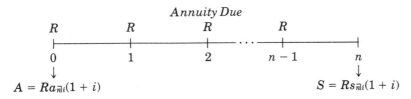

Annuity Due

$A = Ra_{\overline{n}|i}(1 + i)$

$S = Rs_{\overline{n}|i}(1 + i)$

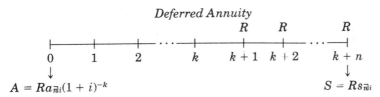

Deferred Annuity

$A = Ra_{\overline{n}|i}(1 + i)^{-k}$

$S = Rs_{\overline{n}|i}$

It is also possible to find the accumulated value of an annuity which earns interest for two or more periods after the last payment. Such an annuity is displayed in the time diagram below and is sometimes called a *forborne annuity*. From the work we did in Exercise 3.2 we know that the accumulated value here is as given:

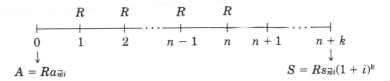

$A = Ra_{\overline{n}|i}$

$S = Rs_{\overline{n}|i}(1 + i)^{k}$

In more complicated problems students are advised to break the problem into simple parts. Every problem can be broken down into single payments and annuities which can be moved to any point in time and an equation of value set up.

Example A couple deposited $300 every half-year in a fund paying interest at $j_2 = 10\%$. The first deposit was made on May 1, 1960, the last deposit on May 1, 1980.
a) How much money was in the fund on (i) May 1, 1970; (ii) November 1, 1980.
b) From November 1, 1990 they plan to draw down their account with semi-annual withdrawals of $8000. How many withdrawals will they make and what is the size and the date of the last withdrawal?
c) If they want to draw down their account with equal semi-annual withdrawals from November 1, 1990 to November 1, 2010 how much will they get every half-year?

Solution a   We arrange the data on the time diagram below.

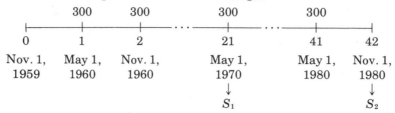

(i) Considering November 1, 1959 as the start of an ordinary annuity, we have $R = 300$, $i = .05$, $n = 21$ and using (12) we calculate
$$S_1 = 300\, s_{\overline{21}|.05} = \$10\ 715.78$$

(ii) Considering November 1, 1980 as the end of an annuity due, we have $R = 300$, $i = .05$, $n = 41$ and using (16) we calculate
$$S_2 = 300\, s_{\overline{41}|.05}(1.05) = \$40\ 269.53$$

Solution b   Using result (ii) we can arrange the data on the time diagram below.

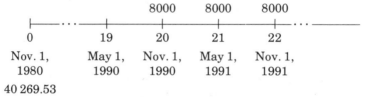

Using May 1, 1990 as the focal date, we can write the equation of value
$$8000\, a_{\overline{n}|.05} = 40\ 269.53(1.05)^{19}$$
$$8000\, a_{\overline{n}|.05} = 101\ 759.10$$
$$a_{\overline{n}|.05} = 12.719\ 887$$
$$\frac{1 - (1.05)^{-n}}{.05} = 12.719\ 887$$
$$1 - (1.05)^{-n} = .635\ 994\ 35$$
$$(1.05)^{-n} = .364\ 005\ 65$$
$$-n \log 1.05 = \log .365\ 005\ 65$$
$$n = 20.712\ 902$$

Thus, there will be 20 full withdrawals of $8000 and a smaller withdrawal X a half year later as shown on the time diagram below.

```
                       8000      8000        X
 ├──···──────────┼─────────┼───···──┼─────────┤
 0               19        20       39        40
 Nov. 1,       May 1,    Nov. 1,   May 1,   Nov. 1,
 1980          1990      1990      2000      2000
                      └──────────────────┘
                       20 full withdrawals
```

Using November 1, 2000 as the focal date, we write the equation of value for X
$$X + 8000\, s_{\overline{20}|.05}(1.05) = 40\ 269.53(1.05)^{40}$$
$$X + 277\ 754.01 = 283\ 497.03$$
$$X = \$5743.02$$
The last withdrawal of $5743.02 will be made on November 1, 2000.

Solution c   We arrange our data on the time diagram below.

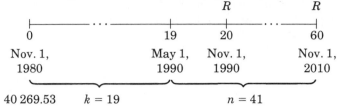

40 269.53 $k = 19$ $n = 41$

Using equation (18) for the discounted value of an ordinary deferred annuity we obtain

$$R\,a_{\overline{41}|.05}(1.05)^{-19} = 40\ 269.53$$

$$R = \frac{40\ 269.53(1.05)^{19}}{a_{\overline{41}|.05}}$$

$$R = \$5883.94$$

Exercise 4.3
Part A
1. Payments of $100 per quarter are made from March 1, 1983 to September 1, 1988 inclusive. If interest is at $j_4 = 18\%$ find:
   a) the discounted value on December 1, 1981;
   b) the accumulated value on March 1, 1990.
2. A couple deposits $500 a year in a fund paying interest at $j_1 = 11\%$. The first deposit is made January 1, 1978, the last deposit January 1, 1987.
   How much money is in the fund on
   a) January 1, 1984 (after the payment is made);
   b) January 1, 1990?
3. Find the accumulated value on December 31, 1994 of an account where deposits of $500 a year were made from December 31, 1970 to December 31, 1989 inclusive if the fund pays $j_1 = 14\%$.
4. From July 1, 1976 to January 1, 1981 a couple made semi-annual deposits of $500 in a special savings account paying $j_2 - 11\%$. Starting July 1, 1985 they start making semi-annual withdrawals of $800. How many withdrawals can they make and what is the size and date of the last withdrawal?
5. If the couple in problem four decided to exhaust their savings with equal semi-annual withdrawals from July 1, 1985, to July 1, 1995 inclusive, how much will they get each half-year?
6. In October 1977, an industrialist gives your school $30 000 to be used for future scholarships of $4000 at each fall convocation starting the year the industrialist dies. If the industrialist died May 1980 and the money earns interest at $j_1 = 8\%$, for how many years will full scholarships be awarded?
7. On February 1, 1970, Allan made the first of a sequence of regular annual deposits of $1000 into a savings account. The last deposit was made February 1, 1986. If the account earned $10\frac{1}{2}\%$ effective the balance after the last deposit would have been $42 472.13 while it would have been $44 500.84 at 11% effective. In fact, the balance in the account immediately after the last deposit was $43 500. What effective rate of interest did the account earn?

Part B

1. Kathy deposited $100 monthly in a fund paying interest at $j_{12} = 12\%$. The first deposit was made on June 1, 1970 and the last deposit on November 1, 1980.
   a) Find the value of the fund on
      (i) September 1, 1975 (after the payment is made);
      (ii) December 1, 1982.
   b) From May 1, 1985 she plans to draw down the fund with monthly withdrawals of $1000. Find the date and the size of the smaller concluding withdrawal one month after the last $1000 withdrawal.
2. Starting on his 45th birthday, a man deposits $1000 a year in a savings account that pays interest at 13% per annum. He makes his last deposit on his 64th birthday. On his 65th birthday he transfers his total savings to a special retirement fund that pays $14\frac{1}{2}\%$ per annum. From this fund he will receive level payments of X at the beginning of each year for 15 years. Find X.
3. Given the following diagram

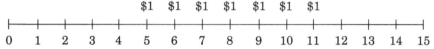

   find simplified expressions for a single sum equivalent to the seven payments shown at times 1, 5, 8, 12, and 15, assuming the rate i per period.

4.4 Perpetuities

Illustration: Let us consider a person who invests $10 000 at rate $j_2 = 10\%$, keeps the original investment intact and collects $500 interest at the end of each half-year. As long as the interest rate does not change and the original principal $10 000 is kept intact interest payments of $500 can be collected forever. We say the interest payments of $500 form a perpetuity.

The present value or discounted value of this infinite series of payments is $10 000, as shown on the diagram below.

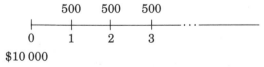

A **perpetuity** is an annuity whose payments begin on a fixed date and continue forever. Examples of perpetuities are the series of interest payments from a sum of money invested permanently at a certain interest rate, a scholarship paid from an endowment on a perpetual basis, and the dividends on a share of preferred stock (Stocks are explained in Chapter 7).

It is meaningless to speak about the accumulated value of a perpetuity, since there is no end to the term of a perpetuity. The discounted value, however, is well defined as the equivalent dated value of the set of payments at the beginning of the term of the perpetuity.

Discounted values of perpetuities are very useful in capitalization problems (see Chapter 8, Section 8.8).

The terminology defined for annuities applies to a perpetuity as well. First we shall discuss an **ordinary simple perpetuity**, that is, a series of level periodic payments, made at the ends of interest periods, which continues forever. The other simple perpetuities, i.e., perpetuities due and deferred, may be handled using the concept of an equation of value.

Let A be the discounted value of an ordinary simple perpetuity; let i be the interest rate per period; and let R be the periodic payment of the perpetuity.

Then A must be equivalent to the set of payments R as shown on the diagram below.

$$
\begin{array}{ccccc}
 & R & R & R & \\
\vdash\!\!\!-\!\!\!-\!\!\!+\!\!\!-\!\!\!-\!\!\!+\!\!\!-\!\!\!-\!\!\!+\!\!\!-\!\!\!-\!\!\cdots\!-\!\!\!-\!\!\!-\!\! & & & & \\
0 & 1 & 2 & 3 &
\end{array}
$$

A

It is evident that A will perpetually provide $R = Ai$ as interest payments on the invested capital A at the end of each interest period as long as it remains invested at rate i.

From $R = Ai$ we obtain the discounted value A of an ordinary simple perpetuity

$$A = \frac{R}{i} \tag{19*}$$

Example 1   How much money is needed to establish a scholarship fund paying scholarships of $1000 each half-year if the endowment can be invested at $j_2 = 10\%$ and if the first scholarships will be provided

a) a half-year from now;
b) immediately;
c) 4 years from now.

Solution a   The payments form an ordinary simple perpetuity and we have $R = 1000$, $i = .05$, and using (19) we calculate

$$A = \frac{1000}{.05} = \$20\ 000$$

Solution b   An extra $1000 is needed immediately. Thus the endowment is the sum of the above perpetuity and $1000, i.e., $21 000.

Solution c   If the first scholarships are awarded 4 years from now, the fund will have to contain $21 000 at that time. We have to find the discounted value of $21 000 for 4 years at $j_2 = 10\%$. We obtain

$$21\ 000(1.05)^{-8} = \$14\ 213.63$$

---

*Some textbooks use the notation $a_{\overline{\infty}|i}$ when referring to the discounted value of a perpetuity. Thus

$$R\,a_{\overline{\infty}|i} = \frac{R}{i}$$

Example 2 A company is expected to pay $3.50 every 3 months on a share of its preferred stock. If money is worth $j_4 = 16\%$, what should a share of the stock be selling for?

Solution We have $R = 3.50$, $i = .04$ and using (19) we calculate

$$A = \frac{3.50}{.04} = \$87.50$$

When the payment interval and the interest period do not coincide, we have a **general perpetuity**. The simplest way to solve a general perpetuity problem is to find the equivalent rate of interest per payment interval (see Chapter 2, Section 2.2) and then use Equation (19).

Example 3 What should a share of the stock in Example 2 be selling for if the money is worth

  a) $j_{12} = 16\%$;
  b) 16% effective?

Solution a We arrange the data on a diagram below using months as the time units.

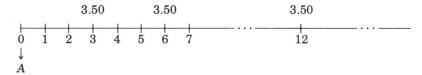

First we replace $j_{12} = 16\%$ by an equivalent rate j_4. The nominal rate $j_4 = 4i$ equivalent to $j_{12} = 16\%$ is found by solving

$$(1 + i)^4 = \left(1 + \frac{.16}{12}\right)^{12}$$

$$1 + i = \left(1 + \frac{.16}{12}\right)^{3}$$

$$i = \left(1 + \frac{.16}{12}\right)^{3} - 1$$

$$i = .040\ 535\ 7$$

If we refer back to our time diagram we can see that we now have an ordinary simple perpetuity with $R = 3.50$, $i = .040\ 535\ 7$ and using (19) we calculate

$$A = \frac{3.50}{i} = \$86.34$$

Solution b First we replace $j_1 = 16\%$ by an equivalent rate j_4. The nominal rate $j_4 = 4i$ equivalent to $j_1 = 16\%$ is found by solving

$$(1 + i)^4 = 1.16$$
$$1 + i = (1.16)^{1/4}$$
$$i = (1.16)^{1/4} - 1$$
$$i = .037\ 801\ 98$$

Again, referring back to our time diagram we see that we now have an ordinary simple perpetuity with $R = 3.50$, $i = .037\ 801\ 98$ and using (19) we calculate

$$A = \frac{3.50}{i} = \$92.59$$

Exercise 4.4
Part A

1. Find the discounted value of an ordinary simple perpetuity paying $50 a month if (a) $j_{12} = 9\%$; (b) $j_{12} = 12\%$; (c) $j_{12} = 15\%$.

2. Find the discounted value of an ordinary simple perpetuity paying $400 a year if interest is
   a) 8% per annum effective;
   b) $j_1 = 12.48\%$.

3. How much money is needed to establish a scholarship fund paying $1500 annually if the fund will earn interest at $j_1 = 14\%$ and the first payment will be made:
   a) at the end of the first year;
   b) immediately;
   c) 5 years from now.

4. A share of preferred stock has a par value of $100 and pays a $6 dividend annually. If money is now worth $j_1 = 19\%$, what should an investor pay for this stock?

5. On September 1, 1983 a philanthropist gives a college a fund of $50 000 which is invested at $j_2 = 10\%$. If semi-annual scholarships are awarded for 20 years from this grant, what is the size of each scholarship if the first one is awarded on
   a) September 1, 1983;
   b) September 1, 1985?
   If these semi-annual scholarships were to be awarded indefinitely, what would be the size of the payments for the two starting dates listed above?

6. It costs the C.N.R. $100 at the end of each month to maintain a level-crossing gate system. How much can the company contribute toward the cost of an underpass which will eliminate the level-crossing system if money is worth 15% per annum payable monthly.

7. How much money is needed to establish a research fund paying $2000 semi-annually forever (first payment at the end of six months) if money is worth
   a) $12\frac{1}{2}\%$ per annum effective;
   b) $12\frac{1}{2}\%$ per annum compounded semi-annually;
   c) 9% per annum compounded monthly?

8. A family is considering putting aluminum siding on their house as it needs painting immediately. Painting the house costs $1200 and must be done every four years. What price can the family afford for the aluminum siding if they earn interest at $j_1 = 12.75\%$ on their savings.

9. The XYZ company has a stock that pays a semi-annual dividend of $4. If the stock sells for $64 what yield j_2 did the investor desire? What is the equivalent rate j_1?

10. The discounted value of a perpetuity is $20 000 and the yield on the fund is $j_2 = 18\%$. What payment will this fund provide:
    a) at the end of each month;
    b) at the beginning of each year?

11. Deposits of $1000 are placed into a fund at the beginning of each year for the next 20 years. At the end of the 20th year annual payments from the fund commence and continue forever. If $j_1 = 12\%$, find the value of these payments.

12. On the basis of an unspecified interest rate, i per annum, a perpetuity paying $330 at the end of each year forever may be purchased for $3000. Find i.

Part B

1. Use an infinite geometric progression to derive formula (19) for the discounted value A of an ordinary simple perpetuity.

2. Derive $a_{\overline{n}|i} = \dfrac{1 - (1 + i)^{-n}}{i}$ as the difference between the discounted value of an ordinary simple perpetuity of $1 per period and the discounted value of an ordinary simple perpetuity of $1 per period deferred for n periods.

3. In 1982 a research foundation was established by a fund of $20 000 invested at a rate that would provide $3000 payments at the end of each year, forever.
   a) What interest rate was being earned in the fund?
   b) After the payment in 1987, the foundation learned that the rate of interest earned on the fund was being changed to $j_1 = 13\%$. If the foundation wants to continue annual payments forever, what size will the new payments be?
   c) If the foundation continues with the $3000 payments annually, how many full payments can be made at the new rate?

4. A college estimates that its new campus centre will require $3000 for upkeep at the end of each year for the next 5 years and $5000 at the end of each year thereafter indefinitely. If money is worth 12% effective, how large an endowment is necessary for the future upkeep of the campus centre?

5. You take out a loan for L at $j_{12} = 18\%$ and repay $300 at the end of each month for as long as necessary. This loan is invested at $j_1 = 10\%$ and provides a perpetuity due which pays the prize in the annual "Liar's Contest." The prize is $200 for the 1st year, and increases by $150 each year until it reaches $500. From then on the prize remains $500. Find the time and amount of the final repayment on the loan.

6. A university receives a certain sum as a bequest and invests it to earn 8% per annum. The fund can be used to pay for a lecturer at $30 000 payable at the end of each year forever, or the money can be used to pay for a new building which the university is planning to erect. The building will be paid for with 25 equal annual payments, the first of which is due 4 years from today when the building will be occupied. Find the amount of each building payment.

4.5 Annuities where Payments Vary

Thus far, all the annuities considered have had a level series of payments. Unfortunately, this is not always the case in real life. Thus, it is necessary to be able to handle situations where the size of the payments may vary.

First we consider situations where *payments vary in terms of a constant ratio*. We present two methods of solution.

Example 1   Mr. Adams wants to buy an annuity of $1000 a year for 10 years that is protected against inflation. The XYZ Trust Company offers to sell him an annuity where payments increase each year by exactly 10%. In particular, the payments will be $1100 at the end of year 1, $1210 at the end of year 2, $1331 at the end of year 3, and so on for 10 years. Find the cost of this annuity if $j_1 = 13\%$.

Solution We arrange the data on a time diagram below.

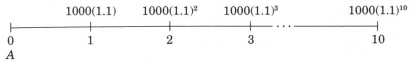

Using 0 as a focal date we write the equation of value for the discounted value A of these payments at $j_1 = 13\%$

$$A = 1000(1.1)(1.13)^{-1} + 1000(1.1)^2(1.13)^{-2} + \ldots + 1000(1.1)^{10}(1.13)^{-10}$$

The expression on the right-hand side is the sum of a geometric progression (see Appendix 2) with first term $t_1 = 1000(1.1)(1.13)^{-1}$ and common ratio $r = (1.1)(1.13)^{-1}$. Thus, applying the formula for the sum of n terms of a geometric progression $S_n = t_1 \dfrac{1 - r^n}{1 - r}$ we obtain

$$A = 1000(1.1)(1.13)^{-1}\left[\frac{1 - (1.1)^{10}(1.13)^{-10}}{1 - (1.1)(1.13)^{-1}}\right] = \$8650.17$$

The cost of the annuity is $8650.17.

It is worth noting that a 10-year $1000 annuity purchased at $j_1 = 13\%$ with no inflation factor would only cost $1000\ a\,\overline{_{10}}|_{13\%} = \$5426.24$.

It is interesting to re-calculate the answer using an ordinary simple annuity of $1000 payments at $j_1 = 3\%$ (13%-10%) which might be considered the "net" rate of return after inflation. We would obtain $1000\ a\,\overline{_{10}}|_{3\%} = \$8530.20$.

Alternate Solution We can re-write the equation for the discounted value A

$$A = 1000\left[\frac{1.1}{1.13} + \left(\frac{1.1}{1.13}\right)^2 + \left(\frac{1.1}{1.13}\right)^3 + \ldots\ 10\ \text{terms}\right]$$

Let i' be a new rate of interest such that

$$1 + i' = \left(\frac{1.1}{1.13}\right)^{-1} = \frac{1.13}{1.1}, \text{ i.e., } i' = .027\ 272\ 73$$

Thus, it is possible to find a new rate of interest, i', and then solve the problem using an ordinary simple annuity. That is

$$A = 1000\left[(1 + i')^{-1} + (1 + i')^{-2} + \ldots\ 10\ \text{terms}\right] = 1000\ a\,\overline{_{10}}|_{i'} = \$8650.17$$

For generalization of the alternate solution see problem 1 of Part B of Exercise 4.5.

Second, we consider situations where *payments vary in terms of a constant difference*. We illustrate a popular method of solution in the following two examples.

Example 2 Find the accumulated and the discounted value of a simple increasing annuity of n payments paid at the end of each interest period at rate i per interest period if the first payment is R, the second $2R$, and so on, the last payment being nR.

Solution We arrange the data on a time diagram below.

$$
\begin{array}{cccccc}
R & 2R & 3R & & (n-1)R & nR \\
\vdash\!\!\!\!\!\!-\!\!\!\!+\!\!\!\!\!\!-\!\!\!\!+\!\!\!\!\!\!-\!\!\!\!+\!\!\!\!\!\!\cdots\!\!\!-\!\!\!\!+\!\!\!\!\!\!-\!\!\!\!+ \\
0 \quad 1 \quad 2 \quad 3 \qquad n-1 \quad n \\
A \qquad\qquad\qquad\qquad\qquad S
\end{array}
$$

Using n as a focal date we write the equation of value for the accumulated value S of the increasing annuity at rate i per period.

$$S = nR + (n - 1)R(1 + i) + \ldots + 3R(1 + i)^{n-3} + 2R(1 + i)^{n-2} + R(1 + i)^{n-1}$$

If we multiply S by $(1 + i)$ we obtain

$$(1 + i)S = nR(1 + i) + (n- 1)R(1 + i)^2 + \ldots + 3R(1 + i)^{n-2} + 2R(1 + i)^{n-1} + R(1 + i)^n$$

Subtracting the first equation from the second, we obtain

$$iS = -nR + R(1 + i) + R(1 + i)^2 + \ldots R(1 + i)^{n-2} + R (1 + i)^{n-1} + R(1 + i)^n$$

$$iS = -nR + R(1 + i)\left[1 + (1 + i) + \ldots + (1 + i)^{n-3} + (1 + i)^{n-2} + (1 + i)^{n-1}\right]$$

The sum of the terms within the square bracket is $s_{\overline{n}|i}$.

Thus

$$iS = -nR + R(1 + i)s_{\overline{n}|i}$$
$$iS = R\left[(1 + i)s_{\overline{n}|i} - n\right]$$
$$S = \frac{R}{i}\left[(1 + i)s_{\overline{n}|i} - n\right]$$

To find the discounted value A of a simple increasing annuity we may discount S at rate i for n periods to obtain

$$A = \frac{R}{i}\left[(1 + i)s_{\overline{n}|i} - n\right](1 + i)^{-n} = \frac{R}{i}\left[(1 + i)a_{\overline{n}|i} - n(1 + i)^{-n}\right]$$

Example 3   Find the discounted value of payments made at the beginning of each year indefinitely at $j_1 = 12\%$, if the first payment is \$100, the second is \$200, the third \$300, and so on.

Solution   We arrange the data on a time diagram below.

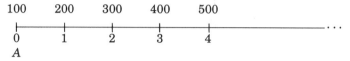

Using 0 as a focal date we write the equation of value for the discounted value A of the increasing simple perpetuity at $j_1 = 12\%$

$$A = 100 + 200(1.12)^{-1} + 300(1.12)^{-2} + 400(1.12)^{-3} + \ldots$$

If we multiply A by $(1 + i) = 1.12$ we obtain

$$1.12A = 100(1.12) + 200 + 300(1.12)^{-1} + 400(1.12)^{-2} + \ldots$$

Subtracting the first equation from the second, we obtain

$$.12A = 100(1.12) + 100\left[1 + (1.12)^{-1} + (1.12)^{-2} + \ldots \right]$$

In the square bracket we have the sum of an infinite geometric progression with first term equal to 1 and ratio equal $(1.12)^{-1}$.
The sum of this infinite geometric progression equals

$$\frac{1}{1 - (1.12)^{-1}} = \frac{1}{1 - \frac{1}{1.12}} = \frac{1.12}{.12}$$

Thus

$$.12A = 100(1.12) + 100\frac{1.12}{.12}$$

$$.12A = 100(1.12)\left[1 + \frac{1}{.12}\right]$$

$$.12A = 100(1.12)\frac{1.12}{.12}$$

$$A = 100\left(\frac{1.12}{.12}\right)^2$$

$$A = \$8711.11$$

Exercise 4.5
Part A

1. Find the discounted value of a series of 20 annual payments of $500 if $j_1 = 15\%$ and we want to allow for an inflation factor of $j_1 = 12\%$.

2. A court is trying to determine the discounted value of the future income of a man paralyzed in a car accident. At the time of the accident the man was earning $25 000 a year and anticipated getting an 8% raise each year. He is 30 years away from retirement. If money is worth $j_1 = 10\%$, what is the discounted value of his future income? (Assume the payments are at the end of each year with the first payment one year hence.)

3. Find the discounted value of a series of 15 payments made at the end of each year at $j_1 = 6\%$ if the first payment is $300, the second payment is $600, the third $900, and so on.

4. A woman has a job that pays $15 000 a year. Each year she gets a $1000 raise. What is the discounted value of her income for the next 10 years if money is worth $j_1 = 17\%$? (Assume the payments are at the end of each year with a first payment of $15 000.)

5. Mrs. Smith invests $10 000 in a preferred stock that pays an annual dividend at 12%. (That is $1200 at the end of each year.) Mrs. Smith invests the dividend payment in her bank account which pays annual interest at $j_1 = 10\%$. What is the total accumulated value of her assets at the end of 5 years? Show that if the two rates of interest (12% and 10%) had been equal (at rate i) the answer would have been $10 000 (1 + i)^5$.

6. An investor deposits $1000 at the beginning of each year in a special fund paying interest at $j_1 = 15\%$. These interest payments are then deposited in a bank account paying interest at $j_1 = 13\%$. How much money has been accumulated at the end of 6 years?

7. A certain site is returning an annual rent of $5000 per year payable at the beginning of the year. It is expected that the rent will increase, on the average, 6% per year. Calculate the present value of the site at 15% effective.

8. Mr. Smith needs to have his house painted immediately. Painting the house will cost $1200 so he is trying to decide if he should put on aluminum siding. If we assume the house must be painted every 5th year (forever) and that the cost of painting will rise by 6% per year (forever), how much should Mr. Smith be willing to pay for aluminum siding if he can earn 14% per annum on his money?

9. In Example 2, we derived the discount value, A, of a simple increasing annuity by taking its accumulated value S and discounting it at rate i for n periods to obtain

$$A = \frac{R}{i}\left[(1 + i)s_{\overline{n}|i} - n\right](1 + i)^{-n}$$
$$= \frac{R}{i}\left[(1 + i)a_{\overline{n}|i} - n(1 + i)^{-n}\right]$$

Starting with the equation:

$$A = R(1 + i)^{-1} + 2R(1 + i)^{-2} + \ldots + (n - 1)R(1 + i)^{-(n-1)} + nR(1 + i)^{-n}$$

derive $A = \frac{R}{i}\left[(1 + i)a_{\overline{n}|i} - n(1 + i)^{-n}\right]$ directly using the methodology illustrated in Example 2.

Part B

1. Consider an annuity where payments vary as represented in the following diagram $(0 < i_1 < 1)$

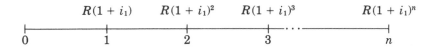

$$
\begin{array}{ccccc}
R(1 + i_1) & R(1 + i_1)^2 & R(1 + i_1)^3 & & R(1 + i_1)^n
\end{array}
$$

Further, assume the interest rate is i_2 per interest period. Let i be the rate such that

$$(1 + i) = \frac{1 + i_2}{1 + i_1}$$

Show that the discounted value A of the above annuity at rate i_2 is

$$A = R\, a_{\overline{n}|i}.$$

2. Derive an algebraic proof of the following identities and interpret by means of time diagrams.

a) $a_{\overline{1}|i} + a_{\overline{2}|i} + a_{\overline{3}|i} + \ldots + a_{\overline{n}|i} = \dfrac{n - a_{\overline{n}|i}}{i}$

b) $s_{\overline{1}|i} + s_{\overline{2}|i} + s_{\overline{3}|i} + \ldots + s_{\overline{n-1}|i} = \dfrac{s_{\overline{n}|i} - n}{i}$

3. Find the discounted value of eleven payments made at the end of each year at rate $j_1 = i\%$ if the dollar size of the respective payments is \$1, \$2, \$3, \$4, \$5, \$6, \$5, \$4, \$3, \$2, \$1.

4. Find the present value of an annuity where payments are \$200 per month at the end of each month during the first year, \$195 per month during the second year, \$190 per month in the third year etc. [with monthly payments decreasing by \$5 after the end of each year]. \$5 monthly will be paid at the end of each month during the 40th year and nothing thereafter. Interest is at $j_{12} = 12\%$.

5. Mr. X has just retired and is trying to decide between two retirement income options as to where he should place his life savings. Fund A will pay him quarterly payments for 25 years starting at \$3000 at the end of the first quarter. Fund A will increase his payments each quarter *thereafter* using an inflation factor equivalent to 10% per annum compounded quarterly. Fund B pays \$4500 at the end of each quarter for 25 years with no inflation factor. Which fund should Mr. X choose if he compares the funds using 12% per annum compounded quarterly?

6. Find the present value of perpetuity under which an amount p is paid at the end of the second year, $p + q$ at the end of the fourth year, $p + 2q$ at the end of the sixth year, $p + 3q$ at the end of the eighth year, etc., interest at the rate i per year.

7. Show that the discounted value A of a simple decreasing annuity whose n payments at the end of each year are $nR, (n - 1)R, (n - 2)R, \ldots, 2R, R$ is

$$A = \frac{R}{i}(n - a_{\overline{n}|i}) \text{ at rate } i \text{ per year.}$$

8. Consider the perpetuity whose payments at the end of each year are $R, R + p$, $R + 2p, \ldots, R + (n - 1)p, R + np, R + np, \ldots$. The payments increase by a constant amount p until they reach $R + np$, after which they continue without change.

Show that the discounted value A of such a perpetuity at rate i per annum is given by

$$A = \frac{R + p\,a_{\overline{n}|i}}{i}$$

9. Given $S = \frac{R}{i}\left[(1 + i)s_{\overline{n}|i} - n\right]$ show that $S = \frac{R}{i}\left[s_{\overline{n+1}|i} - (n + 1)\right]$.

4.6 Review Exercises

1. Instead of paying $450 rent at the beginning of each month for the next 10 years, a couple decides to buy a townhouse. What is the cash equivalent of the 10 years of rent at $j_{12} = 18\%$?

2. A company sets aside $15 000 at the beginning of each year to accumulate a fund for future expansion. What is the amount in the fund at the end of 5 years if the fund earns 15% effective?

3. According to Mr. Smith's will the $100 000 life insurance benefit is invested at 13% effective and from this fund his widow will receive $15 000 each year, the first payment immediately, so long as she lives. On the payment date following the death of his wife, the balance of the fund is to be donated to a local charity. If his wife died 4 years, 3 months later, how much did the charity receive?

4. Five years from now a company will need $150 000 to replace worn-out equipment. Starting now, what monthly deposits must be made in a fund paying $j_{12} = 14\%$ for 5 years to accumulate this sum?

5. Doreen bought a car on September 1 by paying $2000 down and agreeing to make 36 monthly payments of $350, the first due on December 1. If interest is at 18% compounded monthly, find the equivalent cash price.

6. An office space is renting for $3000 a year payable in advance. Find the equivalent monthly rental payable in advance if money is worth 12% compounded monthly.

7. A farmer borrowed $40 000 to buy some farm equipment. He plans to pay off the loan with interest at $j_1 = 13\frac{3}{4}\%$ in 8 equal annual payments, the first to be made 5 years from now. Find the annual payment.

8. What sum of money should be set aside to provide an income of $500 a month for a period of 3 years if the money earns interest at $j_{12} = 15\%$ and the first payment is to be received
   a) one month from now;
   b) immediately;
   c) two years from now?

9. A bank pays interest at 16% compounded quarterly. Interest dates are March 31, June 30, September 30, and December 31. On April 1, 1982, Richard opened an account with a deposit of $200. He continues to make $200 deposits every 3 months until July 1, 1984, when he makes his last deposit. Find the amount in his account
   a) on September 30, 1983;
   b) on September 30, 1987.

10. A certain stock is expected to pay a dividend of $4 at the end of each quarter for an indefinite period in the future. If an investor wishes to realize an annual effective yield of 12%, how much should he pay for the stock?

11. How much money is needed to establish a scholarship fund paying $1000 a year indefinitely, if
    a) the fund earns interest at $j_1 = 12\%$ and the first scholarship is provided at the end of 3 years?
    b) the fund earns interest at $j_{12} = 12\%$ and the first scholarship is provided immediately?

12. On the assumption that a farm will net $15 000 annually indefinitely, what is a fair price for it if money is worth
    a) 18% effective,
    b) $j_{12} = 15\%$?

13. Mr. Jones invests $1000 at the end of each year for 10 years in an investment fund which pays $j_1 = 13\%$. The fund pays the interest out in cheque form at the end of each year and does not allow deposits of less than $1000. Mr. Jones deposits his annual interest payment from the fund into his bank account which pays interest at $j_1 = 10\%$. How much money does he have at the end of 10 years?

14. Show that in question 13, if both rates of interest had been equal to $i\%$, the answer would have been $1000\, s_{\overline{10}|i}$.

15. Find the discounted and the accumulated value of a simple decreasing annuity of 20 payments at the end of each year at $j_1 = 12\%$, if the first payment is $2000, the second $1900, and so on, the last payment being $100.

16. Find the discounted value of a series of payments that start at $18 000 at the end of year one and then increase by $2000 each year forever (i.e., $20 000, $22 000, etc.) if interest is 10% per annum effective.

5

General Annuities

5.1 Introduction

So far, we have assumed that the periodic payments have been made at the same dates as the interest is compounded. This is not always the case. In this chapter, we will consider annuities for which payments are made more or less frequently than interest is compounded. Such a series of payments is called a **general annuity**.

One way to solve general annuity problems is to *replace the given interest rate* by an equivalent rate for which the interest conversion period is the same as the payment period. (A review of Section 2.2. will reacquaint the student with this process.) In effect, the general annuity problems are transformed into simple annuity problems and the methods outlined in Chapter 3 and Chapter 4 can be directly used and thus no new theory is required.

The second, and traditional approach, used in solving general annuity problems is to *replace the given payments* by equivalent payments made on the stated interest conversion dates. In Section 5.2 we develop a replacement formula for converting an ordinary general annuity into an ordinary simple annuity.

In this chapter we illustrate the use of both methods of solution in Sections 5.3 and 5.4. However, in the succeeding topics, we follow the "replacement of the rate" approach, which is the preferred method of solution when calculators are used.

General annuities are very important in Canadian applications, since most of the mortgages in Canada have interest compounded semi-annually but payments made monthly. Canadian mortgages are discussed in Section 5.5.

5.2 Replacement Formula for Converting an Ordinary General Annuity into an Ordinary Simple Annuity

We shall use the following notation:

W = The payment of an ordinary general annuity made p times per year.

p = The number of general annuity payments per year, i.e. frequency of payments.

R = The payment of an ordinary simple annuity, made m times per year, which equitably replaces the ordinary general annuity.

m = The number of interest periods per year, i.e. frequency of compounding.

i = The interest rate per conversion period.

i' = The interest rate per general annuity payment period that is equivalent to i.

Our task is to replace an ordinary general annuity with payments of W made p times a year by an equivalent ordinary simple annuity with payments of R made m times a year.

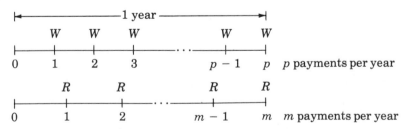

Note m may be greater than, equal to, or less than p.

When replacing one annuity by another one, we must satisfy the following two conditions:
1. the interest rates must be equivalent;
2. the dated values of the two annuities must be the same on any date.

First condition   Rates i' and i are equivalent if and only if

$$(1 + i')^p = (1 + i)^m \tag{i}$$

Second condition   If we chose to equate the value of the two annuities at the end of the year then the accumulated value of the ordinary simple annuity must equal the accumulated value of the ordinary general annuity at the end of the year, i.e.

$$Rs_{\overline{m}|i} = Ws_{\overline{p}|i'} \tag{ii}$$

We now replace the accumulation factors $s_{\overline{m}|i}$ and $s_{\overline{p}|i'}$ by their algebraic expressions

$$s_{\overline{m}|i} = \frac{(1 + i)^m - 1}{i} \text{ and } s_{\overline{p}|i'} = \frac{(1 + i')^p - 1}{i'}$$

and substitute in equation (ii), getting

$$R\frac{(1 + i)^m - 1}{i} = W\frac{(1 + i')^p - 1}{i'}$$

Using equation (i) we see that the numerators of the above fractions are equal, and we can write the last equation in the form

$$\frac{R}{i} = \frac{W}{i'}$$

From equation (i)

$$(1 + i')^p = (1 + i)^m$$
$$(1 + i') = (1 + i)^{m/p}$$
$$i' = (1 + i)^{m/p} - 1$$

Thus

$$R = W\frac{i}{(1 + i)^{m/p} - 1}$$

Comparing the algebraic expression for $\dfrac{1}{s_{\overline{n}|i}} = \dfrac{i}{(1 + i)^n - 1}$

with the factor

$$\frac{i}{(1 + i)^{m/p} - 1}$$

in the above equation, we can write it in the simple form

$$R = \frac{W}{s_{\overline{m/p}|i}} \tag{20}$$

Formula (20) is called a **replacement formula** for converting an ordinary general annuity with payments of W made p times a year into an equivalent ordinary simple annuity with payments of R made m times a year. Shortly we say that formula (20) replaces a general payment W by a simple payment R. For the replacement of a simple payment R by a general payment W we shall use the equivalent form of (20).

$$W = Rs_{\overline{m/p}|i} \tag{21}$$

Example 1   A person receives $2000 at the end of each quarter from a trust fund. What monthly payments are equivalent if money is worth $j_{12} = 9\%$?

Solution   We want to replace $W = 2000$ quarterly by R monthly.

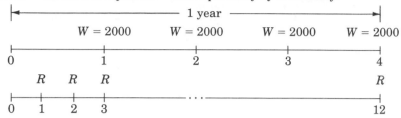

We have $W = 2000$, $p = 4$, $m = 12$, and $i = \frac{3}{4}\%$. Replacement formula (20) gives

$$R = \frac{2000}{s_{\overline{3}|.0075}} = \$661.69$$

The equivalent monthly payment is $661.69. Note that the sum of 3 monthly payments of $661.69 amounts to $1985.07, which is slightly smaller than $2000.

Example 2   A man pays $300 at the end of each month as mortgage payments on a house. Find the equivalent semi-annual payments at 10% per annum compounded semi-annually.

Solution   We want to replace $W = 300$ monthly by R semi-annually.

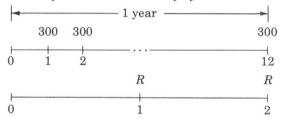

We have $W = 300$, $p = 12$, $m = 2$, and $i = 5\%$. Replacement formula (20) gives

$$R = \frac{300}{s_{\overline{1/6}|.05}} = \$1837.14$$

The equivalent semi-annual payment is $1837.14, which is slightly larger than $1800(6 \times \$300)$.

Example 3   Find an ordinary simple annuity at $j_2 = 11\%$ equivalent to payments of $2000 every 2 years.

Solution   We want to replace $W = 2000$ every 2 years by R semi-annually.

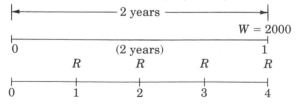

Setting up an equation of value at the end of 2 years we have

$$R\,s_{\overline{4}|.055} = 2000$$
$$R = \frac{2000}{s_{\overline{4}|.055}}$$
$$R = \$460.59$$

Note   We could also use the replacement formula (20) letting $W = 2000$, $p = \frac{1}{2}$
$m = 2$, and $i = 5\frac{1}{2}\%$. Then

$$\frac{m}{p} = \frac{2}{\frac{1}{2}} = 4 \text{ and } R = \frac{2000}{s_{\overline{4}|.055}} = \$460.59$$

Example 4   If money is worth $j_2 = 8\%$, replace an annuity of $1000 at the end of
each half-year by an equivalent annuity payable (a) at the end of each month, and
(b) at the end of each year.

Solution a   We want to replace $R = 1000$ semi-annually by W monthly.

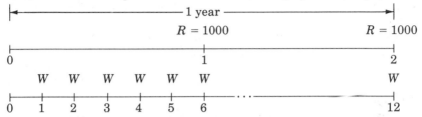

We have $R = 1000$, $m = 2$, $p = 12$, and $i = 4\%$. Replacement formula (21) gives

$$W = 1000s_{\overline{1/6}|.04} = \$163.95$$

Solution b   We want to replace $R = 1000$ semi-annually by W yearly.

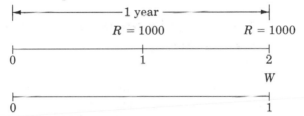

We have $R = 1000$, $m - 2$, $p = 1$, and $i = 4\%$. Replacement formula (21) gives

$$W = Rs_{\overline{2}|.04} = \$2040.00$$

Exercise 5.2

Part A

1. What monthly payments are equivalent to payments of $1000 made at the end
   of each quarter year if $j_{12} = 15\%$?
2. What semi-annual payments are equivalent to payments of $500 at the end of
   each month if $j_{12} = 12\%$?
3. Find the semi-annual payments equivalent to payments of $1000 every 3 years
   if $j_2 = 20\%$.
4. If $j_2 = 10\%$, replace an annuity of $500 payable semi-annually by an equivalent
   annuity payable:
   a) at the end of each month;
   b) at the end of each year.
5. If $150 is needed at the end of each year to pay for your house insurance, how
   much should you set aside at the end of each month for this purpose if your bank
   account pays interest at $j_{12} = 11\%$?

6. Convert an annuity with semi-annual payments of $500 into an equivalent annuity with:
   a) annual payments if money is worth 18% per annum effective;
   b) quarterly payments if money is worth 10% per annum compounded semi-annually.
7. Convert an annuity with quarterly payments of $1000 into an equivalent annuity with:
   a) monthly payments if money is worth $j_{12} = 16\%$;
   b) annual payments if money is worth 13% per annum compounded quarterly.
8. An annuity pays out $1000 at the end of every two years. Find an equivalent simple annuity at $j_2 = 14\%$.
9. Convert a yearly annuity of $500 into an equivalent annuity with quarterly payments if the interest rate is 17% per annum.

Part B
1. Derive replacement formula (20) using a geometric progression.

5.3 Accumulated and Discounted Value of an Ordinary General Annuity

In order to find the accumulated or discounted value of an ordinary general annuity we use the following two-step procedure:
1. Convert the ordinary general annuity into an equivalent ordinary simple annuity, either by replacing the given interest rate (see Section 2.2) or by replacing the given payments (see Section 5.2).
2. Calculate the accumulated or discounted value of an ordinary simple annuity using the methods outlined in Chapter 3.

Example 1   A person deposits $1000 at the end of each year into a Registered Home Ownership Savings Plan (RHOSP), that earns interest at $j_4 = 12\%$. How much money will be accumulated in the plan at the end of 10 years?

Solution   First, find the rate i per year equivalent to 3% per quarter-year, such that

$$1 + i = (1.03)^4$$
$$i = (1.03)^4 - 1$$
$$i = .125\ 508\ 81$$

Second, calculate the accumulated value S of an ordinary simple annuity with $R = 1000, n = 10, i = .125\ 508\ 81$

$$S = 1000\ s_{\overline{10}|i} = \$18\ 022.94$$

At the end of 10 years $18 022.94 will be accumulated in the plan.

Alternate Solution   First, replace $W = 1000$ yearly by R quarterly. We have $W = 1000, p = 1, m = 4$, and $i = 3\%$. Replacement formula (20) gives

$$R = \frac{1000}{s_{\overline{4}|.03}} = \$239.03$$

Second, calculate the accumulated value S of an ordinary simple annuity with $R = 239.03, n = 40, i = 3\%$.

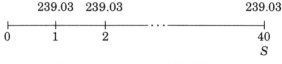

$$S = 239.03\ s_{\overline{40}|.03} = \$18\ 023.16$$

This answer differs slightly from the one obtained by the first method due to rounding off the payment R from replacement formula (20). The first solution is more accurate.

Example 2   A contract calls for payments of $100 at the end of every month for 5 years and an additional payment of $2000 at the end of 5 years. What is the present worth of the contract if money is worth 15% compounded semi-annually?

Solution   First, find the rate i per month equivalent to $7\frac{1}{2}\%$ per half-year, such that

$$(1+i)^{12} = (1.075)^2$$
$$1+i = (1.075)^{1/6}$$
$$i = (1.075)^{1/6} - 1$$
$$i = .012\ 126\ 38$$

Second, find the discounted value, A, of an ordinary simple annuity and of the additional payment of $2000.

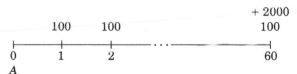

$$A = 100\ a_{\overline{60}|i} + 2000(1+i)^{-60} = 4245.34 + 970.39 = \$5215.73$$

The present value of the contract is $5215.73.

Alternate Solution   First, replace $W = 100$ monthly by R semi-annually. We have $W = 100, p = 12, m = 2$, and $i = .075$ and calculate R using (20)

$$R = \frac{100}{s_{\overline{1/6}|.075}} = \$618.49$$

Second, calculate the discounted value, A, of an ordinary simple annuity and of the additional payment of $2000.

+ 2000
618.49   618.49   618.49

```
├────────┼────────┼── · · · ──────────────────────┤
0        1        2                                10
A
```

$$A = 618.49\ a_{\overline{10}|.075} + 2000(1.075)^{-10} = 4245.37 + 970.39 = \$5215.76$$

This answer differs 3 cents from the one obtained by the first method due to rounding off the payment R from replacement formula (20). The first solution is more accurate.

In the case in which payments are made more frequently than interest is compounded (p is greater than m), financial institutions use different regulations for calculating interest for parts of a conversion period. The three most common possibilities are as follows.

1. *No interest* is given for part of a conversion period. In this case the payment per conversion period is a multiple of payments per general payment interval.
2. *Simple interest* is given for part of a conversion period. In this case the general payments must be accumulated to the end of the conversion period by using the simple interest formula.
3. *Compound interest* is given for part of a conversion period. (This situation is, by far, the most common in Canada.)

Example 3 Payments of \$200 are made at the end of each month in a savings account paying $j_4 = 12\%$. How much money will be accumulated in the account at the end of 5 years if (a) no interest is paid for part of a period? (b) simple interest is paid for part of a period? (c) compound interest is paid for part of a period?

Solution a If no interest is paid for part of a conversion period, then the equivalent payment per quarter is \$600.

We find the accumulated value S of an ordinary simple annuity of \$600 quarterly for 5 years at rate $i = 3\%$ per quarter.

$$S = 600\ s_{\overline{20}|.03} = \$16\ 122.23$$

Solution b First we find an equivalent payment R per quarter by accumulating monthly payments to the end of a 3-month period at simple interest 12%.

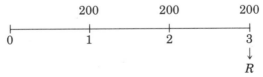

The first payment accumulates 2-months' interest, second payment 1-month's interest, and third payment no interest, or, in other words, the total interest is equal to 3-months' simple interest on \$200,

$$\text{i.e., } 200 \times .12 \times \tfrac{3}{12} = \$6.00.$$

Thus $R = \$606.00$ and the accumulated value S equals

$$S = 606\ s_{\overline{20}|.03} = \$16\ 283.45$$

Solution c First, find the rate i per month equivalent to 3% per quarter-year, such that

$$(1+i)^{12} = (1.03)^4$$
$$1+i = (1.03)^{1/3}$$
$$i = (1.03)^{1/3} - 1$$
$$i = .009\ 901\ 63$$

Second, find the accumulated value S of an ordinary simple annuity with $R = 200$, $n = 60$, $i = .009\ 901\ 63$

$$S = 200 \; s_{\overline{60}|i} = \$16\,282.39$$

Alternate solution c   First, replace $W = 200$ monthly by R quarterly. We have $W = 200$, $p = 12$, $m = 4$ and $i = 3\%$. Replacement formula (20) gives

$$R = \frac{200}{s_{\overline{1/3}|.03}} = \$605.96$$

Second, calculate the accumulated value S of an ordinary simple annuity with $R = 605.96$, $n = 20$, $i = 3\%$.

$$S = 605.96 \; s_{\overline{20}|.03} = \$16\,282.37$$

The 2 cents error is due to rounding off the payment R.

Observation: Not too many people are aware of the fact that simple interest brings more money for a part of a conversion period than compound interest. The difference is not large; however, it is important to know the rules which apply to the particular transaction.

Exercise 5.3
Part A

1. A person deposits $200 at the end of each year in a bank account that earns interest at $j_4 = 16\%$. How much money will be in this bank account at the end of 5 years?

2. A car is purchased by paying $2000 down and then $300 each quarter-year for 3 years. If the interest on the loan was $j_2 = 14\%$, what did the car sell for?

3. How much money must a person have in the bank today to be able to withdraw $100 monthly for 10 years (first withdrawal one month hence) if the bank pays interest at rate $j_2 = 15\%$?

4. Payments of $1000 are to be made at the end of each half-year for the next ten years. Find their discounted value if interest is at rate 12% per annum compounded
   a) half-yearly;
   b) quarterly;
   c) annually.

5. Find the discounted value at $j_2 = 10\%$ of 20 annual payments of $200 each, the first one due five years hence.

6. An experimental forest is to be grown by planting 1000 trees each year on the same day of the year. The trees each contain 0.003 cubic metres of wood when they are planted and increase in volume at the rate of 5% per quarter of a year thereafter. What will be the total volume of all the trees in the forest after 10 years? (Assume no trees die.)

7. What single payment now is equivalent to semi-annual payments of $1000 over 5 years if $j_{12} = 18\%$? (First payment at end of first half-year.)

8. Find the discounted value of an annuity paying $50 at the end of each quarter for 4 years if money is worth $j_{12} = 11\%$.

9. Payments of $200 are made at the end of each month for 5 years into a bank account where interest is paid at $j_4 = 15\%$. Find the accumulated value of the account at the end of 5 years if
   a) no interest is paid for part of a period;
   b) simple interest is paid for part of a period;
   c) compound interest is paid for part of a period.

10. Payments of $500 are made at the end of each half-year for 10 years in an account paying 11% per annum. Find the discounted value of these payments if
   a) no interest is paid for part of a period;
   b) simple interest is paid for part of a period;
   c) compound interest is paid for part of a period.

11. Which is cheaper?
   I. Buy a car for $7000 and after three years trade it in for $2000.
   II. Rent a car for $250 a month payable at the end of each month for three years. Assume maintenance and licence costs are identical and that money is worth 16% effective.

12. An insurance company pays 9% per annum on money left with them. What would be the cost of an annuity certain paying $250 at the end of each month for 10 years if compound interest is paid for each part of a period?

13. Deposits of $100 are made at the end of each quarter to a bank account for 5 years. Find the accumulated value of these payments if
   a) $j_{12} = 15\%$;
   b) $j_4 = 15\%$;
   c) $j_1 = 15\%$.

14. Find the accumulated value of payments of $200 made at the beginning of each month for 3 years at $j_2 = 13\%$.

15. An insurance policy requires premium payments of $15 at the beginning of each month for 20 years. Find the discounted value of these payments at $j_4 = 11\%$.

Part B

1. Using the replacement of rate method fill in the table below to show the accumulated value of an ordinary annuity of $1, p times per year, for 10 years at $j_m = 12\%$.

	$m = 2$	$m = 4$	$m = 12$
$p = 2$			
$p = 4$			
$p = 12$	$i = (1.06)^{1/6} - 1$ $s_{\overline{120}i}$		

2. Using the replacement of payment method fill in the table below to show the discounted value of an ordinary annuity of $1, p times per year, for 10 years at $j_m = 12\%$.

	$m = 2$	$m = 4$	$m = 12$
$p = 2$			$\dfrac{a_{\overline{120}.01}}{s_{\overline{6}.01}}$
$p = 4$			
$p = 12$			

3. Develop the following formulas for the accumulated value S and the discounted value A of an ordinary general annuity with payments W, p times per year, for k years at rate j_m.

$$S = W\frac{(1+i)^{km} - 1}{(1+i)^{m/p} - 1}$$

$$A = W\frac{1 - (1+i)^{-km}}{(1+i)^{m/p} - 1} \text{ where } i = \frac{j_m}{m}$$

4. Develop the following formulas for the accumulated value S and the discounted value A of a general annuity due with payments W, p times per year, for k years at rate j_m.

$$S = W\frac{s_{\overline{km}|i}}{s_{\overline{m/p}|i}}(1+i)^{m/p}$$

$$A = W\frac{a_{\overline{km}|i}}{s_{\overline{m/p}|i}}(1+i)^{m/p} \text{ where } i = \frac{j_m}{m}$$

5. An annuity consists of 40 payments of $300 each made at intervals of three months. Interest is at 12% effective. Find the value of this annuity at each of the following times
   a) three months before the time of the first payment;
   b) at the time of the last payment;
   c) at the time of the first payment;
   d) three months after the last payment;
   e) four years and three months before the first payment.

6. Use an infinite geometric progression to derive the following formula for the discounted value A of an ordinary general perpetuity with payments W, p times per year, at rate j_m

$$A = \frac{W}{i}\frac{1}{s_{\overline{m/p}|i}} \text{ where } i = \frac{j_m}{m}$$

7. A father has saved a fund to provide for his son's 4-year university program. The fund will pay $300 at the beginning of each month for eight months (September through April) plus an extra $2000 each September 1st for four years to cover tuition and books. If $j_4 = 16\%$, what is the value of the fund on the first day of university (before any withdrawals)?

5.4 Finding the Periodic Payment of an Ordinary General Annuity

In order to find the periodic payment of an ordinary general annuity we may use either the "change of rate" approach or the "change of payment" approach.

When using the "change of rate" approach:
   1. Replace the given interest rate by an equivalent interest rate compounded with the same frequency as payments are made.

2. Find the periodic payment of an ordinary simple annuity using formula (14) or (15).

When using the "change of payment" approach:

1. Find the periodic payment R at the ends of interest conversion periods; i.e., the periodic payment of an ordinary simple annuity.

2. Find the periodic payment W of an equivalent ordinary general annuity using replacement formula (21) $W = Rs_{\overline{m/p}|i}$.

Example 1   A property worth $50 000 is sold for $10 000 down and equal monthly payments for the next 20 years. Find the size of the payments if the interest rate is 14% effective.

Solution   First, find the rate i per month equivalent to 14% per year, such that

$$(1+i)^{12} = 1.14$$
$$1+i = (1.14)^{1/12}$$
$$i = (1.14)^{1/12} - 1$$
$$i = .010\ 978\ 85$$

Second, find the monthly payment R of an ordinary simple annuity with $A = 40\ 000$, $n = 240$, and $i = .010\ 978\ 85$ using formula (15)

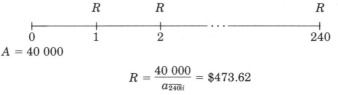

$$R = \frac{40\ 000}{a_{\overline{240}|i}} = \$473.62$$

The monthly payment is $473.62.

Alternate Solution   First, find the annual payment R of an ordinary simple annuity with $A = 40\ 000$, $n = 20$, and $i = 14\%$ using (15).

$$R = \frac{40\ 000}{a_{\overline{20}|.14}} = \$6039.44$$

Second, replace $R = 6039.44$ annually by W monthly. We have $R = 6039.44$, $p = 12$, $m = 1$, and $i = 14\%$. Replacement formula (21) gives

$$W = 6039.44\ s_{\overline{1/12}|.14} = \$473.62$$

The monthly payment is $473.62.

Example 2   A couple would like to accumulate $20 000 in 3 years as a down payment on a house, by making deposits at the end of each week in an account paying interest at $j_{12} = 12\%$. Find the size of the weekly deposit, assuming that compound interest is given for part of a conversion period.

Solution   First, find the rate i per week equivalent to 1% per month, such that

$$(1+i)^{52} = (1.01)^{12}$$
$$1+i = (1.01)^{12/52}$$
$$i = (1.01)^{12/52} - 1$$
$$i = .002\ 298\ 87$$

Second, find the weekly deposit R of an ordinary simple annuity with $S = 20\ 000$, $n = 3 \times 52 = 156$, and $i = .002\ 298\ 87$ using formula (14).

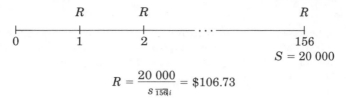

$$R = \frac{20\ 000}{s\ \overline{156}|i} = \$106.73$$

The weekly deposit is $106.73.

Alternate Solution   First, find the monthly payment R of an ordinary simple annuity with $S = 20\ 000$, $n = 36$, and $i = 1\%$ using (14).

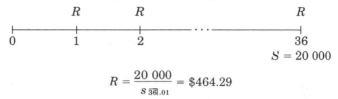

$$R = \frac{20\ 000}{s\ \overline{36}|.01} = \$464.29$$

Second, replace $R = 464.29$ monthly by W weekly. We have $R = 464.29$, $p = 52$, $m = 12$, and $i = 1\%$. Replacement formula (21) gives

$$W - 464.29\ s\ \overline{12/52}|.01 = \$106.73$$

The weekly deposit should be $106.73.

Exercise 5.4
Part A

1. Mr. A borrows $10 000. The loan is to be repaid with equal payments at the end of each month for the next 5 years. Find the size of this payment if
   a) money is worth 18% per annum compounded quarterly;
   b) money is worth 18% per annum effective.

2. Upon graduation, a student determines that he has borrowed $3000 from the provincial loan plan over his three years of college. This loan must be repaid with monthly payments (first payment at the end of the first month) over the next 5 years. If $j_2 = 11\%$, find the monthly payment.

3. How much must be deposited in a bank account at the end of each quarter for 4 years to accumulate $4000 if
   a) $j_{12} = 16\%$;
   b) $j_2 = 16\%$;
   c) $j_{365} = 16\%$.

4. Upon her husband's death, a widow finds that her husband had a $30 000 life insurance policy. One option available to her is a monthly annuity over a ten-year period. If the insurance company pays 10% per annum, what monthly income (at the end of each month) would this provide?

5. A city wants to accumulate $500 000 over the next 20 years to redeem an issue of bonds. What payment will be required at the end of each 6 months to accumulate this amount if interest is earned at 13% per annum, compounded monthly?

Part B

1. On September 1, 1983 a wealthy industrialist gives a college a fund of $100 000 which is invested at 14% compounded daily. If semi-annual scholarships are awarded for 20 years from this grant, what is the size of each scholarship if the first one is awarded on
   a) September 1, 1983;
   b) September 1, 1985?

2. If the semi-annual scholarships in question B1 were awarded indefinitely, what would be the size of the payments for the two starting dates listed above?

3. A condominium owners association will need $100 000, 3 years from now, to be used for major renovations. For the last 2 years they made deposits of $4000 at the end of each quarter into a fund that earns interest at $j_{365} = 12\%$. What quarterly deposits to the fund will be needed to reach the goal of $100 000, 3 years from now?

4. In a recent court case, the ABC Development Company sued the XYZ Trust Company. The ABC Development Company had borrowed $8.2 million from the XYZ Trust Company at 13%. The loan was paid off over 3 years with monthly payments. The ABC Development Company thought the rate of interest was $j_1 = 13\%$. The XYZ Trust Company was using $j_{365} = 13\%$. The court sided with the Development Company and awarded them the total dollar difference (without interest). Find the size of the award.

5. Starting on his 36th birthday, Mr. Adams deposits $2000 a year into a savings fund. His last deposit is at age 65. Starting one month later, he makes monthly withdrawals for 15 years. If $j_4 = 12\%$ throughout, find the size of these monthly withdrawals.

6. A perpetuity paying $1000 at the end of each year is replaced with an annuity paying $X at the end of each month for 10 years. Find $X if $j_4 = 15\%$ in both cases.

7. If, in question six, the annuity paid $250 at the end of each month, how long would the annuity last and what would be the size of the final smaller payment? ($j_4 = 15\%$.)

5.5 Mortgages in Canada

Canadian mortgage regulations require that the interest can be compounded, at most, semi-annually, whereas mortgage payments are usually made monthly.

Thus the mortgage amortizations in Canada are, in effect, general annuities.

There are no legal ceilings on mortgage interest rates in Canada; the rates fluctuate with the price of money on the open market.

While the monthly payment on a Canadian mortgage is usually determined using a repayment period of 20, 25, or 30 years, the interest rate stated in the mortgage is not guaranteed for that length of time. Rather, the interest rate will change after (usually) one, three, or five years depending on the mortgage chosen. At the time the interest rate is renegotiated, the mortgage is open and can be repaid in full. Refinancing of a mortgage will be discussed in Chapter 6.

Example 1 In July 1979, mortgage rates in Canada averaged around $j_2 = 11\%$. Two years later mortgage rates reached the unprecedented level of $j_2 = 22\%$. Given a $50 000 mortgage to be repaid over 25 years find the required monthly payment at the two different rates of interest.

Solution a At $j_2 = 11\%$, first find the rate i per month equivalent to $5\frac{1}{2}\%$ per half-year, such that

$$(1+i)^{12} = (1.055)^2$$
$$1+i = (1.055)^{1/6}$$
$$i = (1.055)^{1/6} - 1$$
$$i - .008\ 963\ 39$$

Second, find the monthly payment R of an ordinary simple annuity with $A = 50\ 000$, $n = 300$, and $i = .008\ 963\ 39$.

$$R = \frac{50\ 000}{a\ \overline{300}|i} = \$481.26$$

At $j_2 = 11\%$ the monthly mortgage payment required is $481.26.

Solution b At $j_2 = 22\%$, first find the rate i per month equivalent to 11% per half-year, such that

$$(1+i)^{12} = (1.11)^2$$
$$1+i = (1.11)^{1/6}$$
$$i = (1.11)^{1/6} - 1$$
$$i = .017\ 545\ 48$$

Second, find the monthly payment R of an ordinary simple annuity with $A = 50\ 000$, $n = 300$, and $i = .017\ 545\ 48$.

$$R = \frac{50\ 000}{a\ \overline{300}|i} = \$882.05$$

At $j_2 = 22\%$ the monthly mortgage payment required is $882.05. Notice the significant effect the rate of interest has on a mortgage payment.

Example 2 A couple is considering a mortgage loan for $60 000 at 18% compounded semi-annually.
a) Calculate the couple's monthly mortgage payment based on the following terms: 25 years, 20 years, 15 years and 10 years.
b) Suppose that the couple could arrange a mortgage loan where only interest due is paid in monthly payments and the principal as a lump-sum is returned at the time of the resale of the home or at the end of 10 years, whichever comes first. Find the monthly interest payment.
c) If the couple can afford to pay $1200 monthly on their mortgage loan, how many full payments will be required and what will be the smaller concluding payment 1 month after the last full payment?

Solution a First, find the rate i per month equivalent to 9% per half-year, such that

$$(1+i)^{12} = (1.09)^2$$
$$1+i = (1.09)^{1/6}$$
$$i = (1.09)^{1/6} - 1$$
$$i = .014\ 466\ 59$$

Second, find the monthly payment R of an ordinary simple annuity with $A = 60\ 000$, $i = .014\ 466\ 59$ and

$n = 300$ (25-year term): $R = \dfrac{60\ 000}{a\,\overline{300}|i} = \$879.83$

$n = 240$ (20-year term): $R = \dfrac{60\ 000}{a\,\overline{240}|i} = \$896.54$

$n = 180$ (15-year term): $R = \dfrac{60\ 000}{a\,\overline{180}|i} = \$938.75$

$n = 120$ (10-year term): $R = \dfrac{60\ 000}{a\,\overline{120}|i} = \$1056.51$

Notice that relatively small increases in the monthly payment will decrease significantly the term of the amortization of the mortgage loan.

The borrower is well advised to choose the term of the loan best suited to his particular situation.

Solution b   Interest rate i per month calculated in part a is $i = .014\ 466\ 59$ and the monthly interest payment is then $60\ 000 \times .014\ 466\ 59 = \$868.00$.

Compare this interest payment with the monthly mortgage payment using a 25-year term to see that most of the mortgage payment pays interest on the outstanding balance and only a very small portion of the mortgage payment is used to reduce the principal. (This is true in the early part of the term of a mortgage.) Detailed discussion of the amortization of a mortgage loan is presented in Chapter 6.

Solution c   We have an ordinary simple annuity with $A = 60\ 000$, $R = 1200$, $i = .014\ 466\ 59$ and we want to calculate n from equation (13).

$$1200\ a\,\overline{n}|i = 60\ 000$$
$$a\,\overline{n}|i = 50$$
$$\frac{1 - (1.014\ 466\ 59)^{-n}}{.014\ 466\ 59} = 50$$
$$1 - (1.014\ 466\ 59)^{-n} = .723\ 329\ 57$$
$$(1.014\ 466\ 59)^{-n} = .276\ 670\ 43$$
$$-n \log 1.014\ 466\ 59 = \log .276\ 670\ 43$$
$$n = 89.461\ 321$$

Thus there will be 89 full monthly payments and a smaller concluding payment $\$X$, 1 month after the last full payment.

Using 90 as a focal date, we obtain the equation of value for unknown X at rate $i = .014\ 466\ 59$

$$1200\ s\,\overline{89}|i\ (1+i) + X = 60\ 000(1+i)^{90}$$
$$217\ 993.19 + X = 218\ 548.91$$
$$X = \$555.72$$

Exercise 5.5
Part A
In each question listed below find the monthly mortgage payment.

No.	Mortgage Loan	Interest Rate	Term
1.	$55 000	$j_2 = 10\frac{1}{4}\%$	25 years
2.	$39 000	$j_2 = 14\frac{3}{4}\%$	20 years
3.	$63 000	$j_2 = 12\frac{1}{2}\%$	22 years
4.	$45 000	$j_2 = 18\frac{1}{4}\%$	12 years

5. A $40 000 mortgage is to be paid off by monthly payments over 25 years. Find the monthly payment, if
   a) $j_2 = 12\%$;
   b) $j_2 = 14\%$;
   c) $j_2 = 16\%$.
6. A $50 000 mortgage is obtained at a rate $j_2 - 16\frac{1}{4}\%$. The mortgage can be paid off over 20, 25, or 30 years. Find the monthly payments necessary under each of these three options.
7. Politicians have sometimes suggested putting a ceiling on mortgage interest rates. Mr. and Mrs. Smith want to buy a house that would require a $60 000, 25-year mortgage. Interest is at rate $j_2 = 15\%$. If the government guaranteed lower mortgage interest rates then we would expect the demand for housing to increase thus forcing house prices upward (given a constant supply). Would Mr. and Mrs. Smith be better off if they could get a government 25-year mortgage at $j_2 = 12\%$ but the price of the house rose such that it required a $70 000 mortgage?
8. A couple is looking at buying one of two houses. The smaller house would require a $55 000 mortgage; the larger house a $70 000 mortgage. If $j_2 = 17\frac{1}{2}\%$, what difference would there be in their monthly payments between these two houses (assume a 25-year mortgage is used in both cases)?
9. Mr. and Mrs. Jones are considering the purchase of a house. They would require a mortgage loan of $35 000 at rate $j_2 = 17\frac{3}{4}\%$. If they can afford to pay $900 monthly, how many full payments will be required and what will be the smaller concluding payment?
10. The Andersons can buy a certain house listed at $100 000 and pay $35 000 down. They can get a mortgage for $65 000 at $j_2 = 16\%$ payable monthly over 25 years. The seller of the house offers them the house for $105 000 and he will give them a $70 000 mortgage at $j_2 = 12\%$ and assume a 25-year amortization period. If these interest rates are guaranteed for 25 years, what should they do?

Part B
In each question listed below find the unknown part.

No.	Mortgage Loan	Interest Rate	Term	Monthly Payment
1.	?	$j_2 = 11\frac{3}{4}\%$	25 years	$575.-
2.	$57 000	$j_2 = ?$	20 years	$832.-
3.	$48 000	$j_2 = 16\frac{1}{2}\%$	?	$750.-
4.	$80 000	$j_2 = 20\frac{3}{8}\%$	30 years	?

5. The Andersons have a $50 000 mortgage with monthly payments over 25 years at $j_2 = 16\%$. Because they each get paid weekly, they decide to switch to weekly payments (still at $j_2 = 16\%$ and paid over 25 years). Compare their weekly payments to their monthly payments.

5.6 Review Exercises

1. Convert an annuity with quarterly payments of $300 into an equivalent annuity with
   a) semi-annual payments if money is worth 15% compounded semi-annually;
   b) monthly payments if money is worth 14% compounded quarterly.

2. Find the accumulated and the discounted value of payments of $100 at the end of each quarter-year for 10 years at $j_{12} = 18\%$.

3. Deposits of $100 are made at the end of each month to a savings account paying interest at 15% compounded semi-annually. How much money will be accumulated in the account at the end of 3 years if
   a) simple interest is paid for part of a conversion period;
   b) compound interest is paid for part of a conversion period?

4. How many monthly deposits of $100 each and what final deposit one month later will be necessary to accumulate $3000 if interest is
   a) at $16\frac{1}{2}\%$ compounded semi-annually?
   b) at 15% compounded quarterly?

5. A company wishes to have $150 000 in a fund at the end of 8 years. What deposit at the end of each month must they make if the fund pays interest at 15% compounded daily?

6. Steve buys a new car worth $7500. He pays $1500 down and agrees to pay $250 at the end of each month as long as necessary. Find the number of full payments and the final payment one month later if interest is at 14.2% effective.

7. If it takes $50 per month for 18 months to repay a loan of $800, what nominal rate compounded semi-annually is being charged? What effective rate is being charged?

8. A lot is sold for $8000 down and 6 semi-annual payments of $3000, the first due at the end of 2 years. Find the cash value of the lot if money is worth 16% compounded daily.

9. Find the accumulated and discounted value of payments of $100 made at the beginning of each month for 5 years at $j_4 = 14\%$.

10. An annuity consists of 60 payments of $200 at the end of each month. Interest is at 11.05% effective. Find the value of this annuity at each of the following times:
   a) at the time of the first payment;
   b) two years before the first payment;
   c) at the time of the last payment.

11. A couple requires a $45 000 mortgage loan at $j_2 = 16\frac{3}{4}\%$ to buy a new house.
   a) Find the couple's monthly mortgage payment based on the following terms: 30 years, 20 years and 10 years.
   b) If the couple can afford to pay $850 monthly on their mortgage loan, how many full payments will be required and what will be the smaller concluding payment?

6

Amortization Method and Sinking Funds

6.1 Amortization of a Debt

In this chapter we shall discuss different methods of repaying interest-bearing loans, which is one of the most important applications of annuities in business transactions.

The first, and most common method, is the **amortization method**. When this method is used to liquidate an interest-bearing debt, a series of periodic payments, usually equal, is made. Each payment pays the interest on the unpaid balance and also repays a part of the outstanding principal. As time goes on the outstanding principal is gradually reduced and the interest on the unpaid balance decreases.

When a debt is amortized by equal payments at equal payment intervals, the debt becomes the discounted value of an annuity. The size of the payment is determined by the methods used in the annuity problems of the preceding chapters. The common commercial practice is to round the payment up to the nearest cent. This practice will be used in this textbook unless specified otherwise. Instead of rounding up to the cent, the lender may round up to the dime or to the dollar. In any case the rounding of the payment up to the cent, to the dime, or to the dollar will result in a smaller concluding payment. An equation of value at the time of the last payment will give the size of the smaller concluding payment.

Example 1 A loan of $20 000 is to be amortized with equal monthly payments over a period of 10 years at $j_{12} = 12\%$. Find the concluding payment if the monthly payment is rounded up to: (a) the cent; (b) the dime.

Solution First we find the monthly payment R, given $A = 20\,000$, $n = 120$, and $i = .01$. Using equation (15) we calculate

$$R = \frac{20\,000}{a_{\overline{120}|.01}} = 286.9419$$

Let X be the concluding payment. We arrange our data on a time diagram below,

and set up an equation of value for X at 120,

$$X + R s_{\overline{119}|.01}(1.01) = 20\,000(1.01)^{120}$$

Solution a If the monthly payment is rounded up to the cent, we have $R = 286.95$ and calculate

$$X = 20\,000(1.01)^{120} - 286.95 s_{\overline{119}|.01}(1.01)$$

$$= 66\,007.74 - 65\,722.65 = \$285.09$$

Solution b If the monthly payment is rounded up to the dime, we have $R = \$287$ and calculate

$$X = 20\,000(1.01)^{120} - 287 s_{\overline{119}|.01}(1.01)$$

$$= 66\,007.74 - 65\,734.10 = \$273.64$$

When interest-bearing debts are amortized by means of a series of equal payments at equal intervals, it is important to know how much of each payment goes for interest and how much goes for the reduction of principal. We construct an **amortization schedule** which shows the progress of the amortization of the debt.

Example 2 A debt of \$2200 with interest at $j_4 = 10\%$ is to be amortized by payments of \$500 at the end of each quarter for as long as necessary. Make out an amortization schedule showing the distribution of the payments as to interest and the repayment of principal.

Solution The interest due at the end of the first quarter is $2\frac{1}{2}\%$ of \$2200 or \$55. The first payment of \$500 at this time will pay the interest and will also reduce the outstanding principal by \$445. Thus the outstanding principal after the first payment is reduced to \$1755. The interest due at the end of the second quarter is $2\frac{1}{2}\%$ of \$1755 or \$43.88. The second payment of \$500 pays the interest and reduces the indebtedness by \$456.12. The outstanding principal now becomes \$1298.88. The procedure is repeated and the results are tabulated below in the amortization schedule.

Payment number	Periodic payment	Payment of interest at $2\frac{1}{2}\%$	Principal repaid	Outstanding principal
				\$2200.00
1	500.00	55.00	445.00	1755.00
2	500.00	43.88	456.12	1298.88
3	500.00	32.47	467.53	831.35
4	500.00	20.78	479.22	352.13
5	360.93	8.80	352.13	0
Totals	2360.93	160.93	2200.00	

It should be noted, that the 5th payment is only $360.93, which is the sum of the outstanding principal at the end of the 4th quarter plus the interest due at $2\frac{1}{2}\%$. The totals at the bottom of the schedule are for checking purposes. The total amount of principal repaid must equal the original debt. Also, the total of periodic payments must equal the total interest plus the total principal returned. Note that the entries in the principal repaid column (except the final payment) are in the ratio $1 + i$. That is

$$\frac{456.12}{445.00} \doteq \frac{467.53}{456.12} \doteq \frac{479.22}{467.53} \doteq 1.025$$

Example 3   A couple purchased a home and signed a mortgage contract for $60 000 to be paid in equal monthly payments over 25 years with interest at $j_2 = 18\%$. Find the monthly payment and make out a partial amortization schedule showing the distribution of the first 6 payments as to interest and the repayment of principal.

How much of the principal is repaid during the first 6 months?

Solution   Since the interest is compounded semi-annually and the payments are paid monthly, we have a general annuity problem. First we calculate rate i per month equivalent to 9% per half-year.

$$(1 + i)^{12} = (1.09)^2$$
$$(1 + i) = (1.09)^{1/6}$$
$$i = (1.09)^{1/6} - 1$$
$$i = .014\ 466\ 59$$

Now $R = \dfrac{60\ 000}{a_{\overline{300}|i}} = \$879.83.$

To make out the amortization schedule for the first 6 months, we follow the method outlined in Example 2 with $i = .014\ 466\ 59$.

Payment number	Periodic payment	Payment of interest at i	Principal repaid	Outstanding principal
				$60 000.00
1	879.83	868.00	11.83	59 988.17
2	879.83	867.82	12.01	59 976.16
3	879.83	867.65	12.18	59 963.98
4	879.83	867.47	12.36	59 951.62
5	879.83	867.30	12.53	59 939.09
6	879.83	867.11	12.72	59 926.37
Totals	5278.98	5205.35	73.63	

During the first 6 months only $73.63 of the original $60 000 debt is repaid. It should be noted that over 98% of each of the first six payments goes for interest and less than 2% goes for the reduction of the outstanding balance.

It is also worth noting that the entries in the principal repaid columns are in the ratio of $(1 + i)$. That is:

$$\frac{12.01}{11.83} \doteq \frac{12.18}{12.01} \doteq \ \cdots \ \doteq \frac{12.72}{12.53} \doteq 1 + i.$$

Exercise 6.1

Part A:

1. A loan of $5000 is to be amortized with equal quarterly payments over a period of 5 years at $j_4 = 12\%$. Find the concluding payment if the quarterly payment is rounded up to a) the cent; b) the dime.

2. A loan of $2000 is to be amortized with equal monthly payments over a 3 year period at $j_{12} = 15\%$. Find the concluding payment if the monthly payment is rounded up to a) the cent; b) the dime.

3. A $5000 loan is to be amortized with 8 equal semi-annual payments. If interest is at $j_2 = 14\%$, find the semi-annual payment and construct an amortization schedule.

4. A loan of $900 is to be amortized with 6 equal monthly payments at $j_{12} = 12\%$. Find the monthly payment and construct an amortization schedule.

5. A loan of $800 is to be repaid over 1 year at $j_2 = 22\%$ with equal monthly payments. Find the monthly payment and construct an amortization schedule.

6. A loan of $1000 is to be repaid over 2 years with quarterly payments. Interest is at $j_{12} = 15\%$. Find the quarterly payment required and construct an amortization schedule to show the interest and principal portion of each payment.

7. A debt of $2000 bearing interest at $j_2 = 12\%$ is amortized by payments of $500 every six months for as long as necessary. Make out an amortization schedule.

8. A debt of $5000 with interest at $j_4 = 20\%$ is to be amortized by payments of $1000 at the end of each quarter for as long as necessary. Make out an amortization schedule.

9. A $1000 loan is to be repaid with semi-annual payments of $250 for as long as necessary. If interest is at $j_{12} = 12\%$, do a complete amortization schedule showing a distribution of each payment into principal and interest.

10. A debt of $2000 will be repaid by monthly payments of $500 for as long as necessary, the first payment made at the end of 6 months. If interest is at $j_{12} = 19\%$, find the size of the debt at the end of 5 months and make out the complete schedule starting at that time.

11. A couple buys some furniture for $1500. They pay off the debt at $j_{12} = 18\%$ by paying $200 a month for as long as necessary. The first payment is at the end of 3 months. Do a complete amortization schedule for this loan showing a distribution of each payment into principal and interest.

12. A $6000 car is purchased by paying $1000 down and then equal monthly payments for 3 years at $j_{12} = 15\%$. Find the size of the monthly payment and complete the first three lines of an amortization schedule.

13. A mobile house worth $26 000 is purchased with a down payment of $6000 and monthly payments for 15 years. If the interest is $j_2 = 21\%$ find the monthly payment required and complete the first 6 lines of an amortization schedule.

14. A couple purchases a home worth $56 000 by paying $6000 down and then taking out a mortgage at $j_2 = 18\%$. The mortgage will be amortized over 25 years with equal monthly payments. Find the monthly payment and do a partial amortization schedule showing the distribution of the first 6 payments as to interest and principal. How much of the principal is repaid during the first 6 months?

15. Re-do question 14 using (a) 14% per annum compounded semi-annually; (b) 22% per annum compounded semi-annually.

Exercise 6.1
Part B:

1. Consider a loan that is to be repaid with annual payments, R, at the end of each year for 5 years at effective rate i per annum. Hence, the original value of the loan is $Ra_{\overline{5}|i}$. Do a complete amortization schedule for this loan. Verify that the sum of the principal column equals the original value of the loan. Verify that the sum of the interest column equals the total payments less the original value of the loan. Finally, verify that the principal payments are in the ratio $1 + i$.

2. A loan is being repaid over 10 years with equal annual payments. Interest is at $j_1 = 10\%$. If the amount of principal repaid in the third payment is $100, find the amount of principal repaid in the seventh payment.

3. The ABC Bank develops a special scheme to help their customers pay their loans off quickly. Instead of making payments of X once a month, mortgage borrowers are asked to pay $\frac{X}{4}$ once a week (52 times a year).
   The Smiths are buying a house and need a $45 000 mortgage. If $j_2 = 18\%$ determine
   a) the monthly payment required to amortize the debt over 25 years;
   b) the weekly payment $\frac{X}{4}$ suggested in the scheme;
   c) the number of weeks it will take to pay off the debt using the suggested scheme;
   d) compare these results and comment.

4. A loan is being repaid by monthly instalment of $100 at $j_{12} = 18\%$. If the loan balance after the fourth month is $1200, find the original loan value.

5. A loan is being repaid with 20 annual instalments at 15% per annum effective. In what instalment are the principal and interest portions most nearly equal to each other?

6. A loan is being repaid with 10 annual instalments. The principal portion of the seventh payment is $110.25 and the interest portion is $39.75. What effective rate of interest is being charged per annum?

7. A loan at 9% per annum effective is being repaid by monthly payments of $750 each. The total principal repaid in the twelve monthly instalments of the 8th year is $400. What is the total interest paid in the 12 instalments of the 10th year?

8. Below is part of a mortgage amortization schedule.

| \multicolumn{2}{c}{Distribution of Payment} | |
Interest	Principal
$243.07	$31.68
242.81	31.94

Determine

a) The monthly payment;
b) The effective rate of interest per month;
c) The nominal rate of interest j_2 (round to nearest $\frac{1}{8}\%$);
d) The outstanding balance just after the first payment shown above;
e) The remaining period of the mortgage if interest rates don't change.

9. On mortgages repaid by equal annual payments covering both principal and interest, a mortgage company pays as a commission to its agents 10% of the portion of each scheduled instalment which represents interest. What is the total commission paid per $1000 of original mortgage loan if it is repaid with n annual payments at rate i per annum effective?

6.2 Outstanding Principal

It is quite important to know the amount of principal remaining to be paid at a certain time. The borrower may want to pay off the outstanding balance of the debt in a lump sum, or the lender may wish to sell the contract.

One could find the outstanding principal by making out an amortization schedule. This becomes rather tedious when a large number of payments are involved. In this section we shall calculate the outstanding principal directly from an appropriate equation of value.

Let P denote the outstanding principal after the kth payment has been made.

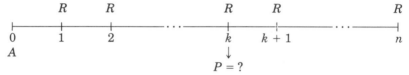

Two methods for finding P are available.

The Restrospective Method. This method uses the past history of the debt—the payments that have been made already. The outstanding principal, P at k, is calculated as the difference between the accumulated value of the debt and the accumulated value of the payments already made. Thus,

$$P = A(1 + i)^k - Rs_{\overline{k}|i} \qquad (22)$$

Equation (22) always gives the correct value of the outstanding principal P and can be used all the time, even if the number of payments is not known or the last payment is an irregular one.

The Prospective Method. This method uses the future prospects of the debt—the payments yet to be made. The outstanding principal, P at k, is calculated as the discounted value of the $(n - k)$ payments yet to be made.

If all the payments, including the last one are equal, we obtain

$$P = Ra_{\overline{n-k}|i} \qquad (23)$$

Equation (23) cannot be used when the concluding payment is an irregular one, however, it is useful if you don't know the original value of the loan or if there have been several interest rate changes in the past. When the concluding payment is an irregular one, it is usually simpler to use the restrospective method, than to discount the $(n - k)$ payments yet to be made.

Example 1   A loan of $2000 with interest at $j_{12} = 12\%$ is to be amortized by equal payments at the end of each month over a period of 18 months. Find the outstanding principal at the end of 8 months.

Solution   First we calculate the monthly payment R, given $A = 2000$, $n = 18$, $i = .01$, and using equation (15)

$$R = \frac{2000}{a_{\overline{18}|.01}} = \$121.97$$

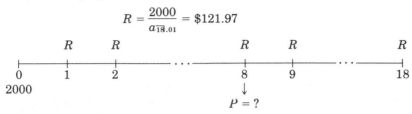

The retrospective method   We have $A = 2000$, $R = 121.97$, $k = 8$, $i = .01\%$, and we calculate P using equation (22).

$$P = 2000(1.01)^8 - 121.97 s_{\overline{8}|.01}$$
$$= 2165.71 - 1010.60 = \$1155.11$$

The prospective method   We have $R = 121.97$, $n - k = 10$, $i = .01$ and calculate P using equation (23).

$$P = 121.97 a_{\overline{10}|.01} = \$1155.21$$

The difference of 10 cents is due to rounding the monthly payment R up to the nearest cent. The concluding payment is in fact slightly smaller than the regular payment $R = 121.97$.

Example 2   On July 15, 1983, a couple borrowed $10 000 at $j_{12} = 15\%$ to start a business. They plan to repay the debt in equal monthly payments over 8 years with the first payment on August 15, 1983. (a) How much principal did they repay during 1983? (b) How much interest can they claim as a tax deduction during 1983?

Solution   We arrange our data on a time diagram below.

	R	R	R	R	R		R
0	1	2	3	4	5	$\cdots$	96
July 15,	Aug. 15,	Sept. 15,	Oct. 15,	Nov. 15,	Dec. 15,		July 15,
1983	1983	1983	1983	1983	1983		1991
10 000					$\downarrow$		
					$P = ?$		

First we calculate the monthly payment R, given $A = 10\,000$, $n = 96$, $i = .0125$, and using equation (15)

$$R = \frac{10\,000}{a_{\overline{96}|.0125}} = \$179.46$$

Then we calculate the outstanding principal P on December 15, 1983 after the 5th payment has been made. We have $A = 10\,000$, $R = 179.46$, $k = 5$, $i = .0125$, and using equation (22) we calculate

$$P = 10\,000(1.0125)^5 - 179.46 s_{\overline{5}|.0125}$$
$$= 10\,640.82 - 920.01$$
$$= \$9720.81$$

The total reduction in principal in 1983 is the difference between the outstanding principal on December 15, 1983 after the 5th payment has been made, and the original debt $10 000. Thus, they repaid 10 000 − 9720.81 = $279.19 on principal during 1983.

To get the total interest paid in 1983, we subtract the amount they repaid on principal from the total of the 5 payments, i.e. Total interest = 5 × 179.46 − 279.19 = $618.11. They can deduct $618.11 as an expense on their 1983 income tax return.

The method of amortization is quite often used to pay off loans incurred in purchasing a property. In such cases, the outstanding principal is called the **seller's equity**. The amount of principal that has been paid already plus the down payment is called the **buyer's equity**, or **owner's equity**. At any point in time we have the following relation

Buyer's equity + Seller's equity = Original selling price

The buyer's equity starts with the down payment and is gradually increased with each periodic payment by the part of the payment which is applied to reduce the outstanding principal. It should be noted that the buyer's equity, as defined above, does not make any allowance for increases or decreases in the value of the property.

Example 3 Mr. and Mrs. Jones bought a cottage worth $38 000 by paying $6000 down and the balance, with interest at $j_2 = 22\%$, in monthly instalments of $800 for as long as necessary. Find Mr. and Mrs. Jones' equity at the end of 5 years.

Solution The monthly payments form a general annuity. First we calculate a monthly rate of interest i equivalent to 11% each half-year.

$$(1 + i)^{12} = (1.11)^2$$
$$(1 + i) = (1.11)^{1/6}$$
$$i = (1.11)^{1/6} - 1$$
$$i = .017\ 545\ 48$$

Using the retrospective method, we calculate the seller's equity

$$P = 32\ 000(1 + i)^{60} - 800s_{\overline{60}|i}$$

$$= 90\ 861.47 - 83\ 869.85 = \$6991.62$$

Mr. and Mrs. Jones' equity is then
Buyer's equity = 38 000 − 6 991.62 = $31 008.38.

Exercise 6.2
Part A:

1. To pay off the purchase of a car, a man got a $5000, 3 year bank loan at $j_{12} = 12\%$. He makes monthly payments. How much does he still owe on the loan at the end of two years (24 payments)? Use both the retrospective and prospective method.

2. A debt of $10 000 will be amortized by payments at the end of each quarter of a year for 10 years. Interest is at $j_4 = 20\%$. Find the outstanding principal at the end of 6 years.

3. On July 1, 1983 a man borrowed $3000 to be repaid with monthly payments (first payment August 1, 1983) over 3 years at $j_{12} = 15\%$. How much principal did he repay in 1983? How much interest?

4. A couple buys a house worth $56 000 by paying $6000 down and then taking a mortgage out for $50 000. The mortgage is at $j_2 = 18\%$ and will be repaid over 25 years with monthly payments. How much of the debt does the couple pay off in the first year?

5. On May 1, 1983 the Smiths borrow $4000 to be repaid with monthly payments over 3 years at $j_{12} = 22\%$. The 12 payments made during 1984 will reduce the principal by how much? What was the total interest paid in 1984?

6. To pay off the purchase of home furnishings, a couple takes out a bank loan of $2000 to be repaid with monthly payments over 2 years at $j_{12} = 15\%$. What is the outstanding debt just after the tenth payment? What is the principal portion of the eleventh payment?

7. A couple buys a piece of land worth $20 000 by paying $5000 down and then taking a loan out for $15 000. The loan will be repaid with quarterly payments over 15 years and is at $j_4 = 12\%$. Find the couple's equity at the end of 8 years.

8. A family buys a $63 000 house. Because they were moving out of a smaller home they are able to pay $23 000 down and then take out a 20-year mortgage for the balance at $j_2 - 17\%$. The mortgage will be repaid by monthly payments. Find the owner's equity at the end of five years.

9. Land worth $20 000 is purchased by a down payment of $3000 and the balance in equal monthly instalments for 15 years. If interest is at $j_{12} = 9\%$, find the buyer's and seller's equity in the land at the end of 9 years.

Part B:

1. With mortgage rates at $j_2 = 22\%$, the XYZ Trust Company makes a special offer to its customers. It will lend mortgage money and determine the monthly payment as if $j_2 = 18\%$. The mortgage will be carried at $j_2 = 22\%$ and any deficiency that results will be added to the outstanding balance. If the Brown's are taking out a $50 000 mortgage to be repaid over 25 years under this scheme, what will their outstanding balance be at the end of 5 years?

2. Mr. Jones can buy a certain home for $90 000. To do so would require taking out a $60 000 mortgage from a bank at $j_2 = 20\%$. The loan will be amortized over 25 years and the rate of interest is fixed for five years.

   The seller of the home is willing to give Mr. Jones a mortgage at $j_2 = 15\%$. The monthly payment will be determined using a 25-year repayment schedule. The seller will guarantee the rate of interest for 5 years at which time Mr. Jones will have to pay off the seller and get a mortgage from a bank. If Mr. Jones accepts this offer, the seller wants $95 000 for the house forcing Mr. Jones to borrow $65 000. If Mr. Jones can earn $j_{12} = 16\%$ on his money, what should he do?

3. The Smiths buy a home and take out a $40 000 mortgage on which the interest rate is allowed to float freely. At the time the mortgage is signed, interest rates are $j_2 = 20\%$ and the Smiths choose a 25-year amortization schedule. Six months into the mortgage, interest rates rise to $j_2 = 22\%$. Three years into the mortgage (36 payments) interest rates drop to $j_2 = 20\%$ and four years into the mortgage, interest rates drop to $j_2 = 18\%$. Find the outstanding balance of the mortgage after 5 years. (The monthly payment is set at issue and does not change.)

4. A young couple buy a house and assume a $45 000 mortgage to be amortized over 25 years. The interest rate is guaranteed at $j_2 = 16\%$. The mortgage allows the couple to make extra payments against the outstanding principal each month. By saving carefully the couple manages to pay off an extra $100 each month. Because of these extra payments, how long will it take to pay off the mortgage and what will be the size of the final smaller monthly payment?

5. A loan of $10 000 is being repaid by instalments of $200 at the end of each month for as long as necessary with a final smaller repayment. If interest is at $j_4 = 16\%$, find the outstanding balance at the end of one year.

6. The ABC Trust Company issues loans where the monthly payments are determined by the rate of interest that prevails on the day the loan is made. After that the rate of interest varies according to market forces but the monthly payments do not change in dollar size. Instead the length of time to full repayment is either lengthened (if interest rates rise) or shortened (if interest rates fall).

Mr. X takes out a 10-year $20 000 loan at $j_2 = 16\%$. After exactly 2 years (24 payments) interest rates change. Find the duration of the loan and the final smaller payment if the new interest rate is
   a) $j_2 = 18\%$;
   b) $j_2 = 14\%$.

7. Five years ago, a man deposited $10 000 into a fund out of which he draws $2000 at the end of each year. The fund guarantees interest at $j_1 = 11\%$. If the fund actually earns interest at a rate in excess of 11%, the excess interest earned during the year is paid to the man at the end of the year in addition to the regular $2000 payment. This past year, the fund earned 18%. What total payment should the man receive now?

6.3 Refinancing a Loan – The Amortization Method

It is a common practice to renegotiate a long-term loan after it has been partially paid off.

If the loan is refinanced at a lower rate, the discounted value of the savings due to lower interest charges must be compared with the cost of refinancing, to decide whether the refinancing would be a profitable one.

Example 1 Mr. Smith buys $5000 worth of home furnishings from the ABC Furniture Mart. He pays $500 down and agrees to pay the balance with monthly payments over 5 years at $j_{12} = 18\%$. The contract he signs stipulates that if he pays the contract off early there is a penalty equal to three months' payments. After two years (24 payments) Mr. Smith realizes that he could borrow the money from the bank at $j_{12} = 12\%$. He realizes that to do so means he will have to pay the three-month penalty on the ABC Furniture Mart contract. Should he refinance?

Solution   First find the monthly payments required under the original contract.

$$R_1 = \frac{4500}{a_{\overline{60}|.015}} = \$114.28 \text{ (rounded up)}$$

Now, find the outstanding balance on the original contract at the end of two years.
$$\text{Outstanding balance} = 4500(1.015)^{24} - 114.28s_{\overline{24}|0.015}$$

$$= \$3160.52$$

If Mr. Smith repays the loan he will also pay a penalty equal to $3 \times R = \$342.84$. Therefore the amount he must borrow from the bank is:

$$3160.52 + 342.84 = \$3503.36$$

Thus, the new monthly payments on the bank loan are

$$R_2 = \frac{3503.36}{a_{\overline{36}|.01}} = \$116.37 \text{ (rounded up)}$$

Therefore, he should not refinance since $116.37 is larger than $114.28.

The largest single loan the average Canadian is likely to make will be the mortgage on one's home. At one time, interest rates on mortgages were guaranteed for the life of the repayment schedule which could be as long as 25 or 30 years. Now, the longest period of guaranteed interest rates available is usually 5 years, although homeowners may choose mortgages where the interest rate is adjusted every three years, every year or even daily to the current interest rates.

A homeowner who wishes to repay the mortgage in full before the defined renegotiation date will have to pay a penalty. In many cases, this penalty is defined as three months of interest on the amount prepaid. In other cases the penalty varies according to market conditions and can be determined by the lender at the time of prepayment (the formula that the lender must use may be defined in the mortgage contract, however). This situation is illustrated in Example 3.

With today's high interest rates, many new and different mortgages are being offered to the prospective borrower. It is important that students are capable of analyzing these contracts fully. Several examples are illustrated in the exercises contained in this chapter.

Example 2   A couple purchased a home and signed a mortgage contract for $50 000 to be paid with monthly payments calculated over a 25-year period at 21% compounded semi-annually. After 5 years, they renegotiate the interest rate and refinance the loan at 17% compounded semi-annually. Find:
a) the monthly payment for the initial 5-year period;
b) the new monthly payment after 5 years;
c) the accumulated value of the savings for the second 5-year period (at the end of that period) at $j_{12} = 15\%$; and
d) the outstanding balance at the end of 10 years;
e) the accumulated value of the payments made in the first 10 years assuming $j_2 = 18\%$ for the first 5 years and $j_4 = 14\%$ in the second 5 years.

Solution a   First we calculate a monthly rate of interest i equivalent to $j_2 = 21\%$

$$(1 + i)^{12} = (1.105)^2$$
$$(1 + i) = (1.105)^{1/6}$$
$$i = (1.105)^{1/6} - 1$$
$$i = .016\ 780\ 12$$

Now $A = 50\ 000$, $n = 300$, $i = .016\ 780\ 12$ and we calculate the monthly payment R_1 for the initial 5-year period.

$$R_1 = \frac{50\ 000}{a\,\overline{300}|i} = \$844.75 \text{ (rounded up to the nearest cent)}$$

Solution b   First we calculate the outstanding balance of the loan after 5 years (call this P_1).

$$P_1 = 50\ 000(1 + i)^{60} - 844.75s\,\overline{60}|i$$

$$= 135\ 704.03 - 86\ 290.78 = \$49\ 413.25$$

This outstanding balance is refinanced at $j_2 = 17\%$ over a 20-year period. First, find the rate i per month equivalent to $j_2 = 17\%$.

$$(1 + i)^{12} = (1.085)^2$$
$$(1 + i) = (1.085)^{1/6}$$
$$i = (1.085)^{1/6} - 1$$
$$i = .013\ 689\ 52$$

Now $A = 49\ 413.25$, $n = 240$, $i = .013\ 689\ 52$ and we calculate the new monthly payment R_2

$$R_2 = \frac{49\ 413.25}{a\,\overline{240}|i} = \$703.36$$

Solution c   The monthly savings after the loan is renegotiated after 5 years at $j_2 = 17\%$ is

$$844.75 - 703.36 = \$141.39$$

If these savings are deposited in an account paying $j_{12} = 15\%$, the accumulated value of the savings at the end of the 5-year period is:

$$141.39s\,\overline{60}|.0125 = \$12\ 523.55$$

Solution d   The outstanding balance P_2 of the loan at the end of 10 years is calculated as in (b). Remember $i = .013\ 689\ 52$.

$$P_2 = 49\ 413.25(1 + i)^{60} - 703.36s\,\overline{60}|i$$

$$= 111\ 722.52 - 64\ 788.63 = \$46\ 933.89$$

The outstanding balance at the end of 10 years is \$46 933.89. That means that only $50\ 000 - 46\ 933.89 = \$3066.11$ of the loan was repaid during the first 10 years (they still owe 93.87% of the original \$50 000 loan). This is despite the fact that payments in the first 10 years totalled \$92 886.60 ($60 \times 844.75 + 60 \times 703.36$).

During the first 10 years, the interest paid on the loan was nearly double the original amount borrowed.

Solution e

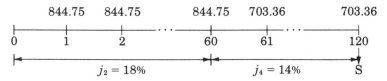

First we need to find rates of interest per month equivalent to $j_2 = 18\%$ and $j_4 = 14\%$.

For $j_2 = 18\%$ find i_1 per month such that

$$(1 + i_1)^{12} = (1.09)^2$$
$$(1 + i_1) = (1.09)^{1/6}$$
$$i_1 = (1.09)^{1/6} - 1$$
$$i_1 = .014\ 466\ 59$$

For $j_4 = 14\%$ find i_2 per month such that

$$(1 + i_2)^{12} = (1.035)^4$$
$$(1 + i_2) = (1.035)^{1/3}$$
$$i_2 = (1.035)^{1/3} - 1$$
$$i_2 = .011\ 533\ 14$$

Now we calculate the accumulated value S of the payments made in the first 10 years.

$$S = 844.75 s_{\overline{60}|i_1}(1 + i_2)^{60} + 703.36 s_{\overline{60}|i_2}$$

$$= 158\ 874.03 + 60\ 363.24 = \$219\ 237.27$$

The accumulated value of the mortgage payments for the first 10 years is $219 237.27. The owner's equity has increased by $3066.11 in the same period of time. One would now have to compare these figures to the increased value of the house and the estimated cost of renting over the same 10-year period.

Example 3 The Smiths buy a house and borrow $40 000 from the ABC Insurance Company. The loan is to be repaid with monthly payments over 30 years at $j_2 = 20\%$. The interest rate is guaranteed for 5 years. After exactly two years of making payments, the Smiths see that interest rates have dropped to $j_2 = 15\%$ in the market place. They ask to be allowed to repay the loan in full, so they can refinance. The Insurance Company agrees to renegotiate but sets a penalty exactly equal to the money the company will lose over the next 3 years. Find the value of the penalty.

Solution First, find the monthly payments R_1 required on the original loan at $j_2 = 20\%$. Find i such that

$$(1 + i)^{12} = (1.10)^2$$
$$(1 + i) = (1.10)^{1/6}$$
$$i = (1.10)^{1/6} - 1$$
$$i = .016\ 011\ 87$$

Now $A = 40\ 000$, $n = 360$, $i = .016\ 011\ 87$, and

$$R_1 = \frac{40\ 000}{a_{\overline{360}|i}} = \$642.59$$

Next we find the outstanding balance P_1 after 2 years.

$$P_1 = 40\ 000(1 + i)^{24} - 642.59 s_{\overline{24}|i}$$

$$= 58\ 564.00 - 18\ 625.31 = \$39\ 938.69$$

Also, we find the outstanding balance P_2 after 5 years if the loan is not renegotiated.

$$P_2 = 40\ 000(1 + i)^{60} - 642.59 s_{\overline{60}|i}$$

$$= 103\ 749.70 - 63\ 960.25 = \$39\ 789.45$$

If the Insurance company renegotiates, it will receive $39 938.69 plus the penalty X now. If they do not renegotiate, they will receive $642.59 a month for 3 years plus $39 789.45 at the end of 3 years. These two options should be equivalent at the current interest rate $j_2 = 15\%$.

option 1   39 938.69 $+X$

	0	1	2	$\cdots$	35	36
option 2		642.59	642.59		642.59	642.59
						+ 39 789.45

Find the monthly rate i equivalent to $j_2 = 15\%$

$$(1 + i)^{12} = (1.075)^2$$
$$1 + i = (1.075)^{1/6}$$
$$i = (1.075)^{1/6} - 1$$
$$i = .012\ 126\ 38$$

Using 0 as a focal date we solve an equation of value for X

$$X + 39\ 938.69 = 642.59 a_{\overline{36}|i} + 39\ 789.45(1 + i)^{-36}$$
$$X + 39\ 938.69 = 18\ 654.90 + 25\ 782.03$$
$$X = \$4498.24$$

Thus the penalty at the end of 2 years is \$4498.24.
If the penalty had been three times the monthly interest on the outstanding balance at the end of 2 years, it would have been:

$$3 \times 39\ 938.69 \times .016\ 011\ 87 = \$1918.48$$

Exercise 6.3
Part A:

1. A borrower is repaying a \$5000 loan at $j_{12} = 15\%$ with monthly payments over 3 years. Just after the twelfth payment (at the end of 1 year) he has the balance refinanced at $j_{12} = 12\%$. If the number of payments remains unchanged, what will be the new monthly payment and what will be the monthly savings in interest?

2. A 5-year \$6000 loan is being amortized with monthly payments at $j_{12} = 18\%$. Just after making the 30th payment, the borrower has the balance refinanced at $j_{12} = 12\%$ with the term of the loan to remain unchanged. What will be the monthly savings in interest?

3. A borrower has a \$5000 loan with the "Easy-Credit" Finance Company. The loan is to be repaid over 4 years at $j_{12} = 24\%$. The contract stipulates an early repayment penalty equal to three months payments. Just after the 20th payment, the borrower determines that his local bank would lend him money at $j_{12} = 16\%$. Should he refinance?

4. The Jones family buys a fridge and stove totalling \$1200 from their local appliance store. They agree to pay off the total amount with monthly payments over 3 years at $j_{12} = 24\%$. If they wish to pay the contract off early they will experience a penalty equal to three months interest on the effective outstanding balance. After 12 payments they see that interest rates at their local bank are $j_{12} = 19\%$. Should they refinance?

5. Consider a couple who bought a house in Canada in 1976. Assume they needed a \$60 000 mortgage which was to be repaid with monthly payments over 25 years. In 1976, interest rates were $j_2 = 10\frac{1}{2}\%$. What was their monthly payment? In 1981 (on the fifth anniversary of their mortgage) their mortgage was renegotiated to reflect current market rates. The repayment schedule was to cover the remaining 20 years and interest rates were now $j_2 = 22\%$. What was the new monthly payment? What effect might this have on homeowners?

6. The Smiths buy a house and take out a $40 000 mortgage. The mortgage is amortized over 25 years with monthly payments at $j_2 = 19\%$. After $3\frac{1}{2}$ years the Smiths sell their house and the buyer wants to set up a new mortgage better tailored to his needs. The Smiths find out that in addition to repaying the loan balance on their mortgage they must pay a penalty equal to three months interest on the outstanding balance. What total amount must they repay?

Part B:

1. A couple buys a home and signs a mortgage contract for $50 000 to be paid with monthly payments over a 25-year period at $j_2 = 19\%$. After 5 years, they renegotiate the interest rate and refinance the loan at $j_2 = 16\%$; find:
   a) the monthly payment for the initial 5-year period;
   b) the new monthly payment after 5 years;
   c) the accumulated value of the savings for the second 5-year period at $j_{12} = 12\%$ valued at the end of the second 5-year period;
   d) the outstanding balance at the end of 10 years;
   e) the face value and accumulated value of all payments at the end of the first 10 years of the mortgage contract assuming money is worth $j_2 = 15\%$ for the first 5 years and $j_2 = 12\%$ for the second 5 years.
2. Mrs. Smith is repaying a debt with monthly payments of $100 over 5 years. Interest is at rate $j_{12} = 12\%$. At the end of the second year she makes an extra payment of $350. She then shortens her payment period by 1 year and renegotiates the loan without penalty and without an interest rate change. What are her new monthly payments over the remaining two years?
3. Mr. Jones is repaying a loan at $j_{12} = 15\%$ with monthly payments of $150 over 3 years. Due to temporary unemployment, Mr. Jones missed making the 13th through 18th payments inclusive. Find the value of the revised monthly payments needed starting in the 19th month if the loan is still to be repaid at $j_{12} = 15\%$ by the end of the original 3 years.
4. Mr. Adams has just moved to Waterloo. He has been told by his employer that he will be transferred out of Waterloo again in exactly three years.
   Mr. Adams is going to buy a house and requires a $50 000 mortgage. He has his choice of two 25-year mortgages with monthly payments.
   Mortgage A is at $j_2 = 10\%$. This mortgage stipulates, however, that if you pay off the mortgage any time before the fifth anniversary, you will have to pay a penalty equal to three times one month's interest on the outstanding balance at the time of repayment.
   Mortgage B is at $j_2 = 10\frac{1}{2}\%$ but can be paid off at any time without penalty. Given that Mr. Adams will have to repay the mortgage in three years and that he can save money at 8% per annum effective, which mortgage should he choose?
5. Write a computer program that will handle amortization schedules for Canadian mortgages. Given the value of the mortgage, the term of amortization and an interest rate j_2, your program should calculate the monthly payment required and be capable of printing out an entire amortization schedule. It should also be able to analyze refinancing possibilities, including the effect on monthly payments because of a change in the rate of interest.

6.4 Refinancing a Loan – The Sum of Digits Method

Some Canadian lending institutions, when determining the outstanding principal on a consumer loan do not use the amortization method outlined in the previous two sections, but rather they use an approximation to the amortization method called the **Sum of Digits Method** or the **Rule of 78**.

We know that under the amortization method, each payment made on a loan is used partly to pay off interest owing and partly to pay off principal owing. We also know that the interest portion of each payment is largest at the early durations and gets progressively smaller over time. Thus if a consumer borrowed $1000 at $j_{12} = 12\%$ and repaid the loan over 12 months we would get the following amortization schedule:

Payment number	Periodic payment	Payment of interest at 1%	Principal repaid	Outstanding principal
				$1000.00
1	88.85	$10.00	78.85	921.15
2	88.85	9.21	79.64	841.51
3	88.85	8.42	80.43	761.08
4	88.85	7.61	81.24	679.84
5	88.85	6.80	82.05	597.79
6	88.85	5.98	82.87	514.92
7	88.85	5.15	83.70	431.22
8	88.85	4.31	84.54	346.69
9	88.85	3.47	85.38	261.31
10	88.85	2.61	86.24	175.07
11	88.85	1.75	87.40	87.97
12	88.85	0.88	87.97	0
Totals	1066.20	66.20	$1000.00	

Under the sum of digits approximation, we find the interest portion of each payment by taking a defined proportion of the total interest paid – that is, $66.20. The proportion used is found as follows.

The loan is paid off over 12 months. If we sum the digits from 1 to 12 we get 78. We now say that the amount of interest assigned to the first payment is $\frac{12}{78} \times \$66.20 = \$10.18$. The amount of interest assigned to the second payment is $\frac{11}{78} \times \$66.20 = \$9.34$. This process continues until the amount of interest assigned to the last payment is $\frac{1}{78} \times \$66.20 = \$0.85$. Notice that the total of the interest column is still $66.20 since $(\frac{12}{78} + \frac{11}{78} + \ldots + \frac{1}{78}) = \frac{78}{78}$. Since many consumer loans are paid off over 12 months the alternative name, the rule of 78, is sometimes used.

If we apply the sum of digits method to the loan described above, we will get the repayment schedule shown overleaf.

Payment number	Periodic payment	Payment of interest	Principal repaid	Outstanding principal
				$1000.00
1	88.85	10.18	78.67	921.33
2	88.85	9.34	79.51	841.82
3	88.85	8.49	80.36	761.46
4	88.85	7.64	81.21	680.25
5	88.85	6.79	82.06	598.19
6	88.85	5.94	82.91	515.28
7	88.85	5.09	83.76	431.52
8	88.85	4.24	84.61	346.91
9	88.85	3.39	85.46	261.45
10	88.85	2.55	86.30	175.15
11	88.85	1.70	87.15	88.00
12	88.85	0.85	88.00	0
Totals	1066.20	66.20	1000.00	

One important point to notice here is that while the error is small, the use of the sum of digits approximation leads to an outstanding balance that is always larger than that obtained by using the amortization method. Thus if you want to refinance your loan to repay the balance early, there is a penalty attached because of the use of the sum of digits approximation.

In fact, in the above illustration we can see that if the consumer paid his loan off in full after one month the lending institution would have realized an interest return of $10.18 on $1000 over one month, or $i = 1.018\%$. This corresponds to $j_{12} = 12.216\%$ as opposed to $j_{12} = 12\%$.

As the term of the loan lengthens and as the interest rate rises, the penalty involved in the use of the Sum of Digits Method increases as Example 1 will show.

Example 1   Consider a $6000 loan that is to be repaid over 5 years at $j_{12} = 15\%$. Find the first three entries in the repayment schedule using: (a) the amortization method; (b) the sum of digits method.

Solution   First we calculate the monthly payment R required

$$R = \frac{6\,000}{a_{\overline{60}|.0125}} = 142.739\,58 = \$142.74$$

a) Using the method outlined in Section 6.1 we would get the repayment schedule using the amortization method as shown below.

Payment number	Periodic payment	Payment of interest at $1\frac{1}{4}\%$	Principal repaid	Outstanding principal
				$6000.00
1	142.74	75.00	67.74	5932.26
2	142.74	74.15	68.59	5863.67
3	142.74	73.30	69.44	5794.23

b) Using the sum of the digits approach we first calculate the total dollar value of all interest payments. We can find the smaller concluding payment X at the end of 5 years using the method of Section 6.1.

$$X = 6000(1.0125)^{60} - 142.74 s_{\overline{59}|.0125}(1.0125)$$

$$= 12\,643.09 - 12\,500.39 = \$142.70$$

and then calculate the total interest in the loan as the difference between the total dollar value of all payments and the value of the loan, i.e.,

$$(59 \times 142.74 + 142.70) - 6000 = \$2564.36$$

The sum of the digits from 1 to 60 is 1830 (Note: The sum of the digits from 1 to n can be found using the formula $n(n + 1)/2$). Thus:

$$\text{Interest in first payment} = \frac{60}{1830} \times 2564.36 = 84.08$$

$$\text{Interest in second payment} = \frac{59}{1830} \times 2564.36 = 82.68$$

$$\text{Interest in third payment} = \frac{58}{1830} \times 2564.36 = 81.28$$

This leads to the following enteries in our repayment schedule.

Payment number	Periodic payment	Amount of interest	Principal repaid	Outstanding balance
				$6000.00
1	142.74	84.08	58.66	5941.34
2	142.74	82.68	60.06	5881.28
3	142.74	81.28	61.46	5819.82

This illustrates the fact that the penalty involved in refinancing a loan where the bank uses the sum of digits approximation can be quite significant on long-term loans at high interest rates. In fact, it is possible under the sum of digits approximation on very long-term loans at very high interest rates, for the interest portion of early payments to exceed the dollar size of these payments which leads to an outstanding balance which is actually larger than the original loan (see question 7 in Exercise 6.4, Part A)

In the above illustration, if the consumer repaid the loan after one month the lending institution would earn $84.08 of interest on their $6000 over one month, or $i = 1.40\%$. This corresponds to $j_{12} = 16.8\%$ as opposed to $j_{12} = 15\%$.

We pointed out in Section 3.6 that most provinces in Canada have "Truth-in-Lending" Acts to protect the consumer. Unfortunately, these acts apply only if the loan is not renegotiated before the normal maturity date. Paying a loan off early constitutes "breaking the contract" and the Truth-in-Lending laws do not apply once the contract is broken.*

If you have a consumer loan from a Canadian lending institution using the Rule of 78, to find the outstanding principal, the loans officer will not go through an entire repayment schedule but rather will use the method outlined in Example 2.

---

*As of January 1, 1983, the Rule of 78 Method will be illegal for consumer loans issued by federally chartered Canadian banks only.

Example 2   To pay off the purchase of a mobile home, a couple takes out a bank loan of $15 000 to be repaid with monthly payments over 5 years at $j_{12} = 18\%$. Using the sum of the digits method find the outstanding debt at the end of 2 years.

Solution a   The monthly payment R required is

$$R = \frac{15\ 000}{a_{\overline{60}|.015}} = 380.901\ 42 = \$380.91$$

Using the non-rounded payment R we may calculate the total interest in the loan as $60R - 15\ 000 = \$7854.09$. (Use of the non-rounded payment R eliminates the calculation of the smaller concluding payment).

Total interest to be repaid over remaining 36 months is called the *interest rebate* and is calculated as

$$\frac{\text{sum of digits 1 to 36}}{\text{sum of digits 1 to 60}} \times 7854.09 = \frac{666}{1830} \times 7854.09 = \$2858.37$$

The couple would be given the following figures:

Original total debt = $60R$	=	22 854.09
Less interest rebate	=	2 858.37
Less payments to date = 24×380.91	=	9 141.84
Outstanding principal at the end of 2 years	=	$10 853.88

It is interesting to note that the outstanding principal at the end of 2 years under the amortization method is

$$15\ 000(1.015)^{24} - 380.91s_{\overline{24}|.015} = 21\ 442.54 - 10\ 906.79$$
$$= \$10\ 535.75$$

Exercise 6.4
Part A:

1. A loan of $900 is to be repaid with 6 equal monthly payments at $j_{12} = 12\%$. Find the monthly payment and construct the repayment schedule using the sum of digits method. (Compare this answer to Ex. 6.1 Q A.4).

2. A loan of $1000 is to be repaid over one year with equal monthly payments at $j_{12} = 18\%$. Find the monthly payment and construct the repayment schedule using the sum of digits method.

3. To pay off the purchase of a car, a man got a $5000, 3 year bank loan at $j_{12} = 21\%$. He makes monthly payments. Find the outstanding balance on the loan just after the twenty-fourth payment using the sum of digits method.

4. A woman borrows $2000 from a bank to be repaid by monthly payments over 3 years at $j_{12} = 24\%$. Find the outstanding balance at the end of 16 months using the sum of digits method.

5. A borrower is repaying a $5000 loan at $j_{12} = 15\%$ with monthly payments over 3 years. Just after the twelfth payment he has the balance refinanced at $j_{12} = 12\%$. The balance is determined by the sum of digits method. If the number of payments remains unchanged, what will be the new monthly payments and what will be the monthly savings in interest? (Compare this to Ex. 6.3 Q A.1).

6. A 5-year $6000 loan is to be repaid with monthly payments at $j_{12} = 18\%$. Just after making the 30th payment, the borrower has the balance refinanced at

$j_{12} = 12\%$ with the term of the loan to remain unchanged. If the balance is determined by the sum of digits method, what will be the monthly savings in interest? (Compare this to Ex. 6.3 Q A.2).

7. Consider a $10 000 loan being repaid with monthly payments over 15 years at $j_{12} = 15\%$. Find the outstanding balance at the end of two years and at the end of five years using both the sum of digits method and the amortization method.

8. A borrower has a $5000 bank loan that is being repaid by monthly payments over 4 years at $j_{12} = 15\%$. The bank uses the sum of digits method to determine outstanding balances. After 1 year of payments the bank interest rate on new loans has dropped to $j_{12} = 12\%$. Will the borrower save money by refinancing the loan? (The term of the loan will not be changed.)

Part B:

1. Mr. X can borrow $15 000 at $j_4 = 15\%$ and repay the loan with monthly payments over 10 years. If he wants to pay the loan off early, the outstanding balance will be determined using the sum of digits method.

    He can also borrow $15 000 with monthly payments over 10 years at $j_4 = 16\%$ and pay the loan off at any time without penalty. The outstanding balance will be determined using the amortization method.

    Mr. X has an endowment insurance policy coming due in 4 years that could be used to pay off the outstanding balance at that time in full. Which loan should he take if he earns $j_{12} = 12\%$ on his savings?

2. A loan of $18 000 is to be repaid with monthly payments over 10 years at $j_2 = 17\frac{1}{2}\%$. Using the sum of digits method

    a) construct the first two and the last two lines of the repayment schedule;

    b) find the interest and the principal portion of the 10th payment;

    c) find the outstanding balance at the end of 2 years and compare it with the outstanding balance at the same time calculated by the amortization method;

    d) advise whether the loan should be refinanced at the end of 2 years at current rate $j_2 = 16\%$ with the term of the loan unchanged.

3. Given the value of a loan, the number of payments, the frequency of payments, and the nominal rate j_m, write a computer program that will print out a complete repayment schedule of a loan using the sum of digits method.

6.5 Sinking Funds

When a specified amount of money is needed at a specified future date, it is a good practice to accumulate systematically a fund by means of equal periodic deposits. Such a fund is called a **sinking fund**. Sinking funds are used to pay off debts (see Section 6.6), to redeem bond issues, to replace worn-out equipment, to buy new equipment, or to return the principal invested in some natural resources when they become depleted (see Section 8.6).

Since the amount needed in the sinking fund, the time the amount is needed, and the interest rate which the fund earns are known, we have an annuity problem in which the size of the payment, the sinking-fund deposit, is to be determined. A schedule showing how a sinking fund accumulates to the desired amount is called a **sinking-fund schedule**.

Example 1 An eight storey condominium apartment building consists of 146 two-bedroom apartment units of equal size. The Board of Directors of the Home-owners Association estimated that the building will need exterior painting and new carpeting in the halls at a cost of $25 800 in 5 years.

Assuming that the association can invest their money at j_{12} = 8%, what should be the monthly sinking fund assessment per unit?

Solution The sinking-fund deposits form an ordinary simple annuity with S = 25 800, i = $\frac{2}{3}$%, n = 60. Using equation (14) we calculate the total monthly sinking-fund deposit

$$R = \frac{25\ 800}{s\ \overline{60}|2/3\%} = \$351.13$$

Per unit assessment should be

$$\frac{351.13}{146} = \$2.41$$

Example 2 Show the first 3 lines and the last 2 lines of the sinking-fund schedule showing the growth of the fund in Example 1.

Solution At the end of the first month, a deposit of $351.13 is made and the fund contains $351.13. This amount earns interest at $\frac{2}{3}$% for 1 month, i.e. $351.13 \times \frac{2}{300}$ = $2.34. Thus the total increase at the end of the second month is the second payment plus interest on the amount in the fund, i.e. $351.13 + 2.34 = \$353.47$, and the fund will contain $704.60. This procedure may be repeated to complete the entire schedule.

In order to complete the last 2 lines of the sinking-fund schedule without running the complete schedule, we may calculate the amount in the fund at the end of the 58th month as the accumulated value of 58 payments, i.e.,

$$351.13s\ \overline{58}|2/3\% = \$24\ 764.04$$

and complete the schedule from that point. The calculations are tabulated below.

End of the month	Interest on fund at $\frac{2}{3}$%	Deposit	Increase in fund	Amount in fund
1	—	351.13	351.13	351.13
2	2.34	351.13	353.47	704.60
3	4.70	351.13	355.83	1 060.43
⋮	⋮	⋮	⋮	⋮
58				24 764.04
59	165.09	351.13	516.22	25 280.26
60	168.54	351.13	519.67	25 799.93*

*The final amount is 7 cents short due to rounding off procedures in calculating the entries in the table.

Exercise 6.5
Part A:

1. A couple is saving a down-payment for a home. They want to have $15 000 at the end of 4 years in an account paying interest at j_1 = 16%. How much must be deposited in the fund at the end of each year? Make out a schedule showing the growth of the fund.

2. A company wants to save $100 000 over the next 5 years so they can expand their plant facility. How much must be deposited at the end of each year if their money earns interest at $j_1 = 18\%$? Make out a schedule for this problem.

3. What quarterly deposit is required in a bank account to accumulate $2000 at the end of 2 years if interest is at $j_4 = 10\%$? Prepare a schedule for this problem.

4. A sinking fund earning interest at $j_4 = 16\%$ now contains $1000. What quarterly deposits for the next 5 years will cause the fund to grow to $10 000? How much is in the fund at the end of 3 years?

5. A cottagers' association decides to set up a sinking fund to save money to have their cottage road widened and paved. They want to have $25 000 at the end of 5 years and they can earn interest at $j_1 = 9\%$. What annual deposit is required per cottager if there are 30 cottages on the road? Show the complete schedule.

6. Find the quarterly deposits necessary to accumulate $10 000 over 10 years in a sinking fund earning interest at $j_4 = 11\%$. Find the amount in the fund at the end of 9 years and complete the rest of the schedule.

7. A city needs to have $200 000 at the end of 15 years to retire a bond issue. What annual deposits will be necessary if their money earns interest at $j_1 = 17\%$? Make out the first three and last three lines of the schedule.

8. What monthly deposit is required to accumulate $3000 at the end of 2 years in a bank account paying interest at $j_4 = 10\%$?

9. A couple wants to save $20 000 to buy some land. They can save $350 each quarter-year in a bank account paying $j_4 = 9\%$. How many years (to the nearest quarter) will it take them and what is the size of the final deposit?

Part B:

1. A homeowners' association decided to set up a sinking fund to accumulate $50 000 by the end of 3 years to improve recreational facilities. What monthly deposits are required if the fund earns 15% compounded daily? Show the first three and the last 2 lines of the sinking fund schedule.

2. Consider an amount that is to be accumulated with equal deposits R at the end of each interest period for 5 periods at rate i per period. Hence, the amount to be accumulated is $Rs_{\overline{5}|i}$. Do a complete schedule for this sinking fund. Verify that the sum of the interest column plus the sum of the deposit-column equal the sum of the increase in the fund-column, and both sums equal the final amount in the fund.

3. Given the amount to be accumulated, the number of payments, the frequency of payments and the nominal rate j_m, write a computer program that will print out a complete sinking fund schedule.

6.6 The Sinking-Fund Method of Retiring a Debt

A common method of paying off long-term loans is to pay the interest on the loan at the end of each interest period and create a sinking fund to accumulate the principal at the end of the term of the loan. Usually, the deposits into the sinking fund are made at the same times as the interest payments on the debt are made to the lender. The sum of the interest payment and the sinking-fund payment is called the **periodic expense** or

cost of the debt. It should be noted that the sinking fund remains under the control of the borrower. At the end of the term of the loan, the borrower returns the whole principal as a lump sum payment by transferring the accumulated value of the sinking fund to the lender.

When the sinking-fund method is used, we define the **book value** of the borrower's debt at any time as the original principal minus the amount in the sinking fund.

Example   A city issues $1 000 000 of bonds paying interest at $j_2 = 9\frac{1}{8}\%$, and by law it is required to create a sinking fund to redeem the bonds at the end of 8 years. If the fund is invested at $j_2 = 8\%$, find (a) the semi-annual expense of the debt; (b) the book value of the city's indebtedness at the beginning of the 7th year.

Solution a

Semi-annual interest payment on the debt:	$1\ 000\ 000 \times 0.045625 = \$45\ 625$	
Semi-annual deposit into the sinking fund:	$R = \dfrac{1\ 000\ 000}{s\,\overline{_{16}}.04}$	$= \$45\ 820$
Semi-annual expense of the debt		$= \$91\ 445$

Solution b   The amount in the sinking fund at the end of the 6th year is the accumulated value of the deposits, i.e.,

$$45\ 820 s\,\overline{_{12}}.04 = \$688\ 482.38$$

The book value of the city's indebtedness at the beginning of the 7th year is then

$$1\ 000\ 000 - 688\ 482.38 = \$311\ 517.62$$

Exercise 6.6

Part A:

1. A borrower of $5000 agrees to pay interest semi-annually at $j_2 = 10\%$ on the loan and to build up a sinking fund which will repay the loan at the end of 5 years. If the sinking fund accumulates at $j_2 = 7\%$ find his total semi-annual expense. How much is in the sinking fund at the end of 4 years?

2. A city borrows $250 000, paying interest annually on this sum at $j_1 = 19\frac{1}{2}\%$. What annual deposits must be made into a sinking fund earning interest at $j_1 = 16\%$ in order to pay off the entire principal at the end of 15 years? What is the total annual expense of the debt?

3. A company issues $500 000 worth of bonds paying interest at $j_2 = 12\%$. A sinking fund with semi-annual deposits accumulating at $j_2 = 9\%$ is established to redeem the bonds at the end of 20 years. Find
   a) the semi-annual expense of the debt;
   b) the book value of the company's indebtedness at the end of the 15th year.

4. A city borrows $2 000 000 to build a sewage treatment system. The debt requires interest at $j_2 = 20\%$. At the same time a sinking fund is established which earns interest at $j_2 = 18\%$ to repay the debt in 25 years. Find
   a) the semi-annual expense of the debt;
   b) the book value of the city's indebtedness at the beginning of the 16th year.

5. On a debt of $4000, interest is paid monthly at $j_{12} = 12\%$ and monthly deposits are made into a sinking fund to retire the debt at the end of 5 years. If the sinking fund earns interest at $j_4 = 8\%$, what is the monthly expense of the debt?

6. On a debt of \$10 000, interest is paid semi-annually at $j_2 = 20\%$ and semi-annual deposits are made into a sinking fund to retire the debt at the end of 5 years. If the sinking fund earns interest at $j_{12} = 16\%$, what is the semi-annual expense of the debt?

Part B:

1. A company issued \$2 000 000 worth of bonds paying interest at $j_{12} = 15\frac{1}{2}\%$. A sinking fund accumulating at $j_4 = 12\%$ is established to redeem the bonds at the end of 15 years. Find
   a) the monthly expense of the debt;
   b) the book value of the company's indebtedness at the beginning of the 6th year.
2. A man is repaying a \$10 000 loan by the sinking fund method. His total monthly expense is \$300. Out of this \$300, interest is paid to the lender at $j_{12} = 12\%$ and a deposit is made to a sinking fund earning $j_{12} = 9\%$. Find the duration of the loan and the final smaller payment.

6.7 Comparison of Amortization and Sinking-Fund Methods

We have discussed the two most common methods of paying off long-term loans: the amortization method and the sinking-fund method. When there are several sources available from which to borrow money, it is important to know how to compare the available loans and choose the cheapest one. The borrower should choose that source for which the periodic expense of the debt is the lowest. When the amortization method is used the periodic expense of the debt is equal to the periodic amortization payment. When the sinking-fund method is used the periodic expense of the debt is the sum of the interest payment and the sinking-fund deposit.

First we shall consider the case where the interest on the debt in the amortization method is the same as the interest rate on the debt in the sinking-fund method.

Let i be the interest rate per period on the debt and r be the interest rate for the same period on the sinking fund, n be the number of conversion periods during the term of the loan, and A be the principal of the loan.

The periodic expense E_1, when the amortization method is used, is

$$E_1 = \frac{A}{a_{\overline{n}|i}}$$

But, from problem 2b of Exercise 3.3, Part B, we know that $\dfrac{1}{a_{\overline{n}|i}} = \dfrac{1}{s_{\overline{n}|i}} + i$.

Therefore, we obtain

$$E_1 = Ai + \frac{A}{s_{\overline{n}|i}}$$

The periodic expense E_2, when the sinking-fund method is used, is

$$E_2 = Ai + \frac{A}{s_{\overline{n}|r}}$$

Comparing the expressions for E_1 and E_2 we may conclude:
If $i > r$, then $s_{\overline{n}|i} > s_{\overline{n}|r}$ (accumulation factors at compound interest increase with the increasing interest rate) and

$$\frac{1}{s_{\overline{n}|i}} < \frac{1}{s_{\overline{n}|r}}$$

Thus for $i > r$, $E_1 < E_2$. (This is normally expected to be true). Similarly we can show that

if $i = r$ then $E_1 = E_2$ and if $i < r$ then $E_1 > E_2$

When the interest rate on the debt under the amortization method is different from the interest rate on the debt under the sinking-fund method, we cannot use the above conclusion and we must calculate and compare the periodic expenses of the debt under the two methods.

Example 1   A company wishes to borrow \$100 000 for 5 years. One source will lend the money at $j_2 = 20\%$ if it is amortized by semi-annual payments. A second source will lend the money at $j_2 = 19\%$ if only the interest is paid semi-annually and the principal is returned in a lump sum at the end of 5 years. If the second source is used, a sinking fund will be established by semi-annual deposits that accumulate at $j_{12} = 14\%$. How much can the company save semi-annually by using the better plan?

Solution   When the first source is used, the semi-annual expense of the debt is

$$E_1 = \frac{100\ 000}{a_{\overline{10}|0.10}} = \$16\ 274.54$$

When the second source is used, the interest on the debt paid semi-annually is $9\frac{1}{2}\%$ of $100\ 000 = \$9500.00$.

To calculate the semi-annual deposit into the sinking fund we first calculate the semi-annual rate i equivalent to $j_{12} = 14\%$

$$(1 + i)^2 = \left(1 + \frac{.14}{12}\right)^{12}$$

$$1 + i = \left(1 + \frac{.14}{12}\right)^{6}$$

$$i = \left(1 + \frac{.14}{12}\right)^{6} - 1$$

$$i = .072\ 073\ 7$$

Now we calculate the semi-annual deposit R into the sinking fund

$$R = \frac{100\ 000}{s_{\overline{10}|i}} = \$7167.16$$

The semi-annual expense of the debt using the second source is:

$$E_2 = 9500 + 7167.16 = \$16\ 667.16$$

Thus, the first source is cheaper and the company can save \$16 667.16 − \$16 274.54 = \$392.62 semi-annually.

Example 2   A firm wants to borrow $500 000. One source will lend the money at $j_4 = 18\%$ if interest is paid quarterly and the principal returned in a lump sum at the end of 10 years. The firm can set up a sinking fund at $j_4 = 16\%$. At what rate j_4 would it be less expensive to amortize the debt over 10 years?

Solution   We calculate the quarterly expense of the debt.

$$\text{Interest payment: } 500\ 000 \times .045 = \$22\ 500.00$$

$$\text{Sinking fund deposit: } \frac{500\ 000}{s_{\overline{40}|.04}} = \underline{\$\ 5\ 261.74}$$

$$\$27\ 761.74$$

The amortization method will be as expensive if the quarterly amortization payment is equal to $27\ 761.74$. Thus we want to find interest rate i per quarter (and then j_4) given $A = 500\ 000$, $R = 27\ 761.74$, $n = 40$.
Substituting in equation (13) we have

$$500\ 000 = 27\ 761.74 a_{\overline{40}|i}$$

$$a_{\overline{40}|i} = 18.010\ 398$$

By trial and error we find the following values:

	$a_{\overline{40}|i}$	j_4		
.3912 {	18.4016	18% } d		$\dfrac{d}{1\%} = \dfrac{.3912}{.6386}$
.6386 {	18.0104	j_4 }	1%	$d \doteq .61\%$
	17.7630	19%		and $j_4 = 18.61\%$.

If the firm can borrow the money and amortize the debt at less than $j_4 = 18.61\%$, then it will be less expensive than a straight loan at $j_4 = 18\%$ with a sinking fund at $j_4 = 16\%$.

Exercise 6.7
Part A:

1. A company borrows $50 000 to be repaid in equal annual instalments at the end of each year for 10 years. Find the total annual cost under the following conditions:
   a) The debt is amortized at $j_1 = 19\%$;
   b) Interest at 19% is paid on the debt and a sinking fund is set up at $j_1 = 19\%$;
   c) Interest at 19% is paid on the debt and a sinking fund is set up at $j_1 = 16\%$.
2. A company can borrow $180 000 for 15 years. They can amortize the debt at $j_1 = 20\%$ or they can pay interest on the loan at $j_1 = 19\%$ and set up a sinking fund at $j_1 = 17\%$ to repay the loan. Which plan is cheaper and by how much per annum?
3. A firm wants to borrow $60 000 to be repaid over 5 years. One source will lend them the money at $j_2 = 10\%$ if it is amortized by semi-annual payments. A second source will lend them money at $j_2 = 9\frac{1}{2}\%$ if only the interest is paid semi-annually and the principal is returned in a lump sum at the end of 5 years. The firm can earn $j_2 = 8\%$ on their savings. Which source should be used for the loan and how much will be saved each half-year?
4. A company can borrow $100 000 for 10 years by paying the interest as it falls due at $j_2 = 19\%$ and setting up a sinking fund at $j_2 = 17\%$ to repay the debt. At what rate, j_2, would an amortization plan have the same semi-annual cost?

5. A city can borrow $500 000 for 20 years by issuing bonds on which interest will be paid semi-annually at $j_2 = 9\frac{1}{8}\%$. The principal will be paid off by a sinking fund consisting of semi-annual deposits invested at $j_2 = 8\%$. Find the nominal rate, j_2, at which the loan could be amortized at the same semi-annual cost.

6. A firm can borrow $200 000 at $j_1 = 19\%$ and amortize the debt for 10 years. From a second source, the money can be borrowed at $j_1 = 18\frac{1}{2}\%$ if the interest is paid annually and the principal is repaid in a lump sum at the end of 10 years. What yearly rate j_1 must the sinking fund earn for the annual expense to be the same under the two options?

7. A company wants to borrow $500 000. One source will lend the money at $j_4 = 18\%$ if interest only is paid quarterly and the principal returned in a lump sum at the end of 15 years. The firm can set up a sinking fund at $j_4 = 16\%$ and will make quarterly deposits. At what rate, j_4, would the quarterly cost be the same if the debt were amortized?

Part B:

1. A company needs to borrow $200 000 for 6 years. One source will lend them the money at $j_2 = 18\%$ if it is amortized by monthly payments. A second source will lend the money at $j_4 = 17\%$ if only the interest is paid monthly and the principal is returned in a lump sum at the end of 6 years. The company can earn interest at $j_{365} = 13\%$ on the sinking fund. Which source should be used for the loan and how much will be saved monthly?

2. Mr. X can borrow $10 000 by paying the interest on the loan as it falls due at $j_2 = 12\%$ and by setting up a sinking fund with semi-annual deposits that accumulate at $j_{12} - 9\%$ over 10 years to repay the debt. At what rate, j_4, would an amortization scheme have the same semi-annual cost?

3. A loan of $10 000 at 16% per annum is to be repaid over 10 years; $2 000 by the amortization method, and $8 000 by the sinking fund method where the sinking fund can be accumulated with annual deposits at $j_4 = 10\%$. What extra annual payment does the above arrangement require as compared to repayment of the whole loan by the amortization method?

4. A company wants to borrow a large amount of money for 15 years. One source would lend the money at $j_2 = 19\%$ provided it is amortized over 15 years by monthly payments. The company could also raise the money by issuing bonds paying interest semi-annually at $j_2 = 18\frac{1}{2}\%$ and redeemable at par in 15 years. In this case the company would set up a sinking fund to accumulate the money needed for the redemption of bonds at the end of 15 years. What rate j_{12} on the sinking fund would make the monthly expense the same under the two options?

6.8 Review Exercises

1. The Smiths borrow $15 000 to be repaid with monthly payments over 10 years at $j_{12} = 15\%$.
   a) Find the monthly payment required.

   b) Find the outstanding balance of the loan after three years (36 payments) and split the 37th payment into principal and interest under:
   i) the amortization method;
   ii) the sum of digits method.

2. A loan of $20 000 is to be amortized by 20 quarterly payments over 5 years at $j_{12} = 18\%$. Split the 9th payment into principal and interest.

3. A loan of $10 000 is to be repaid by 5 equal annual payments at $j_2 = 14\%$. What is the total of the interest paid in the whole loan?

4. A company wants to borrow a large sum of money to be repaid over 10 years. The company can issue bonds paying interest at $j_2 = 17\%$ redeemable at par in 10 years. A sinking fund earning $j_{12} = 15\%$ can be used to accumulate the amount needed in 10 years to redeem the bonds. At what rate, j_2, would the semi-annual cost be the same if the debt were amortized over 10 years?

5. Interest at $j_2 = 12\%$ on a debt of $3000 must be paid as it falls due. A sinking fund accumulating at $j_4 = 8\%$ is established to enable the debtor to repay the loan at the end of four years. Find the *semi-annual* sinking fund deposit and construct the last 2 lines of the sinking fund schedule.

6. For a $60 000 mortgage at $j_2 = 10\%$ amortized over 25 years find:
   a) the level monthly payment required;
   b) the outstanding balance just after the 48th payment;
   c) the principal portion of the 49th payment;
   d) the total interest paid by the first 48 payments.

7. A $10 000 loan at $j_2 = 16\%$ is to be repaid using the amortization method by level monthly payments over 12 years. After 5 years you want to renegotiate the loan. You can refinance by borrowing the money needed to pay off the outstanding balance at $j_2 = 13\%$ and repay this second loan by accumulating the total of principal and interest due after 7 years in a sinking fund earning $j_{12} = 12\%$. You discover the loan company holding the original loan will calculate the outstanding balance using the sum of digits method. Should you refinance?

8. As part of the purchase of a home on January 1, 1983 you negotiated a mortgage in the amount of $55 000. The amortization period for calculation of the level payments (principal and interest) was 25 years and the initial interest rate was 12% per annum compounded semi-annually.
   a) What was the initial monthly payment?
   b) During 1983–87 inclusive (and January 1, 1988) all monthly mortgage payments were made as they became due. What was the balance of the loan owing just after the payment made January 1, 1988?
   c) At January 1, 1988 (just after the payment then due) the loan was renegotiated at 16% per annum compounded semi-annually (with the end date of the amortization period unchanged). What was the new monthly payment?
   d) All payments, as above, have been faithfully made. How much of the September 1, 1988 payment will be principal and how much represents interest?
   e) Of the 12 payments made during 1990 how much will represent interest?

9. A couple has a $50 000, 20-year mortgage at $j_2 = 18\%$ with the interest rate guaranteed for 5 years. After exactly 3 years (36 payments) they could renegotiate a new mortgage at $j_2 = 14\%$. If the bank charges an interest penalty of three times the monthly interest due on the outstanding balance at the time of renegotiation, should they renegotiate?

10. An individual borrows $10 000 to be repaid over 10 years. From one source money can be borrowed at $j_1 = 20\%$ and amortized by annual payments. From a second source, money can be borrowed at $j_1 = 19\%$ if only the interest is paid annually and the principal repaid at the end of 10 years. If the second source is used, a sinking fund will be established by annual deposits that accumulate at $j_4 = 16\%$. How much is saved annually by using the better plan?

7

Bonds

7.1 Introduction and Terminology

When a corporation, a municipality or government needs a large sum of money for a long period of time, they issue **bonds**, sometimes called debentures, which are sold to a number of investors.

A bond is a written contract between the issuer (borrower) and the investor (lender) which specifies:

— the **face value**, or the **denomination**, of the bond which is stated on the front of the bond. This is usually a simple figure such as $100, $500, $1000, $5000, $10 000.

— the **redemption date**, or **maturity date**, that is the date on which the loan will be repaid.

— the **bond rate**, or **coupon rate**, that is the rate at which the bond pays interest on its face value at equal time intervals until the maturity date. In most cases this rate is compounded semi-annually.

The amount of money that will be paid on the redemption date is called the **redemption value**. In most cases it is the same as the face value and in such cases we say the bond is **redeemed at par**. Some bonds are **callable**; they contain a clause that allows the issuer to pay off the loan at a date earlier than the redemption date. Most callable bonds are called at a premium and the redemption value of a bond called before maturity is a previously specified percentage of the face value. For example, the redemption value of a $1000 bond redeemable at 103 during a certain year would be $1030 (during that year).

Bonds (as a contract) may be transferred from one investor to another. Bonds may be bought or sold on the bond market at any time. The buyer of the bond, as an investor, wants to realize a certain return on his investment, specified by the **investment** or **yield rate**. This desired rate of return will vary with the financial climate and will affect the price at which bonds are traded.

As an illustration, consider a $1000 bond redeemable at par in 5 years, paying interest at bond rate $j_2 = 8\%$. If the buyer paid $1000 for the bond, then he receives $40 every half-year in interest and we say his yield rate is $j_2 = 8\%$, that is, the same as the bond rate (coupon rate). If the buyer paid less than the face value, his yield rate will be higher than the bond rate $j_2 = 8\%$, because he receives $40 every half-year in interest and on the redemption date he receives the face value of $1000, i.e. more than he invested. Similarly, if the buyer paid more than the face value, his yield rate will be lower than the bond rate. In the latter case his interest payments at $j_2 = 8\%$ will be partially offset by the loss incurred when the bond is redeemed.

In this chapter we shall use the following notation:

F — the face value or par value of the bond.
C = the redemption value of the bond.
r = the bond rate per interest period (coupon rate).
i = the yield rate per interest period.
n = the number of interest periods until the redemption date.
P = the purchase price of the bond to yield rate i.
Fr = the bond interest payment or coupon.

The two fundamental problems relating to bonds, which will be discussed in this chapter, are

1. to determine the purchase price P of a bond to yield a given yield rate i;
2. to determine the investment rate i that a bond will yield when bought for a given price P.

7.2 Purchase Price to Yield a Given Investment Rate

We want to determine the purchase price of a bond on a bond interest date, n interest periods before maturity so that it earns interest at a specified investment rate i. We shall assume that the bond rate and the yield rate have the same conversion period.

A buyer of a bond will receive two types of payments: (i) bond interest payment Fr at the ends of interest periods; (ii) the redemption value C on the redemption date.

The buyer of a bond who wishes to realize an investment rate i on his investment should pay a price equal to the discounted value of the above payments at rate i. Thus

$$P = Fra_{\overline{n}|i} + C(1 + i)^{-n} \qquad (24)$$

Example 1   A $1000 bond that pays interest at $j_2 = 14\%$ is redeemable at par at the end of 5 years. Find the purchase price to yield an investor

a) 16% compounded semi-annually;
b) 12% compounded semi-annually.

Solution The bond pays 7% of $1000 semi-annually, i.e., $Fr = 1000 \times .07 = \$70$, and $1000 at the end of 5 years.

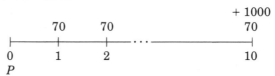

(a) The purchase price P to yield $j_2 = 16\%$ is the discounted value of the above payments at $j_2 = 16\%$.
$P = 70\ a_{\overline{10}|.08} + 1000(1.08)^{-10} = 469.71 + 463.19 = \$932.90.$
The purchase price of $932.90 will yield a buyer a return of $j_2 = 16\%$ on his investment. The buyer is buying the bond for less than the redemption value, he is buying it at a *discount*, because the yield rate is higher than the bond rate.
(b) The purchase price P to yield $j_2 = 12\%$ is
$P = 70\ a_{\overline{10}|.06} + 1000(1.06)^{-10} = 515.21 + 558.39 = \$1073.60.$
The purchase price of $1073.60 will yield a buyer a return of $j_2 = 12\%$ on his investment. The buyer is buying the bond for more than the redemption value, he is buying it at a *premium*, because the yield rate is lower than the bond rate.

Example 2   A $5000 bond maturing at 105 on September 1, 2005 has semi-annual coupons at 13%. Find the purchase price on March 1, 1984 to guarantee a yield of at least $j_2 = 12\frac{1}{2}\%$.

Solution   Each coupon is of dollar size $6\frac{1}{2}\%$ of $5000 = \$325.00$ semi-annually. The bond matures on September 1, 2005 for $5000 \times 1.05 = \$5250$.

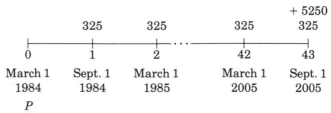

The purchaser receives 43 coupons plus the maturity value. The purchase price P on March 1, 1984 to guarantee a yield of $j_2 = 12\frac{1}{2}\%$ is
$$P = 325.00\ a_{\overline{43}|.0625} + 5250(1.0625)^{-43}$$
$$= 4816.42 + 387.27 = \$5203.69.$$

In this example, the buyer wants a yield rate smaller than the coupon rate on the bond and yet, since the price is less than the redemption value, he has bought the bond at a discount. This apparent contradiction can be explained by remembering that while the bond is redeemed for \$5250, which affects the price of the bond, the coupons are determined by taking $6\frac{1}{2}\%$ of \$5000 not $6\frac{1}{2}\%$ of \$5250.

We will study the concepts of premium and discount in more detail in section 7.5.

The above two examples illustrate that in the bond investment market the price of a bond depends on the bond rate, the yield rate acceptable to investors, the time to maturity, and the redemption value.

Note   Unless it is specified otherwise, we assume the bonds are redeemed at par.

Bond Tables   Until recently, companies that bought and sold bonds used bond tables to calculate the price of a bond, or the yield rate for a price set by market forces.

Bond tables are available in large volumes with answers to 4 or 6 decimal places. The tables give the market prices of bonds for a wide range of yield and bond interest rates and lengths of time to maturity. Almost all bond tables make assumptions that redemption is at par and the bond rate as well as the yield rate are compounded semi-annually.

Today, companies that buy and sell bonds use electronic calculators to calculate the information previously found in the bond tables. The formulas they must use, are those developed in this chapter.

7.3 An Alternate Purchase-Price Formula

We shall develop an alternate formula for the purchase price of a bond sold on a bond interest date, which is somewhat simpler than formula (24)

$$P = Fra_{\overline{n}|i} + C(1 + i)^{-n}$$

Using the identity

$$a_{\overline{n}|i} = \frac{1 - (1 + i)^{-n}}{i}$$

from Chapter 3, we can get the factor $(1 + i)^{-n}$ as

$$(1 + i)^{-n} = 1 - ia_{\overline{n}|i}$$

and eliminate it in formula (24). Thus

$$P = Fra_{\overline{n}|i} + C(1 - ia_{\overline{n}|i})$$

or

$$P = C + (Fr - Ci)a_{\overline{n}|i} \tag{25}$$

Formula (25) is often more efficient than formula (24) since it requires only one calculation, $a_{\overline{n}|i}$, whereas formula (24) requires two, $a_{\overline{n}|i}$ and $(1 + i)^{-n}$.

Example 1   A corporation decides to issue 15-year bonds in the amount of $10 000 000. Under the indenture, interest payments will be made at the rate $j_2 = 10\%$. The bonds were priced to yield $j_2 = 8\%$ to maturity. What is the issue price of the bonds? What is the price of a $1000 bond to yield $j_2 = 8\%$?

Solution   The bond issue will provide interest payments of 5% of $10 000 000 semi-annually, that is $Fr = \$500\ 000$, and redemption price $10 000 000 at the end of 15 years.

The alternate purchase-price formula will give us
$$P = 10\ 000\ 000 + (500\ 000 - 400\ 000)a_{\overline{30}|.04}$$
$$= 10\ 000\ 000 + 1\ 729\ 203.32$$
$$= \$11\ 729\ 203.32$$

The issue price of the bonds to the public is $11 729 203.32. The bonds will provide the investor with a yield $j_2 = 8\%$ if held to maturity. The price of a $1000 bond is
$$\frac{11\ 729\ 203.32}{10\ 000} = \$1172.92$$

In all examples so far we have considered the case where the bond interest payments Fr form an ordinary simple annuity, that is, where the bond interest period coincides with the period the yield rate is compounded. In cases when these periods are different, the bond interest payments form an ordinary general annuity, and the techniques of Chapter 5 may be used to replace an ordinary general annuity with an ordinary simple annuity. The following example will illustrate the procedure.

Example 2   Find the issue price of the bonds in Example 1 to yield (a) 8% per annum compounded monthly; (b) 8% per annum effective.

Solution a   Find a rate of interest, i, per half year such that:
$$(1 + i)^2 = \left(1 + \frac{.08}{12}\right)^{12}$$
$$1 + i = \left(1 + \frac{.08}{12}\right)^6$$
$$i = \left(1 + \frac{.08}{12}\right)^6 - 1$$
$$i = .040\ 672\ 62$$

Now $P = 10\ 000\ 000 + (500\ 000 - 406\ 726.24)a_{\overline{30}|i}$
$$= 10\ 000\ 000 + 1\ 599\ 802 = \$11\ 599\ 802$$

The issue price of the bonds to the public is $11 599 802. The purchase price of a $1000 bond is then $1159.98.

Solution b   Find a rate of interest, i, per half year such that:
$$(1 + i)^2 = 1.08$$
$$1 + i = (1.08)^{\frac{1}{2}}$$
$$i = (1.08)^{\frac{1}{2}} - 1$$
$$i = .039\ 230\ 48$$

Now $P = 10\ 000\ 000 + (500\ 000 - 392\ 304.84)a_{\overline{30}|i}$
$$= 10\ 000\ 000 + 1\ 879\ 792.10 = \$11\ 879\ 792.10$$

The issue price of the bonds to the public is $11 879 792.10. The purchase price of a $1000 bond is then $1187.98.

Exercise 7.3
Part A
Questions 1 to 8 use the following information. Using either formula find the purchase price of the bond.

No.	Face Value	Redemption	Bond interest rate	Years to redemption	Yield Rate
1.	$ 500	at par	$j_2 = 9\%$	20	$j_2 = 8\%$
2.	$1 000	at par	$j_2 = 9\%$	15	$j_2 = 10\%$
3.	$2 000	at par	$j_2 = 13\%$	15	$j_4 = 14\%$
4.	$5 000	at par	$j_2 = 12\%$	20	$j_2 = 10\%$
5.	$1 000	at 110	$j_2 = 9\%$	18	$j_2 = 12\%$
6.	$2 000	at 105	$j_2 = 13\%$	20	$j_2 = 14\%$
7.	$10 000	at 110	$j_2 = 10\frac{1}{2}\%$	15	$j_{12} = 15\%$
8.	$5 000	at 103	$j_2 = 11\%$	17	$j_4 = 10\%$

9. The XYZ Corporation needs to raise some funds to pay for new equipment. They issue $1 000 000 worth of 20-year bonds with semi-annual coupons at 12%. These bonds are redeemable at 105. At the time of issue, interest rates in the market place are $j_{12} = 15\%$. How much money did they raise?

10. Mr. Smith buys a $1000 bond paying bond interest at $j_2 = 13\%$ and redeemable at par in 20 years. Mr. Smith's desired yield is $j_4 = 14\%$. How much did he pay for the bond? After exactly five years he sells the bond. Interest rates have dropped and the bond is sold to yield a buyer $j_1 = 10\%$. Find the sale price.

Part B

1. Prove the following formula for a *par value* bond

$$P = F(1 + i)^{-n} + \frac{r}{i}\left[F - F(1 + i)^{-n}\right]$$

This purchase-price formula is known as Makcham's formula and requires the use of only $(1 + i)^{-n}$ factors.

2. The XYZ Corporation issues a special 20-year bond issue that has no coupons. Rather, interest will accumulate on the bond at a rate $j_2 = 11\%$ for the life of the bond. At the time of maturity, the total value of the loan will be paid off, including all accumulated interest. Find the price of a $1000 bond of this issue to yield $j_2 = 15\%$.

3. A $1000 bond bearing coupons at $j_2 = 13\%$ and redeemable at par is bought to yield $j_2 = 12\%$. If the present value of the redemption value at this yield is $140, what is the purchase price?

4. Two $1000 bonds redeemable at par at the end of n years are bought to yield $j_2 = 10\%$. One bond costs $1153.72 and has semi-annual coupons at 12%. The other bond has semi-annual coupons at 8%. Find the price of the second bond.

5. A $1000 bond with semi-annual coupons at $j_2 = 12\%$ and redeemable at the end of n years at $1050 sells at $930 to yield $j_2 = 15\%$. Find the price of a $1000 bond with semi-annual coupons at $j_2 = 10\%$ redeemable at the end of $2n$ years at $1040 to yield $j_2 = 15\%$. (Do not find n).

7.4 Callable Bonds

Some bonds contain a clause which allows the issuer to redeem the bond prior to the maturity date. These bonds are referred to as **callable bonds**.

Callable bonds present a problem with respect to the calculation of price, since the term of the bond is not certain. Since the corporation issuing the bond controls when the bond is redeemed (or called), the investor must determine a price that will guarantee him his desired yield regardless of the call date.

Example 1   The XYZ Corporation issues a 20-year $1000 bond with coupons at $j_2 = 11\%$. The bond can be called, at par, at the end of 15 years. Find the purchase price that will guarantee an investor a return of

a) $j_2 = 13\%$;
b) $j_2 = 9\%$.

Solution a   The bond matures at the end of 20 years, but may be called at the end of 15 years. Given a desired yield rate of $j_2 = 13\%$ we calculate the price of the bond for these two different dates using formula (25).

(i) If it is called after 15 years
$$P = 1000 + (55 - 65)a_{\overline{30}|.065} = 1000 - 130.59 = \$869.41$$
(ii) If it matures after 20 years
$$P = 1000 + (55 - 65)a_{\overline{40}|.065} = 1000 - 141.46 = \$858.54$$

The purchase price to guarantee a return of $j_2 = 13\%$ is the lower of these two answers, or $858.54. If the investor pays $858.54 and the bond runs the full 20 years to maturity, the investor's yield will be exactly $j_2 = 13\%$. If the investor pays $858.54 and the bond is called after 15 years, the investor's return exceeds $j_2 = 13\%$.

If the investor pays $869.41 for the bond, however, he will yield $j_2 = 13\%$ only if the bond is called after 15 years. If the bond runs to its full maturity, the rate of return will be less than $j_2 = 13\%$.

Solution b   Again we calculate the price of the bonds at the two different dates using a yield of $j_2 = 9\%$ and formula (25).

(i) If it is called after 15 years
$$P = 1000 + (55 - 45)a_{\overline{30}|.045} = 1000 + 162.89 = \$1162.89.$$
(ii) If it matures after 20 years
$$P = 1000 + (55 - 45)a_{\overline{40}|.045} = 1000 + 184.02 = \$1184.02.$$

The purchase price to guarantee a return of $j_2 = 9\%$ is $1162.89. Regardless of the outcome, the investor's yield will equal or exceed $j_2 = 9\%$ at this price.

In the above example, we have shown, in effect, that the investor must assume that the issuer of the bond will exercise his call option to the disadvantage of the investor and must calculate the price accordingly. The example above also illustrates a useful principle *for bonds that are callable at par*. That is:

If the yield rate is less than the coupon rate (if the bond sells at a premium) then you use the earliest possible call date in your calculation.

If the yield rate is greater than the coupon rate (if the bond sells at a discount), then you use the latest possible redemption date in your calculation.

These rules can be explained logically. For a bond purchased at a premium, the earliest call date is the worst for the investor since he gets only $1000 for his bond whenever it is called. On the other hand, for a bond purchased at a discount, the earliest call date is the best for the investor, since at that early call date he will get a full $1000 for a bond that he values at something less than $1000. Thus, the most unfavourable situation is the latest possible redemption.

Unfortunately, when a bond is called early, it is usually done so at a premium. In that case we are forced to calculate all possible purchase prices and pay the lowest price calculated.

Example 2 The ABC Corporation issues a 20-year $1000 bond with bond interest at $j_2 = 12\%$. The bond is callable at the end of 10 years at $1100, or at the end of 15 years at $1050. Find the price to guarantee an investor a yield rate of $j_2 = 11\%$.

Solution Calculate the purchase price using formula (25)

(i) If the bond is called after 10 years
$$P = 1100 + (60 - 60.50)a_{\overline{20}|.055} = 1100 - 5.98 = \$1094.02$$
(ii) If the bond is called after 15 years
$$P = 1050 + (60 - 57.75)a_{\overline{30}|.055} = 1050 + 32.70 = \$1082.70$$
(iii) If the bond is redeemed at par after 20 years
$$P = 1000 + (60 - 55)a_{\overline{40}|.055} = 1000 + 80.23 = \$1080.23$$

In this case, despite the fact that the desired yield rate is less than the bond coupon rate, the correct answer is found by using the latest possible redemption date. That is because of the premium value in the early call dates.

Exercise 7.4

Part A

1. A $2000 bond paying interest at $j_2 = 10\%$ is redeemable at par in 20 years. It is callable at par in 15 years. Find the price to guarantee a yield
   a) $j_2 = 8\%$;
   b) $j_2 = 12\%$.
2. A $5000 bond paying interest at $j_2 = 11\%$ is redeemable at par in 20 years. It is callable at 105% of its face value in 15 years. Find the price to guarantee a yield
   a) $j_2 = 9\%$;
   b) $j_2 = 13\%$.
3. A $1000 bond with coupons at $j_2 = 10\%$ is redeemable at par in 20 years. It is callable after 10 years at $1100 and after 15 years at $1050. Find the price to guarantee a yield
   a) $j_2 = 8\%$;
   b) $j_2 = 12\%$.

Part B

1. A $2000 bond with semi-annual coupons at $j_2 = 13\%$ is redeemable at par in 20 years. It is callable at a 5% premium in 15 years. Find the price to guarantee a yield
   a) $j_4 = 16\%$;
   b) $j_1 = 11\%$.

2. A $1000 bond with coupons at $j_2 = 11\%$ is redeemable at par in 20 years. It also has the following call options:

Call Date	Redemption
15 years	$1050
16 years	1040
17 years	1030
18 years	1020
19 years	1010

Find the price to guarantee a yield
a) $j_1 = 10\%$;
b) $j_{12} = 12\%$.

7.5 Premium and Discount

If the purchase price of a bond exceeds its redemption value, i.e., $P > C$, then the bond is said to sell **at a premium**, and the difference $P - C$ is called the **premium**. Similarly, if the purchase price is less than the redemption value, i.e. $P < C$, then the bond is said to sell **at a discount**, and the difference $C - P$ is called the **discount**.

From the alternate purchase-price formula (25) we can derive expressions for the premium and the discount

$$\text{Premium} = P - C = (Fr - Ci)a_{\overline{n}|i} \tag{26}$$
$$\text{Discount} = C - P = (Ci - Fr)a_{\overline{n}|i} \tag{27}$$

Remarks
a) When the bond is to be redeemed at par, i.e. $C = F$, from (26) we can conclude that $P > C$ if $r > i$, i.e., premium will occur when the bond rate is higher than the yield rate. Similarly, we can conclude that $P < C$ if $r < i$, i.e., a bond is sold at a discount when the bond rate is less than the yield rate.
b) Some authors call $P - C$ the *excess* and $C - P$ the *deficiency*, when the bond is not to be redeemed at par, i.e., $C \neq F$. When the bond is to be redeemed at par, they call $P - F$ the premium and $F - P$ the discount.

When the bond is purchased at a premium, i.e., $P > C$, then only C of the original principal is returned on the redemption date. There will be a loss, equal to the premium, at the redemption date, unless part of each bond interest payment is used to amortize the premium. The remaining principal $P - C$, or the premium is returned in instalments as a part of the bond interest payments.

Each bond payment, in addition to paying interest on the investment (at a yield rate), provides a partial return of the principal P. These payments of principal will continually reduce the value of the bond from the price on the purchase date to the redemption value on the redemption date. These adjusted values of the bond are called the **book values** of the bond and are used by many investors in reporting the asset values of bonds for financial statements. The process of gradually decreasing the value of the bond from the purchase price to the redemption value is called **amortization of a premium** or **writing down**. A **bond amortization schedule** is a table which shows the division of each interest payment into its interest-paid and principal-adjustment portion together with the book value after each bond interest payment is paid.*

Example 1   A $1000 bond, redeemable at par on December 1, 1985, pays interest at $j_2 = 13\%$. The bond is bought on June 1, 1983 to yield $j_2 = 12\%$. Find the price and construct a bond schedule.

Solution   The purchase price P on June 1, 1983 can be determined using the alternate purchase-price formula

$$P = 1000 + (65 - 60)a_{\overline{3}|.06} = 1000 + 21.06 = \$1021.06$$

The premium of $21.06 must be saved out of the bond interest payments in order to recover the entire principal originally invested in the bond. To construct the amortization schedule for this bond, we shall calculate how much of each coupon is used as return on the investment at the desired yield rate and how much is used to adjust the principal (i.e., amortize the premium).

At the end of the first half-year on December 1, 1983, the investor's yield should be $1021.06 \times 0.06 = \$61.26$. Since he actually receives $65, the difference of $3.74 can be regarded as part of the original principal being returned and is used to adjust (reduce) the principal, or amortize the premium. The adjusted value, or book value, after the coupon payment is $1021.06 - 3.74 = \$1017.32$. This book value can be computed independently by the alternate purchase price formula using $F = C = 1000$, $r = 6\frac{1}{2}\%$, $i = 6\%$ and $n = 4$. The above procedure is continued until the bond matures.

The following is a complete bond schedule.

Schedule for a bond purchased at a premium

Date	Coupon	Interest on Book Value at Yield Rate	Principal Adjustment	Book Value
June 1, 1983	—	—	—	1021.06
Dec. 1, 1983	65.00	61.26	3.74	1017.32
June 1, 1984	65.00	61.04	3.96	1013.36
Dec. 1, 1984	65.00	60.80	4.20	1009.16
June 1, 1985	65.00	60.55	4.45	1004.71
Dec. 1, 1985	65.00	60.28	4.72	999.99*
Totals	325.00	303.93	21.07*	

*The 1-cent error is due to the accumulation of round-off errors.
Several observations are possible:

1. All the book values can be reproduced using either of the purchase price formulas.
2. The sum of the principal adjustments is equal to the amount of premium.
3. The book value is gradually decreasing from the original purchase price to the redemption value.

---

*There are several methods available to accountants for setting up a bond amortization schedule. The method presented in this text is that based on compound interest theory and is, perhaps, the most direct method.

4. Successive principal adjustments are in the ratio $1 + i$,

i.e., $\dfrac{3.96}{3.74} \doteq \dfrac{4.20}{3.96} \doteq \dfrac{4.45}{4.20} \doteq \dfrac{4.72}{4.45} \doteq 1.06$

This provides a quick check of entries in the bond table.

When the bond is purchased at a discount, i.e., $P < C$, the investor's return is more than just the bond interest payments. There will be a profit, equal to the discount, at the redemption date, unless the book value is gradually increased. The process of gradually increasing the value of the bond from the purchase price to the redemption value is called **accumulation of a discount** or **writing up**.

A **bond accumulation schedule** is a table which shows the division of the investor's interest (at a yield rate) into the bond interest payment and the increase in the value of the bond, or the principal-adjustment, together with the book value after each bond interest payment is paid.

Example 2 A $1000 bond, redeemable at par on December 1, 1985, pays interest at $j_2 = 9\%$. The bond is bought on June 1, 1983 to yield $j_2 = 10\%$. Find the price and construct a bond schedule.

Solution The purchase price P on June 1, 1983 can be determined by the alternate purchase-price formula

$$P = 1000 + (45 - 50)a_{\overline{5}|.05} = 1000 - 21.65 = \$978.35$$

The discount is $21.65.

To construct the accumulation schedule for this bond we shall calculate the investor's interest at the end of each half-year and gradually increase the book value of the bond by the difference between investor's interest and the bond interest payment.

At the end of the first half-year, on December 1, 1983, the investor's interest should be $978.35 \times 0.05 = \$48.92$. Since the bond interest payment is only $45 we increase the book value of the bond by $48.92 - 45.00 = \$3.92$. We say, $3.92 is used for accumulation of a discount or $3.92 is the principal adjustment.

The adjusted value, or book value, after the bond interest payment on December 1, 1983, is $978.35 + 3.92 = \$982.27$. This book value can be computed independently by the alternate purchase-price formula, using $F = C = 1000$, $r = 4\frac{1}{2}\%$, $i = 5\%$, and $n = 4$. The above procedure is continued until the bond matures. The following is a complete bond schedule.

Schedule for a bond purchased at a discount

Date	Bond interest payment	Interest on book value at yield rate	Principal adjustment	Book value
June 1, 1978	—	—	—	978.35
Dec. 1, 1978	45.00	48.92	3.92	982.27
June 1, 1979	45.00	49.11	4.11	986.38
Dec. 1, 1979	45.00	49.32	4.32	990.70
June 1, 1980	45.00	49.54	4.54	995.24
Dec. 1, 1980	45.00	49.76	4.76	1000.00
Totals	225.00	246.65	21.65	

Several observations are possible:
1. All the book values can be reproduced using either of the purchase price formulas.

2. The sum of the principal adjustments is equal to the amount of discount.
3. The book value is gradually increasing from the original purchase price to the redemption value.
4. Successive principal adjustments are in the ratio $1 + i$,

i.e., $\dfrac{4.76}{4.54} \doteq \dfrac{4\ 54}{4.32} \doteq \dfrac{4.32}{4.11} \doteq \dfrac{4.11}{3.92} \doteq 1.05$

This provides a quick check of entries in the bond table.

Exercise 7.5
Part A
In each question listed below, determine logically, before calculation, if the bond is purchased at a premium or a discount. Then find the purchase price of the bond and make out a complete bond schedule showing the amortization of the premium or the accumulation of the discount.

No.	Face Value	Redemption	Bond interest rate	Years to Redemption	Yield rate
1.	$1 000	at par	$j_2 = 10\%$	3	$j_2 = 9\%$
2.	$5 000	at par	$j_2 = 12\%$	3	$j_2 = 14\%$
3.	$2 000	at par	$j_2 = 13\%$	$2\frac{1}{2}$	$j_2 = 11\%$
4.	$1 000	at 105	$j_2 = 10\%$	$2\frac{1}{2}$	$j_2 = 12\%$
5.	$2 000	at 103	$j_2 = 15\%$	3	$j_2 = 14\%$
6.	$10 000	at 110	$j_2 = 14\%$	$2\frac{1}{2}$	$j_2 = 16\%$

7. A $1000 par value bond paying interest at $j_2 = 12\%$ has book value $1100 on March 1, 1984 at a yield rate of $j_2 = 9\%$. Find the amount of amortization of the premium on September 1, 1984 and the new book value on that date.

Part B
1. A 20-year bond with annual coupons is bought at a premium to yield $j_1 = 13\%$. If the amount of amortization of the premium in the 3rd payment is $6, determine the amount of amortization of the premium in the 16th payment.
2. A $1000 bond, redeemable at par, with annual coupons at 16% is purchased for $1060. If the write-down in the book value is $7 at the end of the first year, what is the write-down at the end of the fourth year?
3. A bond with $160 annual coupons is purchased at a discount to yield $j_1 = 15\%$. The write-up for the first year is $44. What was the purchase price?
4. A $1000 bond redeemable at $1050 on December 1, 1985 pays interest at $j_2 = 13\%$. The bond is bought on June 1, 1983. Find the price and construct a bond schedule if the desired yield is
   a) $j_{12} = 12\%$;
   b) $j_1 = 11\%$.
5. A $1000, 20-year par value bond with semi-annual coupons is bought at a discount to yield $j_2 = 10\%$. If the amount for accumulation of the discount in the last entry in the schedule is $5, find the purchase price of the bond.
6. A bond with $80 semi-annual coupons is purchased at a premium to yield $j_2 = 14\%$. If the first write-down is $4.33, find the purchase price of the bond.

7. A \$1000, 14% bond pays coupons on January 1 and July 1 and will be redeemed at par on July 1, 1988. If the bond was bought on January 1, 1980 to yield 12% per annum compounded semi-annually, find the interest due on the book value on January 1, 1984.

7.6 Price of a Bond between Bond Interest Dates

The bond purchase price formulas (24) and (25) were derived for bonds purchased on bond interest dates. In that case, the seller keeps the bond interest payment due on that date and the buyer receives all the future bond payments. In practice, bonds are purchased at any time and consequently we need a method of valuation of bonds between bond interest dates.

Suppose a bond is purchased between bond interest dates to yield the buyer interest at rate i.

Let P_0 denote the purchase price of the bond on the preceding bond interest date to yield i;

P_1 denote the purchase price of the bond on the following bond interest date to yield i;

f be the fractional part of an interest period that has elapsed since the preceding bond interest date.

In actual practice we use linear interpolation between P_0 and P_1 to get the so-called **market price** Q (also known as the **"and interest"** price, or the **quoted price**). This price does not include the **accrued bond interest**, I, which is a proportional share of the next bond interest payment the seller is entitled to because he held the bond for part of the bond interest period. The formulas for Q and I are

$$Q = P_0 + f(P_1 - P_0) \tag{28}$$
$$I = f \times Fr \tag{29}$$

The total purchase price P, called the **flat price** of a bond, is the money which changes hands at the date of sale, i.e.,

$$P = Q + I$$

Note   We could get P by accumulating P_0 at simple interest i for time f.

Summary of the procedure to calculate the purchase price P between bond interest dates:

1. Determine the prices P_0 and P_1.
2. Interpolate between P_0 and P_1 to get the market price Q.
3. Add the accrued bond interest I to get the total purchase price P.

Example   A $1000 bond, redeemable at par on October 1, 1985, is paying bond interest at $j_2 = 10\%$. Find the purchase price on June 16, 1983, to yield $j_2 = 9\%$.

Solution   The preceding bond interest date is April 1, 1983 and the following bond interest date is October 1, 1983. The exact time elapsed from April 1, 1983 to June 16, 1983 is 76 days, the exact time between April 1, 1983 and October 1, 1983, is 183 days. Thus $f = \frac{76}{183}$.

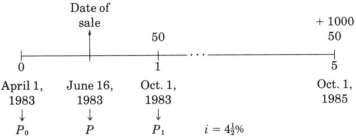

Using the alternate purchase-price formula we have

$P_0 = 1000 + (50 - 45)a_{\overline{5}|.045} = \$1021.95$

$P_1 = 1000 + (50 - 45)a_{\overline{4}|.045} = \$1017.95$

The market price on June 16, 1983, is

$Q = 1021.95 + \frac{76}{183}(1017.95 - 1021.95)$

   $= 1021.95 - \frac{76}{183} \times 4 = 1021.95 - 1.66 = \$1020.29$

The accrued bond interest is

$I = \frac{76}{183} \times 50 = \$20.77$

The total purchase price on June 16, 1983, is

$P = 1020.29 + 20.77 = \$1041.06$

Note   We could get P by accumulating $P_0 = 1021.95$ at simple interest $i = 4\frac{1}{2}\%$ for time $f = \frac{76}{183}$.

$P = 1021.95\left[1 + (0.045)\left(\frac{76}{183}\right)\right] = \$1041.05$

The 1-cent difference is due to the rounding off errors.

The relationship between the flat price P, the market price Q and the accrued bond interest can be sketched in the Figure on page 152.

Note that the market price approaches the par value of the bond and finally equals it on the maturity date. The actual purchase price (the flat price) of the bond is equal to the market price only on interest dates. The market price (or quoted price) does not include the accrued bond interest.

If the actual purchase price were quoted, there would be a big price change before and after a bond interest date due to the accrued bond interest. This is why bond prices are usually quoted as market prices plus accrued bond interest.

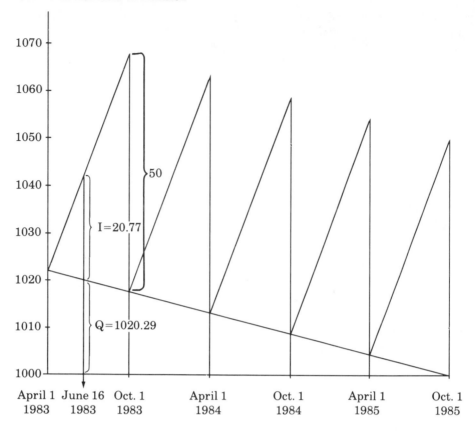

Exercise 7.6

Part A

Find the purchase price of the following bonds.

No.	Face Value	Redemption	Bond Interest Rate	Yield Rate	Redemption Date	Date of Purchase
1.	1 000	at par	$j_2 = 8\%$	$j_2 = 10\%$	Jan. 1, 2003	May 8, 1983
2.	500	at par	$j_2 = 12\%$	$j_2 = 11\%$	Jan. 1, 1998	Oct. 3, 1983
3.	2 000	at par	$j_2 = 14\%$	$j_2 = 15\%$	Nov. 1, 1994	July 20, 1983
4.	10 000	at par	$j_2 = 13\%$	$j_2 = 14\%$	Feb. 1, 2001	Oct. 27, 1983
5.	1 000	at 105	$j_2 = 16\%$	$j_2 = 14\%$	July 1, 1994	July 30, 1983
6.	2 000	at 110	$j_2 = 11\%$	$j_2 = 13\%$	Oct. 1, 1999	Apr. 17, 1984

7. A $1000 bond, redeemable at par on October 1, 1985 is paying bond interest at rate $j_2 = 9\%$. Find the purchase price on August 7, 1983 to yield $j_2 = 10\%$. Do a diagram similar to that found at the end of Section 7.6 for this bond.

Part B

1. Let: P_t be the value of a bond on a coupon date at time t to yield i.
P_{t+1} be the value of a bond on the following coupon date to yield i.

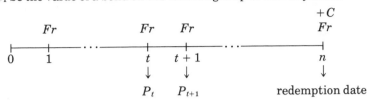

Show that $P_{t+1} = P_t(1 + i) - Fr$.

2. A \$1000 bond, redeemable at \$1100 on November 7, 1992 has coupons at $j_2 = 11\%$. Find the purchase price on April 18, 1983 if the desired yield is

a) $j_{12} = 15\%$;

b) $j_1 = 10\%$.

7.7 Buying Bonds on the Market

In Section 7.6 we developed a method of determining the price an investor should pay for a given bond to yield a specified interest rate. In most cases, bonds are purchased on the bond market (bond exchange) where they are sold to the highest bidder. Trading of bonds is done through agents acting on behalf of the buyer and seller. The seller indicates the minimum price he is willing to accept (ask) and the buyer the maximum price he is willing to pay (bid). The agents, who work for a commission, try to get the best possible price for their client. Many newspapers publish tables of bond information. The numbers in the column at the extreme left in the bond markets table shown, give the coupon rate or bond interest rate. The due date is the year the bond will mature. Bid and ask represent prices being offered and asked on the bond market assuming a unit of \$100. The yield rate listed is that which will be earned if the price paid is half-way between the bid and the ask and the bond is held to maturity.

Bond prices will vary over time as general interest rates available vary. If investment rates of return rise, bond values will fall. If investment rates of return fall, bond values will rise. (This is illustrated in questions 9 and 10 of the exercises.)

Since bonds are issued in different denominations, it is customary to give the **market quotation, q**, on the basis of a \$100 bond rounded off to the nearest eighth.

Example 1 A \$1000 bond, paying interest at $j_2 = 9\frac{1}{2}\%$ is redeemable at par on August 15, 2004. This bond was sold on September 1, 1983 at a market quotation of $103\frac{1}{8}$. What did the buyer pay?

Solution   The market price was $Q = 10 \times 103\frac{1}{8} = \$1031.25$.

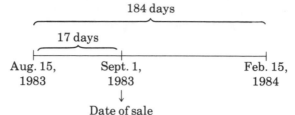

Date of sale

The accrued bond interest from August 15, 1983, to September 1, 1983 is

$$I = \tfrac{17}{184} \times 47.50 = \$4.39$$

and the total purchase price is

$$P = Q + I = 1031.25 + 4.39 = \$1035.64$$

Example 2   A \$500 bond, paying interest at $j_2 = 8\%$, is redeemable at par on February 1, 1994. What should the market quotation be on November 15, 1985 to yield the buyer 9% per annum compounded semi-annually?

Solution

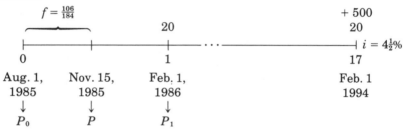

The purchase price on August 1, 1985, to yield $j_2 = 9\%$, would be

$P_0 = 500 + (20 - 22.50)a_{\overline{17}|.045} = 500 - 29.27 = \$470.73$

The purchase price on February 1, 1986 to yield $j_2 = 9\%$ would be

$P_1 = 500 + (20 - 22.50)a_{\overline{16}|.045} = 500 - 28.09 = \$471.91$

The market price on November 15, 1985 to yield $j_2 = 9\%$, would be

$Q = P_0 + f(P_1 - P_0) = 470.73 + \tfrac{106}{184}(471.91 - 470.73) = \$471.41$

Reducing Q to a \$100 bond we get the market quotation

$$q = \frac{471.41}{5} = 94.282$$

and rounding off to the nearest eighth

$$q = 94\tfrac{1}{4}$$

Note   An alternate method of computing Q from P, obtained by accumulating P_0 at simple interest i for time f, will give the same answer.

The purchase price on November 15, 1985 to yield $j_2 = 9\%$, would be

$$P = P_0(1 + if) = 470.73\left(1 + 0.045 \times \tfrac{106}{184}\right) = \$482.93$$

The accrued bond interest from August 1, 1980, to November 15, 1985 is

$$I = \tfrac{106}{184} \times 20 = \$11.52$$

The market price on November 15, 1985, would be

$$Q = P - I = 482.93 - 11.52 = \$471.41$$

Bond Markets

Corporate bonds, debentures

Supplied by Richardson Securities of Canada
Approximate market prices at
December 4, 1981

BONDS		DUE	BID	ASK	YIELD
9¾	*Abitibi Paper	90	71.38	72.38	16.10
10¾	AEC Power Ltd	96	72.75	73.75	15.51
9⅝	Do.	97	65.75	66.75	15.51
9¾	*Alta Gas Tk	90	71.13	72.13	16.08
8⅛	Do	92	59.50	60.50	16.10
11⅜	Do.	95	74.13	75.13	16.10
9⅝	Alta Oil Sands	97	65.88	66.88	15.48
9⅞	Algoma Cen Rly	97	63.00	64.00	16.51
10⅝	*Algoma Steel	94	71.00	72.00	15.75
11	Do	95	73.75	74.75	15.75
9⅜	Alum Co. of Can	91	69.75	70.75	15.74
10¾	*Do	94	72.75	73.75	15.74
10.45	Amoco Cda Pete	84	91.25	92.25	15.26
9¾	Asbestos Corp.	90	69.50	70.60	16.50
10⅝	Ashland Oil Cda	96	70.50	71.50	15.49
12¾	Atrium On Bay	05	90.38	91.38	15.29
9¾	Avco Fin Service	84	87.75	88.75	16.24
9½	Do	93	83.50	84.50	16.23
9	Bank of Montreal	84	90.00	94.00	14.35
9¼	Do.	84	88.00	92.00	14.56
8¼	Bank of NScotia	82	98.50	99.00	14.76
9	Do	84	88.13	89.13	15.23
9½	Do	97	65.38	66.38	15.39
9⅝	BBC-RI Services	83	90.75	91.25	16.03
10½	Bell Canada	85	87.13	88.13	15.25
8⅛	Do	94	60.25	61.25	15.39
10	Do	96	69.38	70.38	15.39
9⅞	*Do	99	66.88	67.88	15.39
9.40	Do	02	63.38	64.38	15.30
11	Do	04	72.38	73.38	15.39
9.85	Do	05	65.38	66.38	15.30
9⅜	BM-RT Ltd.	82	99.00	100.00	18.25
8¾	Do.	82	94.50	95.00	15.44
9⅜	BC Cen Credit	87	96.00	96.50	16.43
9¾	BC Forest	92	66.38	67.38	16.48
9½	BC Sugar Ref	87	88.00	89.00	12.47
11	B.C. Tele	96	71.38	72.38	16.21
9.70	*Do	99	62.50	63.50	16.20
10¼	Do	01	64.88	65.88	16.20
9⅞	Do	03	62.25	63.25	16.19
11	Brunswick Mng	96	68.75	69.75	16.75
9⅛	Calgary Power	94	65.38	66.38	15.50
10¾	Do	01	71.00	72.00	15.50
9¾	*Cdn Cement Laf	97	63.88	64.88	16.09
8⅞	Cda Accept Co	92	83.13	84.13	16.49
9⅜	Cdn-Dmn Leasing	82	95.63	96.13	16.53
10.10	Cdn Imperial Bank	84	89.50	90.50	15.25
9¾	Do	95	86.88	87.88	15.24
9½	Do	96	80.75	81.75	15.24
9¼	Do	98	76.88	77.88	15.12
10⅝	Cdn Industries	96	72.13	73.13	15.48
11⅜	Cdn Pacific Hotel	95	75.13	76.13	15.91
11¼	Cdn Pacific	95	76.38	77.38	15.41
5	Cdn Pacific Railway	83	89.63	90.62	15.05
8⅞	*Cdn Pac Railway	92	67.00	68.00	15.39
9⅜	*Cdn Pacific Sec	90	71.00	72.00	15.51
10¾	*Cdn Tire	95	71.13	72.13	16.00
8⅛	Cdn Utilities	92	64.38	65.38	15.39

Provincial

December 4, 1981

			Bid	Ask	Yield
8⅛	Alta	Jun 91	64.75	65.25	15.26
7⅞	Alberta	Oct 91	63.00	63.50	15.24
5½	Alta Mun Fin Co	Nov 86	67.75	68.25	15.01
7½	Alta Gov Tel	Dec 91	60.75	61.25	15.27
6	Alta Gov Tel	Apr 92	52.50	53.00	15.26
6½	BC Elec	Apr 90	59.50	60.00	15.24
5¾	BC Hydro	Apr 91	53.50	54.00	15.22
10	BC Hydro	Oct 00	92.25	92.75	14.78
9	Manitoba	Dec 81	100.00	100.50	9.00
8¾	Manitoba	Oct 93	65.38	65.88	15.11
10	Manitoba	Dec 99	68.63	69.13	15.11
8½	Man Hy	Sep 91	66.75	67.25	15.11
7⅞	Man Hy	Apr 92	62.75	63.25	15.10
7¼	Man Hy	Aug 93	57.50	58.00	15.10
10	Man Hy	Jun 94	71.63	72.13	15.11
7	Man Tele	Feb 93	56.88	57.38	15.09
8¾	Man Tele	Mar 99	61.38	61.88	15.09
7¾	New Bruns	Jul 88	67.50	68.00	15.89
7¾	New Bruns	Mar 96	56.50	57.00	15.34
9⅞	New Bruns	Jul 98	67.13	67.63	15.40
13¼	New Bruns Elec	Mar 85	96.38	96.87	14.65
13¾	New Bruns Elec	May 85	97.75	98.25	14.59
10⅜	New Bruns Elec	May 95	72.00	72.50	15.35
7⅞	New Bruns Elec	Nov 96	56.63	57.13	15.35
8½	New Bruns Elec	Nov 98	59.00	59.50	15.35
11	New Bruns Elec	Oct 99	73.38	73.88	15.41
10	New Bruns Elec	Mar 00	67.25	67.75	15.40
10¼	New Bruns Elec	Dec 03	67.75	68.25	15.41
13⅜	Nfld	May 86	94.88	95.38	14.99
7½	Nfld	Feb 88	69.38	69.88	15.31
10½	Nfld	Oct 96	71.25	71.75	15.49
10¾	Nfld	Jun 97	72.38	72.88	15.49
10	Nfld	Jan 99	67.25	67.75	15.50
10¼	Nfld & Lab Hy	Oct 01	67.88	68.38	15.49
10	Nfld & Lab Hy	Sep 02	66.00	66.50	15.51
10	Nfld & Lab Hy	Jun 03	65.88	66.38	15.51
5½	Nova Scotia	Mar 84	82.88	83.38	14.73
13¾	Nova Scotia	May 85	97.75	98.25	14.60
8⅝	Nova Scotia	Jan 86	81.50	52.00	14.79
7¼	Nova Scotia	Mar 91	60.25	60.75	15.47
7⅝	Nova Scotia	Dec 91	60.75	61.25	15.46
10	NS Power	Mar 01	66.50	67.00	15.49
9¾	NS Power	Oct 01	64.75	65.25	15.51
9¼	NS Power	Jul 02	61.50	62.00	15.50
9⅜	NS Power	Jan 03	62.13	62.63	15.50
11½	NS Power	Jul 05	74.88	75.38	15.51
5¾	Ontario	May 87	66.75	67.25	14.92
10¼	Ontario	Dec 87	81.88	82.38	14.92
7	Ontario	Feb 88	68.75	69.25	14.88
7¾	Ontario	Dec 97	59.63	60.13	14.20
9¾	Ontario	Mar 98	85.13	85.63	14.51
9	Ontario	Jul 98	92.13	92.63	14.76
8⅜	Ont Hy	Aug 83	90.62	91.13	14.80
13¼	Ont Hy	Mar 85	96.75	97.25	14.50
10¼	Ont Hy	Oct 85	87.63	88.13	14.50
13¼	Ont Hy	Oct 85	96.38	96.87	14.49
7¾	Ont Hy	May 94	59.25	59.75	15.11
9	Ont Hy	Jun 95	65.00	65.50	15.15

Source: The Financial Post

Exercise 7.7

Part A

Find the purchase price of the following $1000 bonds if bought at the given market quotation

No.	Redemption value	Bond interest rate	Market quotation	Redemption date	Date of purchase
1.	par	$j_2 = 10\%$	$98\frac{1}{2}$	Sept. 1, 2002	June 8, 1984
2.	par	$j_2 = 11\%$	$104\frac{1}{4}$	Feb. 1, 1998	Oct. 2, 1984
3.	$1050	$j_2 = 9\%$	$101\frac{3}{4}$	Oct. 1, 1999	Nov. 29, 1986
4.	$1100	$j_2 = 13\%$	$112\frac{1}{2}$	Apr. 1, 1998	Jan. 12, 1983

What would be the market quotation on the following $1000 bonds?

No.	Redemption value	Bond interest rate	Yield rate	Redemption date	Date of purchase
5.	par	$j_2 = 11\%$	$j_2 = 14\%$	Nov. 1, 2002	Feb. 8, 1984
6.	par	$j_2 = 12\%$	$j_2 = 10\%$	Mar. 1, 2005	Aug. 19, 1986
7.	$1050	$j_2 = 11\%$	$j_2 = 13\%$	June 1, 1998	Oct. 30, 1983
8.	$1100	$j_2 = 13\%$	$j_2 = 11\%$	Oct. 1, 1994	Nov. 2, 1986

Problems 9 and 10 which follow are designed to show how volatile and risky investing in bonds can be.

9. A $1000 bond paying coupons at $j_2 = 12\%$ is redeemable at par in 20 years. Find the price to yield an investor
   a) $j_2 = 14\%$;
   b) $j_2 = 12\%$;
   c) $j_2 = 10\%$.

10. a) A $1000 bond paying interest at $j_2 = 10\%$ is redeemable at par on September 1, 2003. Find the price on its issue date of September 1, 1983 to yield $j_2 = 12\%$.
    b) Find the book value of the bond on September 1, 1985 (just after the coupon is cashed).
    c) Find the sale price of this bond on September 1, 1985 if the buyer wants a yield of
       (i) 9% compounded semi-annually
       (ii) 15% compounded semi-annually.

Part B

1. A $5000 bond with semi-annual coupons at $j_2 = 12\%$ is redeemable at par on November 1, 2003.
   a) Find the price on November 1, 1983 to yield $j_4 = 16\%$.
   b) Find the book value of the bond on May 1, 1986 (just after the coupon is cashed).
   c) What should the market quotation of this bond be on August 17, 1986 if the buyer wants a yield of 11% per annum effective?

2. Refer to the Bond Market Quotations on page 155. Assume the Algoma Steel bond paying semi-annual coupons at $10\frac{3}{8}\%$ is due on December 4, 1994 and is purchased on December 4, 1981 to yield $j_2 = 15.75\%$. Find the price per $100 unit.

7.8 Finding the Yield Rate

One of the fundamental problems relating to bonds is to determine the investment rate i a bond will yield to the buyer when bought for a given price P. In practice, the market price is often given without stating the yield rate. The investor is interested in finding the true rate of return on his investment, i.e., the yield rate. Based on the yield rate he can decide whether the purchase of the particular bond is an attractive investment or not, and also find out which of several bonds available is the best investment.

There are different methods available for finding the yield rate. The method most frequently used in practice was interpolation in *bond tables*, which are tables of market prices of bonds for wide ranges of bond interest rates, yield rates and terms to maturity. This method has become obsolete with the advent of electronic calculators. In this section we will calculate the yield rate in two ways.

The Method of Averages (or Bond Salesman's Method)
This method is simple and usually leads to fairly accurate results. It calculates an approximate value of the yield rate i as the ratio of the average interest payment over the average amount invested.

Example 1   A \$500 bond, paying interest at $j_2 = 9\frac{1}{2}\%$, redeemable at par on August 15, 1998, is quoted at $109\frac{1}{2}$ on August 15, 1986. Find the approximate value of the yield rate j_2 to maturity.
Solution   The purchase price $P = 5 \times 109\frac{1}{2} = \$547.50$, since the bond is sold on a bond interest date. If the buyer holds the bond until maturity he will receive 24 bond interest payments of \$23.75 each, plus the redemption price 500, in total $24 \times 23.75 + 500 = \$1070$. He pays \$547.50 and receives \$1070. The net gain $1070 - 547.50 = \$522.50$ is realized over 24 interest periods, so that the average interest per period is

$$\frac{522.50}{24} = \$21.77$$

The average amount invested is the average of the purchase price (the original value) and the redemption value (the final value), i.e., $\frac{1}{2}(547.50 + 500) = \$523.75$. The approximate value of the yield rate is

$$i = \frac{21.77}{523.75} = 0.0416 = 4.16\% \quad \text{or} \quad j_2 = 8.32\%.$$

If n is the number of interest periods from the date of sale until the redemption date we can conclude that

The average interest payment $= \dfrac{n \times Fr + C - P}{n}$

The average amount invested $= \dfrac{P + C}{2}$

The approximate value of $i = \dfrac{\text{the average interest payment}}{\text{the average amount invested}}$

In most cases the answer is correct to the nearest tenth percent. If a more accurate answer is desired, the method of averages should be followed by the interpolation technique described below.

The Method of Interpolation

This method of determining the yield rate consists of finding two adjacent rates by trial and error such that the market price of the bond lies between the prices determined. The standard method of interpolation between the two adjacent rates is then used to determine i or j_2. Usually the method of averages is used to get rates to be used in the method of interpolation.

Example 2   Compute the yield rate j_2 in Example 1 by the method of interpolation.

Solution   By the method of averages we found that $i = 4.16\%$. Now we compute the market prices (which are equal to purchase prices) to yield $j_2 = 8\%$ and $j_2 = 9\%$.

$$Q \text{ (to yield } j_2 = 8\%) = 500 + (23.75 - 20)a_{\overline{24}.04} = \$557.18$$

and

$$Q \text{ (to yield } j_2 = 9\%) = 500 + (23.75 - 22.50)a_{\overline{24}.045} = \$518.12$$

Arranging the data in the interpolation table, we have

	Q	j₂
	557.18	8%
	547.50	j₂
	518.12	9%

$$\frac{d}{1\%} = \frac{9.68}{39.06}$$
$$d \doteq .25\%$$
$$\text{and } j_2 = 8.25\%$$

Note Q (to yield $j_2 = 8.25\%) = 500 + (23.75 - 20.63)a_{\overline{24}.04125} = \$546.97$

The two methods described in this section apply equally well to bonds purchased between interest dates. The computations are more tedious as is illustrated in the following example.

Example 3   A \$1000 bond paying interest at $j_2 = 11\%$ matures at par on June 1, 1994. On February 3, 1984 this bond is quoted at $95\frac{3}{8}$. What is the yield rate, j_2?

Solution   First we use the method of averages to get an estimate of the yield rate assuming that the bond was quoted on the nearest coupon date, in this case December 1, 1983 or 21 interest periods before maturity. The market price on February 3, 1984 is $Q = \$953.75$.

The average interest payment $= \dfrac{21 \times 55 + 1000 - 953.75}{21} = \$57.20$.

The average amount invested $= \dfrac{953.75 + 1000}{2} = \$976.88$.

The approximate value of $i = \dfrac{57.20}{976.88} = 0.0586$ or 5.86%.

The approximate value of $j_2 = 11.71\%$.

If we want a more accurate answer, we select 2 rates, $j_2 = 11\%$, and $j_2 = 12\%$, and compute the corresponding market prices on February 3, 1984 using the method outlined in Section 7.6.

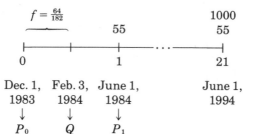

$$f = \tfrac{64}{182}$$

Dec. 1, 1983 → P_0; Feb. 3, 1984 → Q; June 1, 1984 → P_1; ... ; June 1, 1994.

Points: 0, 1, 21 with 55, 55 and 1000, 55.

At $j_2 = 11\%$: $\quad P_0 = P_1 = Q = \$1000$ without calculation.

At $j_2 = 12\%$: $\quad P_0 = 1000 + (55 - 60)a_{\overline{21}|.06} = 1000 - 58.82 = \$941.18$

$\qquad\qquad\qquad P_1 = 1000 + (55 - 60)a_{\overline{20}|.06} = 1000 - 57.35 = \$942.65$

$$Q = 941.18 + \tfrac{64}{182}(942.65 - 941.18) = \$941.70$$

Arranging the data in an interpolation table, we have

	Q on Feb. 3, 1984	j_2		
	1000.00	11%		
58.30 { 46.25 {	953.75	j_2	} d } 1%	
	941.70	12%		

$$\frac{d}{1\%} = \frac{46.25}{58.30}$$
$$d \doteq .79\%$$
and $j_2 = 11.79\%$.

Exercise 7.8
Part A
In problems 1 to 4, find the yield rate by the method of averages.

No.	Face Value	Redemption Value	Bond Interest	Years to Redemption	Purchase Price
1.	$2000	at par	$j_2 = 11\%$	12	$1940
2.	$5000	at par	$j_2 = 13\%$	10	$5640
3.	$1000	at 105	$j_2 = 12\%$	15	$1120
4.	$ 500	at 110	$j_2 = 11\%$	11	$450

5-8. Find the yield rate in problems 1 to 4 by the method of interpolation.

9. A $1000 bond paying bond interest at $j_2 = 6\%$ matures at par on August 1, 1991. If this bond was quoted at 70 on August 1, 1984 what was the yield rate, j_2
a) using the method of averages;
b) using the method of interpolation?

10. A $1000 bond redeemable at par at the end of 20 years and paying bond interest at $j_2 = 11\%$ is callable in 15 years at $1050. Find the yield rate, j_2, if the bond is quoted now at 110 assuming
a) it is called;
b) it is not called.

11. A $1000 bond redeemable at par in 20 years, pays bond interest at $j_2 = 10\%$. It is callable at $1050 at the end of 10 years. If it is quoted at 96, find the yield rate, j_2, assuming
a) it is called;
b) it is not called.

12. A $1000 bond paying interest at $j_2 = 10\%$ matures at par on June 1, 1999. On August 17, 1983 this bond is quoted at $98\frac{1}{2}$. What is the yield rate?

13. A $1000 bond paying interest at $j_2 = 11\%$ matures at par on October 1, 1995. On April 28, 1984 this bond is quoted at 102. What is the yield rate?

14. The XYZ Corporation has a $1000 bond that pays bond interest at $j_2 = 10\%$. The bond is redeemable at par on June 1, 1999. On June 1, 1983 an investor buys this bond on the open market at 97. On June 1, 1991 he sells this bond on the open market at 101. Find the yield rate j_2.

15. Mr. Adams buys a $1000 bond that pays bond interest at $j_2 = 11\%$ and is redeemable at par in 15 years. The price he pays will give him a yield of $j_2 = 12\%$ if held to maturity. After 5 years, Mr. Adams sells this bond to Mr. Brown who desires a yield of $j_2 = 10\%$ on his investment.
   a) What price did Mr. Adams pay?
   b) What price did Mr. Brown pay?
   c) What yield j_2 did Mr. Adams realize?

Part B

1. The XYZ Corporation issues a $1000 bond with semi-annual coupons at $j_2 = 11\%$ redeemable at par in 20 years or callable at par in 15 years. Mr. Smith buys the bond to guarantee a yield rate $j_{12} = 12\%$.
   a) Find the purchase price.
      After 15 years, the XYZ Corporation calls the bond in and pays Mr. Smith his $1000.
   b) Find his overall yield stated as a rate j_{12}.

2. In our "method of averages" formula we said

$$\text{Average amount invested} = \frac{P + C}{2}$$

A slightly more accurate formula uses:

$$\text{Average amount invested} = C + \frac{n + 1}{2n}(P - C)$$

Using this latter modification, try some of the above problems again and see if your approximations improve.

3. The XYZ Corporation has a bond due December 4, 1994 paying bond interest at $j_2 = 10\frac{3}{8}\%$. The price bid on December 4, 1981 is 68. What yield, j_2, does the investor desire? What comment would you make on the risk involved in investing in the XYZ bond versus the Algoma Steel Bond listed on page 155.

4. Mr. Smith buys a $1000 bond with semi-annual coupons at $j_2 = 12\%$. The bond is redeemable at par in 20 years. The price he pays will guarantee him a yield of $j_4 = 16\%$ if held to maturity. After 5 years, Mr. Smith sells this bond to Miss Jones who desires a yield of $j_1 = 11\%$ on her investment.
   a) What price did Mr. Smith pay?
   b) What price did Miss Jones pay?
   c) What yield, j_4, did Mr. Smith realize?

5. The ABC Corporation issues a $1000, 11% bond with coupons payable January 1 and July 1 redeemable at par on July 1, 1995.
   a) How much would an investor pay for this bond on September 1, 1985 to yield $j_2 = 13\%$?
   b) Given the purchase price from part a), if each coupon is deposited in a bank account paying interest at $j_4 = 10\%$, and the bond is held to maturity, what is the effective annual yield rate, j_1, on this investment?

6. A bond paying semi-annual coupons at $j_2 = 14\%$ matures at par in n years and sells for 110 to yield rate j_2. A bond paying semi-annual coupons at $j_2 = 14\frac{1}{2}\%$ matures at par in n years and sells for 112 on the same yield basis.
   a) Find the unknown yield rate, j_2.
   b) Determine n to the nearest half-year.

7. An issue of bonds, redeemable at par in n years, is to bear coupons at $j_2 = 9\%$. An investor offers to buy the entire issue at a premium of 15%. At the same time, he advises the issuer that if the coupon rate were raised from $j_2 = 9\%$ to $j_2 = 10\%$, he would offer to buy the entire issue at a premium of 25%. At what yield rate, j_2, are these two offers equivalent?

8. In March, 1980, interest rates in the bond markets were such that an investor could expect a yield of $j_2 = 17\%$. On March 1, 1980, an investor bought a bond with semi-annual coupons at 12% which was to mature in 20 years at par. By September 1, 1980 interest rates had fallen to $j_2 = 13\%$. This same investor sold his bond on September 1, 1980 on the bond market. Find the yield j_2 on this investment.

7.9 Other Types of Bonds

Canada Savings Bonds

Every fall since the end of World War II, the Canadian government has borrowed the savings of individual Canadians through the issuing of Canada Savings Bonds. These bonds are available in values ranging from $50 to $25 000 and are the favorite investment of the average citizen, in fact, they account for one quarter of the total value of all bonds—both corporate and government. Canada Savings Bonds have the yearly interest coupons attached to the bond and are redeemable on any banking day at any bank for their full face value, plus any interest accrued up to that time. In some years the coupons are arranged in such a way that if a certain number of coupons are not clipped, then bonus coupons also come into effect, i.e. these bonds will pay compound interest on them. The bonds are guaranteed by the federal government and are registered. They are nontransferable and there is a limit on the value that can be held by any person, partnership or corporation. Canada Savings Bonds are heavily advertised every year. Any Canadian resident can buy them without any formality at any branch of any chartered bank or trust company, as well as through a stockbroker or investment dealer. They can also be purchased through payroll deductions. Since the Canada Savings Bonds are redeemable at par on any banking day, purchase-price formula (24) or (25) does not apply to their valuation.

Serial Bonds

When companies borrow by means of an issue of bonds, they occasionally issue a series of bonds with staggered redemption dates instead of with a common redemption date. Such bonds are called **serial bonds**. Serial bonds can be thought of simply as several bonds covered under one bond indenture. If the redemption date of each individual bond is known, then the valuation of any one bond can be performed by methods already described. The value of the entire issue of the bonds is just the sum of the values of the individual bonds.

Example   The directors of a company authorized the issuance of $30 000 000 of serial bonds on September 1, 1984. Interest is to be paid annually on September 1 at nominal rate 9%. The indenture provides the following redemption provisions:

(i) $5 000 000 of the issue is to be redeemed on September 1, 1989.
(ii) $10 000 000 of the issue is to be redeemed on September 1, 1994.
(iii) $15 000 000 of the issue is to be redeemed on September 1, 1999.

a) Find the purchase price of the issue on September 1, 1984, which would yield $j_1 = 8\%$.

b) What would be the value of the bonds on September 1, 1991?

Solution a   We consider the serial issue to be composed of 3 issues, represented by the following diagrams

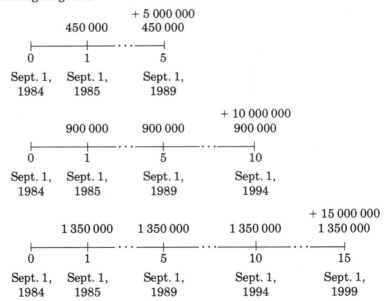

The purchase price of the entire serial issue P on September 1, 1984, is the sum of the purchase prices of the 3 individual issues $P^{(1)}$, $P^{(2)}$, $P^{(3)}$.

$$P^{(1)} = 5\,000\,000 + (450\,000 - 400\,000)a_{\overline{5}|.08} \quad = \quad 5\,199\,635.50$$
$$P^{(2)} = 10\,000\,000 + (900\,000 - 800\,000)a_{\overline{10}|.08} = 10\,671\,008.14$$
$$P^{(3)} = 15\,000\,000 + (1\,350\,000 - 1\,200\,000)a_{\overline{15}|.08} = 16\,283\,921.80$$

$$P = P^{(1)} + P^{(2)} + P^{(3)} \quad\quad\quad\quad\quad\quad\quad = 32\,154\,565.44$$

Solution b   The value of the entire serial issue P on September 1, 1991, is the sum of the values of the 2nd and 3rd individual issues $P^{(2)}$ and $P^{(3)}$. (First individual issue was already redeemed at that time.)

$$P^{(2)} = 10\,000\,000 + (900\,000 - 800\,000)a_{\overline{3}|.08} \quad = 10\,257\,709.70$$
$$P^{(3)} = 15\,000\,000 + (1\,350\,000 - 1\,200\,000)a_{\overline{8}|.08} = 15\,861\,995.84$$

$$P \quad = P^{(2)} + P^{(3)} \quad\quad\quad\quad\quad\quad\quad\quad = 26\,119\,705.54$$

Annuity Bonds

An **annuity bond**, with face value F, is a contract promising the payment of an annuity whose present value is F at the bond rate. When face value F and the bond rate are given, the periodic payment R of the bond is computed by the methods developed in the annuity chapters. At any date, the price of the annuity bond is obtained as the present value of the future payments of the bond at the investor's interest rate.

Problems of this nature have been already solved in this text and will be illustrated in the following example.

Example   An annuity bond promises to repay $20 000 principal with interest at $j_2 = 10\%$ by equal payments at the end of each half-year for 10 years. How much will an investor offer for this bond if he wants to realize $j_2 = 9\%$ on his investment?
Solution   First we find the semi-annual payment R of an ordinary simple annuity.

$$R = \frac{20\ 000}{a_{\overline{20}|.05}} = \$1604.85$$

The price P the investor should offer to pay in order to realize $j_2 = 9\%$ is equal to the present value of the future payments at $j_2 = 9\%$.

$$P = 1604.85\, a_{\overline{20}|.045} = \$20\ 875.79$$

Exercise 7.9

Part A

1. A $10 000 serial bond is to be redeemed in instalments of $2000 at the end of each of the 21st through 25th years from the date of issue. The bonds pay interest at $j_2 = 11\%$. What is the price to yield 14% per annum compounded semi-annually?

2. A $100 000 issue of serial bonds issued July 1, 1984 and paying interest at rate $j_2 = 13\%$ is to be redeemed in instalments of $25 000 each on the first day of July in 1989, 1991, 1993, and 1995. Find the price to yield 12% per annum compounded semi-annually.

3. An annuity bond offers to repay $10 000 principal and interest at $j_2 = 18\%$ by equal payments at the end of each half-year for 10 years. How much will an investor offer for this bond if he wants to realize

   a) $j_2 = 16\%$;
   b) $j_2 = 20\%$?

Part B

1. In question B1 of Exercise 7.3 we introduced Makeham's formula for a bond redeemable at par:

$$P = F(1 + i)^{-n} + \frac{r}{i}\left[F - F(1 + i)^{-n}\right]$$

For serial bonds with k individual issues we have

$$P^{(k)} = F_k(1 + i)^{-n_k} + \frac{r}{i}\left[F_k - F_k(1 + i)^{-n_k}\right]$$

$$\text{and } \sum_k P^{(k)} = \sum_k F_k(1 + i)^{-n_k} + \frac{r}{i}\left[\sum_k F_k - \sum_k F_k(1 + i)^{-n_k}\right]$$

where $\sum_{k} P^{(k)}$ ... purchase price of the entire serial issue.

$\sum_{k} F_k(1 + i)^{-n_k}$ ... total present value of all redemptions.

$\sum_{k} F_k$ ... total face value of k individual issues.

Try this formula on questions 1 and 2 of Part A.

2. To finance an expansion of production capacity, Minicorp Ltd. will issue, on March 15, 1983, $30 000 000 of serial bonds. Bond interest at 13% per annum is payable half yearly on March 15 and September 15, and the indenture provides for redemption as follows:

$10 000 000 of the issue to be redeemed March 15, 1988
$10 000 000 of the issue to be redeemed March 15, 1993
$10 000 000 of the issue to be redeemed March 15, 1998

Calculate the purchase price of the issue to the public, to yield 12% effective on those bonds redeemable in 5 years, and 14% effective on the remaining bonds.

3. An annuity bond promises to repay $50 000 principal with interest at $j_2 = 14\%$ by 20 equal payments at the end of each half-year for 10 years, first payment in 3 years. How much should an investor, who wants to yield 16% effective, pay for this bond

a) now;
b) in 2 years;
c) in 5 years.

7.10 Common and Preferred Stock

We have seen that a bond is a type of promissory note in that a person who buys a bond is lending money to a corporation or government agency, is paid interest at a defined rate, and is repaid his capital investment at a set point in time.

A stockholder, on the other hand is part owner of the company and does not have all the guarantees of the bondholder.

There are two basic types of stocks: preferred and common.

Preferred stock is a type of security which earns a fixed rate of interest called a dividend and in that sense it is similar to bonds. In general, preferred stock has no maturity date since it is an ownership security. Preferred stock has a claim on earnings before payment may be made on common stocks, but, in terms of degree of security, preferred stock ranks behind bonds and other debt instruments, since all payments on indebtedness must be made first.

Most preferred stock is cumulative which means that any dividends which the corporation is not able to pay are accumulated (without interest) and must be paid in the future before any dividends are paid to common stockholders.

Some preferred stock is convertible. Owners of this type of preferred stock have the option to convert their preferred stock to common stock under certain conditions.

Declines outnumbered advances 590 to 237 on the Toronto Stock Exchange this week. Issues unchanged totalled 224.

Volume for the week was 25,822,872 shares down from the previous week's 28,844,001. Volume for the year-to-date is 1,438,579,116. (Quotations in cents unless marked $ and occasionally when traded in both cents and dollars).

Distributed by The Canadian Press

Stock	This Week Sales	Week Ending Dec. 11 High	Low	Close	Ch'ge	1981 High	Low
A and B							
A.G.F.M	2617	$7	6¾	7	+ ⅛	7⅞	5¼
AZL Res	z80	$29⅜	29⅜	29⅜		38	32⅞
AMCA Int	16238	$23¾	22⅝	23		27¼	18½
Abti Prce	4039	$22	21¼	21¼	— ⅜	32¼	19⅛
Abitibi 7½p	761	$26⅛	26	26⅛	+ ⅛	39	26
Abitibi 10	1708	$37	36	36		50	36
Acklands	1125	$14	14	14		16	13½
Acklnd 2p	300	$13½	13½	13½		14½	12½
Adanac M	55288	100	95	96	—4	425	85
Advocate	18300	70	51	51	— 23	225	20
Aero E	37533	$7¼	6¼	6¾	— ½	7¼	5⅝
Agassiz	18300	74	63	65	—7	135	60
Agnico E	46237	$7¼	6⅞	7⅛	— ¼	10½	6⅞
Agra Ind A	910	$8	7¾	7¾		10⅝	6½
Ahed C	700	27	27	27	+1	115	26
Akaitcho	15200	70	55	60	— 15	260	55
Albany	33950	96	92	93	—2	330	80
Alt Energy	89261	$16¼	15¾	16		27¾	14
Alta Nat	3050	$24¼	24¼	24¼	+ ¼	31	19
Alcan	136665	$28	26¼	26¼	—1⅝	47½	23½
Algo Cent	897	$16	15½	16		24	15½
Algoma St	21302	$43¼	42¼	43	+ ⅝	49¼	37¼
Algoma St p	5100	$17⅝	17½	17½	— ⅛	23½	16⅞
Algon Merc	900	$11½	11½	11½	+ ¼	14	10¼
Alum 3rd p	4000	$20	19¾	20		24	19⅝
Amcan	1000	115	115	115	+ 40	445	75
Am Eagle	82625	345	320	330	—5	5¾	240
Am Leduc	53500	42	38	38	—3	120	38
Andres W A	2965	$13⅞	13½	13⅞	+ ⅜	17¼	10
Andres W B	225	$13½	13½	13½		16¾	11
Ang CT 4½	345	$15½	15½	15½	—1	22¾	14½
Ang CT 265	725	$18¾	18	18	—1	26	18
Ang CT 290	825	$20	19½	19½	—1½	28½	19⅝
Ang CT 315	2510	$22½	21	22	— ⅝	30	20½
Ang D Gld	25000	60	40	45	— 10	460	40
Ang U Dev	5360	115	100	100	— 11	279	100
Anthes	13300	240	215	220	—5	290	200
Arbor C	2500	335	330	335	+ 10	5¼	300
Argosy	19450	25½	22	23	—2½	159	22
Argus	6694	480	460	460	+ 10	13	375
Args 250 p	455	$17½	17½	17½	— ½	24	17½
Args 260 p	1645	$18	18	18		24	17⅛
Argus B pr	1030	$17¾	17½	17½	— ⅜	25	16¼
Argus C pr	10000	460	460	460		7¾	375
Asamera	72995	$16⅞	14½	16⅝	+2	21½	9
Asbestos	16435	$19¼	17⅛	17¼	—2½	45	17⅛
Asoc Porc	9993	365	330	340	— 40	13½	280
Astral	8025	$5¾	5½	5⅝	— ⅛	6	305
Atco I	12196	$9⅛	8¼	8⅝	— ⅝	11¼	6½
Atco II	2755	$8⅝	8¼	8⅜	— ¼	11⅛	6½
Atl C Cap	2200	100	100	100	— 20	180	85
Atlas Yk	62100	60	53	60	+3	210	50
Atlas w	35714	19	16	19	+1	25	9
Augmitto	38500	135	120	130	+ 15	7¾	105
Ato Hard A	3400	$10¾	10⅜	10¾	+ ⅜	13½	10
BC Sugar A	2786	$17½	16½	17¼	+ ¼	24½	16⅛
BC Sugar P	500	$10	10	10	— ¼	11¾	8
BP Can	174772	$36½	33¼	34	—1¼	59½	28½
Bachelor	8800	405	365	365	— 45	6⅞	315
Bakertalc	54800	40	30	40	—1	205	30
Banister C	20695	$6⅝	5⅛	5¾	+ ¾	15¾	400
Bank BC	3913	$46	45½	46	+ ⅜	50	38½
Bk BC 228	1200	$17¼	16¼	16¼	—1½	19½	15
Bank Mtl	146488	$24¾	23¾	23⅞	— ⅞	33½	22⅝
Claiborne A	680	100	80	80	— 20	210	80
Clarion	27702	460	410	430	— 30	9⅜	260
Coastal	z30	$7⅜	7⅜	7⅜		14	8½
Coastal A	5700	460	450	460	+ 35	9¾	375
Cockfield	10069	$6⅝	6	6⅝	+ ¼	6¾	350
Coho A	6587	$9¾	8¾	8¾	— ⅝	15½	5¾
Coin Lake	10200	38	36	36	—4	175	36
Color Y W	200	350	350	350	— 50	5½	350
Comaplex	31341	90	82	82	—3	365	82
Comiesa	900	70	70	70	—2	305	70
Cominco	92165	$55¾	53½	54	—1½	72	43¾
Cominco A	6850	$17	16½	16⅝	— ⅝	24	16½
Comrcl O G	94100	127	113	115	— 15	450	100
Computlog	24250	$6¼	5½	6	— ⅛	17½	5⅜
Computel	100	$7½	7½	7½	—1½	18	330
Comtech	3879	400	400	400		6	350
Coniagas	28200	260	247	250	.	5¼	140
Con Bath A	11305	$19½	18½	18⅞	— ¾	29⅞	16½
Con Bath B	z37	$19¼	19¼	19¼		28⅞	18¾
Con Bath p	545	$12¼	12	12		17	10⅜
Con Fardy	21861	221	215	215	— 10	395	210
Con Copper	43900	51	42	45	—3	175	25
C Durham	62550	205	182	185	— 15	5¾	120
C Louanna	8248	271	220	225	— 55	315	220
C Marben	21800	51	45	46	—5	214	45
Cons Pipe	1800	$7½	7¼	7½	+1	8¼	5¾
Cons Prof	69355	205	175	200	— 10	385	90
C Rambler	3100	460	450	450		5	410
C Rexspar	30050	33	25	25	—6	125	25
C Summit	2500	60	60	60	—5	80	35
Consoltex	1800	310	300	305	+5	7½	300
Con Distrb	13600	$7⅜	6⅛	6¼	—1¼	12	6⅛
Con Gas A	z45	$41	39¾	40		53	37
Con Gas B	z60	$41	39¾	39¾		53	37
Con Glass	100	$15½	15½	15½		20	14⅜
CTL Bank	64935	$9¼	8⅝	8⅝	— ⅝	13¼	6½
CTL Bk 5¾	200	$11	11	11	—1	16¼	11
Control F	1200	190	180	180	— 20	450	180
Conventrs	23600	$10⅛	9¼	9½	+ ⅜	15½	6½
Conwest A	7415	410	380	395	—5	9	350
Conwest B	16712	390	365	365	— 10	8½	320
Cooper C	2400	$5½	5¼	5¼	— ½	8¼	5¼
Cop Fields	10410	$11½	10¾	11	— ½	21¼	10¾
Corby vt	873	$26	24½	25¾	— ½	31	21
Corp Food	550	$49	49	49	+2	49	28⅝
C Falcon C	228655	$13¾	12¾	13¼	— ¼	19⅛	8¾
Coseka R	54155	$11¾	10⅝	11	— ¾	25½	10
Coseka 7 p	20900	$7¼	6⅝	6¾	— ¾	13	6
Costain Ltd	650	$9	8½	9	+ ½	15	8¼
Courvan	27200	39	29½	30	— 12	190	29½
Craigmt	27908	190	180	180	—5	6⅞	160
Crain R L	1950	$12½	12⅛	12⅛	— ¼	15¾	11¼
Crestbrk	570	$31	31	31	+1	40	26
Crwn Life	503	$82	82	82	+5	121	75
Crwn Trst	101	$17	17	17	+1	22¾	16
Crown 8¾	100	$13½	13½	13½	+1½	17⅛	11½
C Zeirba A	8959	$28½	27½	28¼	+ ¼	33⅞	24
Cullaton	41413	$13⅞	13	13⅛	— ⅜	16¾	8½
Cuvier M	5900	40	35	35	—3	149	35
Czar Res	680950	$5¼	450	5	+ 35	17½	425
Czar Wt	5965	70	65	70	+ 10	175	25
D to G							
DRG A	1300	$7	6½	6½	— ½	10¼	6
Dalco Pet	43450	165	141	141	— 19	6¾	141
Dalmys	10300	$10	9⅝	9⅝		13	9⅛
Dalmy C	13800	$9½	9	9	— ⅜	10½	8
Daon Dev	120776	$5⅜	475	490	— 22	13⅜	385
Daon A	200	480	475	475	— 10	7	410
Daon 8⅝ p	8200	$5⅛	460	470	— 42	8⅝	435
Daon 9½ p	5000	$5⅝	5	5	— ⅝	9¼	450
Dejour Mn	123100	51	43	45	—5	195	30
D Eldona	78100	98	85	85	— 15	355	80
Delhi Pac	78700	85	76	80	—9	245	32
Denison	33415	$35	33½	33⅞	— ½	58¾	26⅛
Dicknsn A	28093	275	245	245	— 29	14¼	240
Dicknsn B	54018	265	210	210	— 40	13½	200
Digtech	1950	485	475	480	—5	12½	450
Discovry	12096	164	150	161		5¼	120
Dist Tr A	300	285	280	285	+5	7½	280
Dofasco A	10525	$42	40	40½		49½	37½
Dofasco 4¾	175	$38½	38½	38½		48	34

An example of a weekly review of trading on the Toronto Stock Exchange.

Common stock is a type of ownership security, as is preferred stock, but it does not earn a set dividend rate as is the case with preferred shares. Common stock dividends are paid only after interest payments have been made on all bonds and other debt instruments and all dividends on preferred stock are paid. The board of directors of the corporation decide what common stock dividend will be paid, if any. While common stock has the highest risk factor of all securities mentioned, there is no ceiling on the possible profit to be made on a common stock. If the corporation is successful, common stocks benefit from both increasing dividends and a rising value in market price. All residual profits after dividends to the preferred stockholders belong to the common stockholders.

Stocks are traded (bought and sold) on the floor of a stock exchange. On page 165 is a sample of the weekly review of trading on the Toronto Stock Exchange as distributed by the Canadian Press. This would appear in many Saturday editions across the country.

For each stock listed it gives an abbreviation of the corporation's name, the volume of shares traded (in this case over the past week), the highest and lowest price paid for the stock (over the past week), and the price of the last trade (close). Finally it lists the change in value of the stock since the last publication and the high and low prices paid for the year to date. The letters "pr" after a stock mean this is a preferred share. The numerals after some of the stocks listed refer to dividends paid either as a percent or as an amount in cents per share. Quotations are in cents unless marked $.

7.11 Review Exercises

1. The Acme Corporation issues $10 000 000 of 20-year bonds on March 15, 1984, with semi-annual coupons at 13%. The contract requires that Acme will set up a sinking fund earning interest at $j_2 = 10\%$ to redeem the bonds at maturity, the first sinking fund deposit to be made September 15, 1984. Find
   a) the purchase price of the bond issue to yield $j_2 = 14\%$;
   b) the necessary sinking fund payment.

2. Refer to question 1. Rather than issuing 20 year bonds assume that Acme Corporation decided to issue serial bonds on March 15, 1984 with the following redemption schedule
   (1) $5 000 000 on March 15, 1994;
   (2) $3 000 000 on March 15, 1999;
   (3) $2 000 000 on March 15, 2004.
   Compute the purchase price of this serial bond issue to the public on March 15, 1984 to yield $j_2 = 14\%$.

3. The XYZ Corporation issues a $1000, 12% bond with coupons payable February 1 and August 1 and redeemable at par on August 1, 1999.
   a) How much should be paid for this bond on February 1, 1984 to yield $j_2 = 11\%$.
   b) If the purchase price was $950, and the bond is held to maturity, determine the overall yield, j_2.

4. A $1000 bond with semi-annual coupons at 10% payable January 1 and July 1 each year matures on July 1, 1989 for $1050.
   a) Find the price on January 1, 1984 to yield $j_2 = 10\frac{1}{2}\%$.
   b) Is the bond purchased at a premium or a discount?
   c) Calculate the entries in the bond schedule on July 1, 1984 and January 1, 1985.

5. The ABC Corporation $2000 bond, paying bond interest at $j_2 = 13\%$, matures at par on September 1, 1997.
   a) What did a buyer pay for this bond on July 20, 1984 if the market quotation for the bond was $85\frac{3}{4}$?
   b) Estimate, using linear interpolation, the yield rate for the buyer in part a).
   c) What should the market quotation for this bond be on July 20, 1984 if the desired yield is $j_2 = 18\%$?

6. The ABC Corporation issues a 20-year par value bond on February 1, 1985 with coupons at 13% payable February 1 and August 1. Mr. Brown buys a $1000 bond from this issue on February 1, 1985 to yield $j_2 = 14\%$. On August 1, 1989 Mr. Brown sells this bond to Mr. Black who wants a yield $j_2 = 12\%$.
   a) Find the original purchase price.
   b) Find the sale price on August 1, 1989.
   c) What yield, j_2, did Mr. Brown realize?
   d) Find the sale price if the transaction took place on September 1, 1989.

7. Jones invested $10 000 in the Ace Manufacturing Company four years ago. He was to be paid interest on the loan at $j_2 = 11\%$. The principal amount of $10 000 was to be returned after 10 years. Now, having just received the eighth interest payment in full, Jones has been informed that Ace has just been declared bankrupt. Jones has been offered, as a settlement, 25% of the present value of all monies due to him determined at $j_1 = 13\%$. How much can he expect to receive?

8. A $1000 bond has semi-annual coupons at $j_2 = 9\%$. The bond matures after 20 years at par but can be called after 15 years at $1050.
   a) Find the price to guarantee a yield of $j_2 = 11\%$.
   b) What maturity date was assumed in answering part a)?
   c) Determine the yield, j_2, realized if the bond is redeemed other than anticipated in part a). (Your answer must be larger than $j_2 = 11\%$.)

9. Write a computer program that determines the price of a bond given its coupon rate, duration to maturity, value at maturity, and desired yield. The program should be able to determine the price even if the bond is not purchased on a coupon date.

8

Depreciation and Related Topics

8.1 Definitions

Assets, purchased at a particular point in time, provide services over a finite future accounting period. Since the economic life of most assets (land being a notable exception) is limited, it is necessary to allocate the cost of the asset to the accounting periods in which it generates revenues. This periodic charge to income to measure the consumption of the asset is called **depreciation** and is an expense item.

An account, which usually bears the name **accumulated depreciation**, or allowance for depreciation expense, is used to record the total depreciation expense from period to period. The difference between the original cost of an asset and its accumulated depreciation is its **book value**. The book value is not necessarily the same as its market value or resale value. Rather, the book value represents the remaining amount of the original cost of the asset which has yet to be charged as an expense.

At the end of its useful lifetime, the book value of an asset will equal its estimated **scrap** or **salvage value**. Both the economic lifetime of the asset and its salvage value are estimates made by persons familiar with the particular asset. The **depreciation base** of an asset is its original cost less its estimated scrap value and represents the total amount which should be recorded as depreciation over the useful lifetime of the asset.

There are many accounting methods for handling depreciation as an operating expense. We shall consider only a few: the straight-line method, the constant percentage method, (also called the declining balance method), the sum-of-digits method, the physical service method, and the sinking-fund method.

In this chapter we will use the following notation:

C ...   the original cost of the asset.

S ...   the estimated scrap, salvage or residual value of the asset at the end of its useful lifetime (this could be negative).

n ...   the estimated useful lifetime of the asset in years.

W ...   the depreciation base of the asset. By definition $W = C - S$.

R_k ...   the yearly depreciation expense or simply yearly depreciation for the kth year.

B_k ...   the book value of the asset at the end of k years, $k \leqslant n$. Note that $B_0 = C$ and $B_n = S$.

D_k ...   the accumulated depreciation expense or simply accumulated depreciation at the end of k years, $k \leqslant n$. Note that $D_0 = 0$ and $D_n = W$.

For every method of depreciation we shall set up a **depreciation sched- ule** showing the status of the depreciation expense at various stages during the lifetime of the asset, namely the yearly depreciation expense, the book value at the end of each year, and the accumulated depreciation to date. For all methods, the accumulated depreciation, D_k, plus the book value of the asset, B_k, must equal the original cost of the asset C. That is, $D_k + B_k = C$.

8.2 The Straight-Line Method

The simplest and by far the most popular method for depreciating an asset is the straight-line method. This method assumes that the asset contributes it services equally to each year's operation so that the total depreciation base is evenly allocated over the lifetime of the asset and the yearly depreciation expense R is a constant given by

$$R_k = \frac{W}{n} = \frac{C-S}{n} \tag{30}$$

The accumulated depreciation D_k at the end of k years is then given by

$$D_k = k \cdot R_k$$

If we think of k as changing continuously, and not merely taking integral values, then the graph of D_k as a function of k is a straight line (see Section 8.7). This accounts for the name given to this method.

The book value B_k of the asset at the end of k years is:

$$B_k = C - k \cdot R_k$$

Example Equipment costing $5000 is estimated to have a useful lifetime of 5 years and scrap value of $500. Prepare a depreciation schedule using the straight-line method.

Solution   The depreciation base of the asset is $5000 - $500 = $4500 and the yearly depreciation is

$$R_k = \frac{4500}{5} = \$900$$

The accumulated depreciation increases by $900 each year and the book value of the asset decreases by $900 each year. This is shown in the following schedule:

End of Year	Yearly Depreciation	Accumulated Depreciation	Book Value
0	0	0	5000
1	900	900	4100
2	900	1800	3200
3	900	2700	2300
4	900	3600	1400
5	900	4500	500

While the straight-line method is the most popular, other depreciation methods which charge a greater proportion of the depreciation base to the early years or conversely charge more of the expense to the later years are used because they may match more suitably the perceived service consumption of the asset.

Exercise 8.2
Part A
1. Equipment costing $60 000 is estimated to have a useful lifetime of 5 years and a scrap value of $8000. Prepare a depreciation schedule using the straight-line method.
2. A machine costing $26 000 is installed. Its expected useful lifetime is 6 years. At the end of that time it will have no scrap value, in fact, it is estimated that it will cost the company $1000 to remove the old machine (i.e., $S = -\$1000$). Prepare a depreciation schedule using the straight-line method.
3. A machine costing $50 000 has an estimated useful lifetime of 20 years and a scrap value of $2000 at that time. Find the accumulated depreciation and the book value of this asset at the end of 8 years using the straight-line method.
4. A machine costing $20 000 has an estimated lifetime of 15 years and zero scrap value at that time. At the end of 6 years, the machine becomes obsolete because of the development of a better machine. What is the accumulated depreciation and the book value of the asset at that time using the straight-line method.

Part B
1. Under the straight-line method the book value at the end of k years is
$$B_k = C - kR_k$$

Because of the straight-line nature of this depreciation method it is also possible to find the book value at the end of year k by linear interpolation between C, the original cost of the asset and S, the salvage value of the asset at the end of n years. Thus,

$$B_k = \left(1 - \frac{k}{n}\right)C + \frac{k}{n}S$$

Prove this formula is equivalent to:

$$B_k = C - kR_k$$

and try this formula on questions 3 and 4 of Part A.

8.3 The Constant-Percentage Method

The constant-percentage method is used for income tax purposes in Canada for almost all capital-cost allowance calculations. The regulations in Canada state that all items in a certain class may be pooled together and depreciated at a fixed percentage of the total capital cost (book value) in that particular pool during that year. The percentage to be used is defined by the act and varies from class to class.

In general, under the constant-percentage method each year's depreciation is a fixed percentage of the preceding book value. When this method is used, it is customary to assign a value to the **rate of depreciation**, d, rather than to estimate the useful lifetime n, and scrap value S. The yearly depreciation for the k-th year R_k is different for each year and is given by

$$R_k = B_{k-1}d \qquad\qquad (31)$$

At the end of the 1st year:
the depreciation is $\qquad\qquad\qquad\qquad\qquad Cd$
the book value is $\qquad\qquad\qquad\qquad\quad C - Cd = C(1-d)$

At the end of the 2nd year:
the depreciation is $\qquad\qquad\qquad\qquad\quad C(1-d)d$
the book value is $\qquad\qquad\qquad\quad C(1-d) - C(1-d)d =$
$\qquad\qquad\qquad\qquad\qquad\quad C(1-d)(1-d) = C(1-d)^2$

At the end of the 3rd year:
the depreciation is $\qquad\qquad\qquad\qquad\quad C(1-d)^2 d$
the book value is $\qquad\qquad\qquad\quad C(1-d)^2 - C(1-d)^2 d =$
$\qquad\qquad\qquad\qquad\quad C(1-d)^2(1-d) = C(1-d)^3$

Continuing in this manner for k years the book value B_k at the end of k years is given by

$$B_k = C(1-d)^k \qquad\qquad (32)$$

The accumulated depreciation D_k at the end of k years may then be calculated by $D_k = C - B_k$ or

$$D_k = C - C(1-d)^k$$

Example 1   A car costing $6500 depreciates 30% of its value each year. Make out a depreciation schedule for the first 3 years; find the book value at the end of 5 years and the depreciation expense for the 6th year.

Solution   A depreciation schedule is set up below.

End of Year	Yearly Depreciation	Accumulated Depreciation	Book Value
0	0	0	6500.00
1	1950.00	1950.00	4550.00
2	1365.00	3315.00	3185.00
3	955.50	4270.50	2229.50

We calculate the book value B_5 by equation (32)

$$B_5 = 6500(1-.3)^5 = 6500(.7)^5 = 6500(.16807) = \$1092.46$$

The depreciation expense for the 6th year is obtained using equation (31)
$$R_6 = dB_5 = .3(1092.46) = \$327.74$$

If we estimate the useful lifetime n and the scrap value S of the asset, it is necessary first to compute the rate of depreciation d.

The constant percentage method can be used only if S is positive.

Example 2   Find the rate of depreciation and construct the depreciation schedule for the equipment in the example given in Section 8.2 if the constant percentage method is used.

Solution   We have $C = 5000$, $S = 500$, $n = 5$. Noting that $S = B_5$, i.e., the scrap value is the book value at the end of 5 years, we substitute into equation (34) to obtain

$$B_5 = C(1-d)^5$$
$$500 = 5000(1-d)^5$$
$$(1-d)^5 = .1$$
$$(1-d) = (.1)^{1/5}$$
$$(1-d) = .630\ 957\ 34$$
$$d = .369\ 042\ 66$$

The schedule can now be set up using the rate of depreciation $d = .369\ 042\ 66$.

End of Year	Yearly Depreciation	Accumulated Depreciation	Book Value
0	0	0	5000.00
1	1845.21	1845.21	3154.79
2	1164.25	3009.46	1990.54
3	734.59	3744.05	1255.95
4	463.50	4207.55	792.45
5	292.45	4500.00	500.00

Exercise 8.3
Part A

1. Equipment costing $60 000 is estimated to have a useful lifetime of 5 years and a scrap value of $8000. Prepare a depreciation schedule using the constant percentage method. (Note, you must find d). Compare to question 1 of Exercise 8.2.

2. A machine costing $45 000 depreciates 20% of its value each year. Make out a depreciation schedule for the first 5 years.

3. A machine costing $50 000 has an estimated useful lifetime of 20 years and a scrap value of $2000 at that time. Find the accumulated depreciation and the book value of this asset at the end of 8 years using the constant percentage method. (Note, you must find d). Compare to question 3 of Exercise 8.2.

4. Equipment costing $18 000 depreciates 10% of its value each year. Make out a depreciation schedule for the first 3 years. Find the book value at the end of 5 years and the depreciation expense for the 6th year.

5. A machine that costs $40 000 will depreciate to $3000 in 12 years. Find its book value at the end of 7 years and the depreciation expense for the eighth year using the constant percentage method.

6. Equipment worth \$30 000 depreciates 10% of its value each year. How long in years will it take before the equipment is worth less than \$15 000?
7. A machine costing \$28 000 depreciates to \$4000 over 15 years. How long will it take for the machine to depreciate to less than $\frac{1}{2}$ of its original value?

Part B

1. Use mathematical induction to prove formula (32)

$$B_k = C(1-d)^k$$

2. Show that

$$d = 1 - \left(\frac{S}{C}\right)^{\frac{1}{n}}$$

where n is the estimated lifetime of the asset.

8.4 The Sum-of-Digits Method

This is one of the accelerated depreciation methods which accounts for larger depreciation expenses during the early years of the useful lifetime of the asset. The yearly depreciation is a specified fraction of the depreciation base $C-S$. The denominator of the fraction is the sum of digits from 1 to n. Let us denote this sum by s and using the formula for the sum of an arithmetic progression (see Appendix 2) we obtain

$$s = 1 + 2 + 3 + \ldots + n = \frac{n(n+1)}{2}$$

The yearly depreciation expenses are determined as follows:

1st year depreciation	$R_1 = \dfrac{n}{s}(C-S)$
2nd year depreciation	$R_2 = \dfrac{n-1}{s}(C-S)$
3rd year depreciation	$R_3 = \dfrac{n-2}{s}(C-S)$

• •

$(n-1)$st year depreciation	$R_{n-1} = \dfrac{2}{s}(C-S)$
nth year depreciation	$R_n = \dfrac{1}{s}(C-S)$

Thus the depreciation expense for the k-th year is given by

$$R_k = \frac{n-k+1}{s}(C-S) \tag{33}$$

It is easy to see that the sum of all yearly depreciation expenses equals the depreciation base $C-S$:

$$R_1 + R_2 + R_3 + \ldots + R_n = \frac{n+(n-1)+(n-2)+\ldots+2+1}{s}(C-S) = C-S$$

Example   Construct the depreciation schedule for the equipment in the example in Section 8.2 if the sum-of-digits method is used.

Solution   We have $C = 5000$, $S = 500$, $n = 5$ and $C - S = 4500$. We calculate the sum of digits

$$s = 1 + 2 + 3 + 4 + 5 = \frac{5(5+1)}{2} = 15$$

The yearly depreciation expenses are calculated below

$$R_1 = \frac{5}{15}(4500) = 1500$$

$$R_2 = \frac{4}{15}(4500) = 1200$$

$$R_3 = \frac{3}{15}(4500) = 900$$

$$R_4 = \frac{2}{15}(4500) = 600$$

$$R_5 = \frac{1}{15}(4500) = 300$$

A depreciation schedule is now set up below:

End of Year	Yearly Depreciation	Accumulated Depreciation	Book Value
0	0	0	5000
1	1500	1500	3500
2	1200	2700	2300
3	900	3600	1400
4	600	4200	800
5	300	4500	500

Exercise 8.4

Part A

1. Equipment costing $60 000 is estimated to have a useful lifetime of 5 years and a scrap value of $8000. Prepare a depreciation schedule using the sum-of-digits method. Compare your answer to question 1 of Exercise 8.2 and 8.3.

2. A machine costing $26 000 is installed. Its expected useful lifetime is 6 years. At the end of that time it will have no scrap value, in fact, it is estimated that it will cost the company $1000 to remove the old machine (i.e. $S = -\$1000$). Prepare a depreciation schedule using the sum-of-digits method. Compare your answer to question 2 of Exercise 8.2.

3. A machine costing $50 000 has an estimated useful lifetime of 20 years and a scrap value of $2000 at that time. Find the accumulated depreciation and the book value of this asset at the end of 8 years using the sum-of-digits method. Compare your answer to question 3 of Exercise 8.2 and 8.3.

4. A machine costing $20 000 has an estimated lifetime of 15 years and zero scrap value at that time. At the end of 6 years, the machine becomes obsolete because of the development of a better machine. What is the accumulated depreciation and the book value of the asset at that time using the sum-of-digits method? Compare your answer to question 4 of Exercise 8.2.

Part B

1. Given s_n is the sum-of-digits to n, prove:

$$B_k = S + \frac{s_{n-k}}{s_n}(C-S)$$

8.5 The Physical-Service Method and Depletion

If assets are purchased to supply a service, the cost of using any asset should be spread in relation to the amount of service received in each period. The asset's useful lifetime is expressed in terms of service units and the depreciation expense is then expressed in dollars per service unit. The depreciation charge per period will then fluctuate with the amount of activity of the asset. The service units can be expressed in many ways. Examples include: hours, units of production, mileage etc.

Example 1 A machine costing $5000 is estimated to have a useful lifetime of 5 years and a scrap value of $500. It is expected to run for 20 000 hours. Determine the depreciation rate per hour of useful service and prepare a depreciation schedule assuming the actual hours worked are as follows.

Year	Production Hours
1	5000
2	4400
3	4000
4	3400
5	3200

Solution The depreciation base of the asset is $5000 - $500 = $4500.

The depreciation rate is $\frac{4500}{20\ 000} = 22\frac{1}{2}$¢ per hour.

The full depreciation schedule is as follows:

End of Year	Production Hours	Yearly Depreciation	Accumulated Depreciation	Book Value
0	0	0	0	5000
1	5000	1125	1125	3875
2	4400	990	2115	2885
3	4000	900	3015	1985
4	3400	765	3780	1220
5	3200	720	4500	500

Depletion

Certain kinds of assets, such as mines, gravel pits, oil wells, timber tracts, and sources of natural gas diminish in value because the natural resources they originally held become used up. This gradual loss in value due to the using up of an asset is called **depletion**. While any of the preceding methods of calculating depreciation expense could also be used in calculating depletion expenses, the normal method of calculation used is similar to the physical service method as the following example will illustrate.

Example 2   A mine has an original acquisition cost of $1 000 000. It is estimated to hold 50 000 grams of recoverable silver. After the mineral worth is exhausted, the land will be sold for $80 000. If, in the first year 10 000 grams are recovered and, in the second year 15 000 grams are recovered, determine the depletion deduction in years one and two.

Solution   The depletion base of the asset is 1 000 000 − 80 000 = $920 000.

The depletion rate is $\dfrac{920\ 000}{50\ 000}$ = $18.40 per gram.

The depletion deduction in year one: $18.40 × 10 000 = $184 000.
The depletion deduction in year two: $18.40 × 15 000 = $276 000.

Exercise 8.5

1. A transport truck costs $80 000 and has an estimated useful lifetime of 100 000 miles at which time it can be sold for $15 000. If the truck actually logs the following miles, do a depreciation schedule.

Year	Miles Driven
1	25 000
2	21 000
3	38 000
4	16 000

2. A machine costing $50 000 will last 5 years when it will be worth $5000. In that time, it is expected to produce 90 000 units of production. If its production follows the following pattern, do a depreciation schedule.

Year	Units Produced
1	23 000
2	16 000
3	21 000
4	17 000
5	13 000

3. An airplane costing $10 000 000 is purchased and will be used for three years by a company at which time it is estimated that it can be sold for $6 000 000. The accountant sets up a depreciation schedule based on miles flown and estimates that the plane will fly 450 000 miles in the next three years. Given the following, do a depreciation schedule.

Year	Miles Flown
1	130 000
2	210 000
3	110 000

4. A mine is purchased for $300 000 and has an expected reserve of 400 000 units of ore. After mining is complete, the land will be worth $20 000. If 100 000 units of ore are extracted in the first year, find the depletion deduction in year one.

5. Petro Canada purchases some land containing oil wells for $20 000 000. The total reserves of crude oil are estimated at 4 000 000 barrels. After the oil is gone, the land can be sold for $140 000. If Petro Canada removes 400 000 barrels in year one and 560 000 barrels in year two, determine the respective depletion deductions.

8.6 The Sinking-Fund Method

The sinking-fund method of depreciation uses a compound interest methodology to calculate the yearly depreciation expense. While it is not physically required, it is easier to understand this method if one assumes that a sinking-fund is set up to accumulate to an amount equal to the depreciation base $(C - S)$ of the asset at the end of its lifetime. If the sinking-fund is assumed to accumulate at rate i per year, then the equal annual sinking-fund deposit is calculated using the methods outlined in section 6.5 and equals $\dfrac{C - S}{s_{\overline{n}|i}}$.

The yearly depreciation expense for the k-th year, R_k, is equal to the sinking-fund deposit plus the interest earned by the sinking-fund during the k-th year. Thus the depreciation expense is different each year and increases over time.

The depreciation schedule in this case is the same as an ordinary sinking-fund schedule except for the added column giving the book value of the asset.

The accumulated depreciation, D_k, at the end of k years is equal to the accumulated value of the sinking fund:

$$D_k = \left(\frac{C - S}{s_{\overline{n}|i}} \right) \cdot s_{\overline{k}|i} \tag{34}$$

Example 1 Equipment costing \$5000 is estimated to have a useful lifetime of 5 years and scrap value of \$500. Prepare a depreciation schedule using the sinking-fund method with $j_1 = 9\%$. (This is the same example we have used throughout this chapter.)

Solution We have $C = 5000$, $S = 500$, $n = 5$, and $i = 9\%$ and we calculate the required annual sinking-fund deposit:

$$\frac{C - S}{s_{\overline{n}|i}} = \frac{5000 - 500}{s_{\overline{5}|.09}} = \$751.92.$$

A depreciation schedule can now be set up:

End of Year	Sinking-Fund Deposit	Interest on Fund	Yearly Depreciation	Accumulated Depreciation	Book Value
0	0	0	0	0	5000.00
1	751.92	0	751.92	751.92	4248.08
2	751.92	67.67	819.59	1571.51	3428.49
3	751.92	141.44	893.36	2464.87	2535.13
4	751.92	221.84	973.76	3438.63	1561.37
5	751.92	309.48	1064.40	4500.03	499.97*

*The 3¢ error is due to round-off.

We can check the accumulated depreciation, D_3, at the end of 3 years by calculating the accumulated value of the sinking-fund.

$$D_3 = 751.92 \, s_{\overline{3}|.09} = \$2464.87.$$

Exercise 8.6

Part A

1. Equipment costing $60 000 is estimated to have a useful lifetime of 5 years and a scrap value of $8000. Prepare a depreciation schedule using the sinking-fund method and $j_1 = 16\%$. Compare your answer to question #1 Exercise 8.2, 8.3, 8.4.
2. A machine costing $26 000 is installed. Its expected useful lifetime is 6 years. At the end of that time it will have no scrap value, in fact, it is estimated that it will cost the company $1000 to remove the old machine (i.e., $S = -\$1000$). Prepare a depreciation schedule using the sinking-fund method and $j_1 = 9\%$. Compare your answer to question #2 Exercise 8.2, 8.4.
3. A machine costing $50 000 has an estimated useful lifetime of 20 years and a scrap value of $2000 at that time. Find the accumulated depreciation and the book value of this asset at the end of 8 years using the sinking-fund method and $j_1 = 8\%$. Compare your answer to question #3 Exercise 8.2, 8.3, 8.4.
4. A machine costing $20 000 has an estimated lifetime of 15 years and zero scrap value at that time. At the end of 6 years, the machine becomes obsolete because of the development of a better machine. What is the accumulated depreciation and the book value of the asset at that time using the sinking-fund method and $j_1 = 12\%$. Compare your answer to #4 Exercise 8.2, 8.4.
5. Redo question #1 using $j_4 = 16\%$.
6. Redo question #4 using $j_{12} = 12\%$.
7. Equipment costing $30 000 is estimated to have a useful lifetime of 20 years and scrap value of $4000. The depreciation schedule is prepared using the sinking fund method with $j_1 = 10\%$. Find
   a) the amount in the sinking fund at the end of 10 years,
   b) the book value of the asset at the end of 10 years and
   c) the depreciation expense for the eleventh year.

Part B

1. Show that, under the sinking-fund method
   a) the book value, B_k, of the asset at the end of k years is

$$B_k = C - \left(\frac{C-S}{s_{\overline{n}|i}}\right) s_{\overline{k}|i}$$

   b) the depreciation expense R_k in year k is

$$R_k = \left(\frac{C-S}{s_{\overline{n}|i}}\right)(1+i)^{k-1}$$

2. Show that if $i = 0$, the sinking-fund method is equivalent to the straight-line method.

8.7 Comparison of Methods

The Tables and Graphs below are for Example 1, of Section 8.2, as it was calculated under several depreciation methods.

Straight-Line Method

Year	Yearly Depreciation	Accumulated Depreciation	Book Value
0	0	0	5000
1	900	900	4100
2	900	1800	3200
3	900	2700	2300
4	900	3600	1400
5	900	4500	500

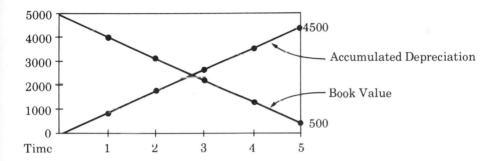

Constant-Percentage Method

Year	Yearly Depreciation	Accumulated Depreciation	Book Value
0	0	0	5000.00
1	1845.21	1845.21	3154.79
2	1164.25	3009.46	1990.54
3	734.59	3774.05	1255.95
4	463.50	4207.55	792.45
5	292.45	4500.00	500.00

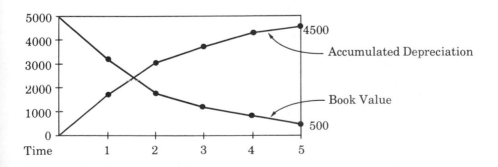

Sum-of-Digits Method

Year	Yearly Depreciation	Accumulated Depreciation	Book Value
0	0	0	5000
1	1500	1500	3500
2	1200	2700	2300
3	900	3600	1400
4	600	4200	800
5	300	4500	500

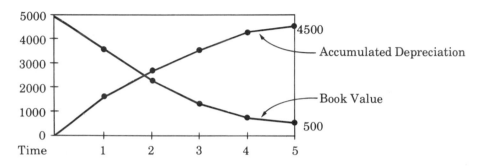

Sinking-Fund Method

Year	Yearly Depreciation	Accumulated Depreciation	Book Value
0	0	0	5000.00
1	751.92	751.92	4248.08
2	819.59	1571.51	3428.49
3	893.36	2464.87	2535.13
4	973.76	3438.63	1561.37
5	1064.40	4500.03	499.97

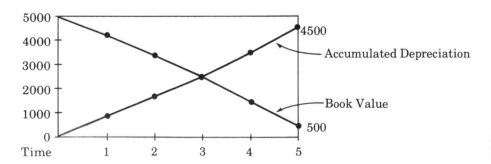

As pointed out earlier, the straight-line method is used mainly because of its simplicity. As a method of allocating the cost of an asset, however, its merits are more limited. This level allocation of the cost of the asset assumes that the services of the asset are consumed uniformly over its estimated lifetime. Further, it assumes that there is no decrease in the efficiency or quality of the service received as the asset ages. These two assumptions often may not be true.

The constant-percentage method and the sum-of-digits method can both be referred to as accelerated depreciation methods since they allow for larger depreciation allowances in the early years and smaller ones later on. If maintenance costs of an asset increase with time, this may result in a better matching of revenues with expenses throughout the life of the asset.

The constant-percentage method is popular since it is the prescribed method for most assets when it comes time to determine taxable income. For companies wishing to keep only one set of records, it may be easier to use the constant-percentage method throughout.

The sinking-fund method leads to a smaller depreciation allowance in the early years and a larger depreciation allowance in the later years. This pattern, however, may not be practicably applicable in all situations.

The physical-service method is set up to match the revenue and the expenses of the asset as closely as possible. That it is not possible to draw a general graph for the method, should be clear after completing the exercises of Section 8.5.

8.8 Capitalized Cost and Capital Budgeting

In Section 4.4 of Chapter 4 we saw that the discounted value of a perpetuity could be considered as the value of an investment that yields interest payments equal to the payments of that perpetuity.

The process of obtaining the discounted value of a perpetuity may be called capitalization of the perpetuity. The notion of capitalization may be extended to include physical assets that must be continually replaced. We define the **capitalized cost** of an asset as the original value of the asset plus the discounted value of an infinite number of replacements plus periodic maintenance costs.

If K denotes the capitalized cost, C the original cost, S the salvage value of an asset that is to be replaced every n years, M the annual cost of maintenance (operating expenses and expenses for repairs), and i the rate of interest per year, then

$$K = C + \frac{C-S}{is_{\overline{n}|i}} + \frac{M}{i} \tag{35}$$

The capitalized cost K can be regarded as the sum of money that, if invested now at rate i per year, would be sufficient to maintain the identical asset in operation indefinitely.

The concept of capitalized cost is useful in capital budgeting, when the objective is the selection of the lowest cost alternative to provide a specific level of benefits to the owner. In making comparisons between two physical assets that are employed for the same purpose but that vary with respect to original costs, salvage values, expected useful lifetimes, and maintenance costs, we may compare the capitalized costs of the assets.

Example 1   A farmer can purchase a steel barn with an estimated lifetime of 20 years. It will cost $200 000 and will require $1000 a year to maintain. Alternatively, he can purchase a wooden barn with an estimated lifetime of 14 years. It will cost $160 000 and require $2000 a year to maintain. If the farmer requires a return of $j_1 = 15\%$ on his investment, what should he do?

Solution   Capitalized cost, K_1, of the steel barn is:

$$K_1 = 200\ 000 + \frac{200\ 000}{(.15)s_{\overline{20}.15}} + \frac{1000}{.15}$$
$$= 200\ 000 + 13\ 015.29 + 6666.67 = \$219\ 681.96$$

Capitalized cost K_2 of the wooden barn is:

$$K_2 = 160\ 000 + \frac{160\ 000}{(.15)\ s_{\overline{14}.15}} + \frac{2000}{.15}$$
$$= 160\ 000 + 26\ 334.39 + 13\ 333.33 = \$199\ 667.72$$

The farmer should purchase the wooden barn.

Different assets may produce items at a different rate per unit of time. In that case it is necessary to divide the capitalized cost by the number of items produced per unit of time. If U_1 and U_2 are the numbers of items produced per unit of time by machine 1 and machine 2 with capitalized cost K_1 and K_2, respectively, then the two machines are economically equivalent if

$$\frac{K_1}{U_1} = \frac{K_2}{U_2}$$

Example 2   A machine costing $4000 has an estimated useful lifetime of 10 years, and estimated salvage value of $500. It produces 1600 items per year and has an annual maintenance cost of $800. How much can be spent on increasing its productivity to 2000 units per year if its lifetime, salvage value, and maintenance costs remain the same? The owners want a rate of return of $j_1 = 18\%$ on their investment.

Solution   Let X be the maximum amount to be spent on increasing the productivity of the machine.

The capitalized cost K_1 of the original machine is

$$K_1 = 4000 + \frac{3500}{(.18)s_{\overline{10}.18}} + \frac{800}{.18} = 4000 + 826.67 + 4444.44 = \$9271.11$$

The capitalized cost K_2 after remodelling is

$$K_2 = (4000 + X) + \frac{3500 + X}{(.18)s_{\overline{10}.18}} + \frac{800}{.18} = 9271.11 + X + \frac{X}{.18s_{\overline{10}.18}}$$
$$= 9271.11 + 1.236\ 192\ 5\ X$$

The machine after remodelling will be economically equivalent to the original one if

$$\frac{K_1}{1600} = \frac{K_2}{2000}$$
$$K_2 = \frac{2000}{1600}\ K_1$$
$$9271.11 + 1.236\ 192\ 5\ X = \frac{2000}{1600}\ 9271.11$$
$$1.236\ 192\ 5\ X = 2317.78$$
$$X = \$1874.93$$

Exercise 8.8

Part A

1. A certain machine costs $8000 and has an expected lifetime of 10 years and scrap value of $1000. The annual maintenance cost is $1500. Find the capitalized cost of the machine if $j_1 = 12\%$.

2. A company can build a steel warehouse with an estimated lifetime of 25 years at a cost of $250 000 plus annual maintenance of $1500 a year. Alternatively, they can build a cement block warehouse with an estimated lifetime of 20 years at a cost of $180 000 plus annual maintenance of $1200 a year. If money is worth $j_1 = 14\%$, what should they do?

3. A company uses batteries costing $45 with a useful lifetime of 2 years. Another model costing $60 has a useful lifetime of 3 years. If money is worth $j_1 = 11\%$ which should be purchased?

4. Widget-producing machines can be purchased from Manufacturer A or Manufacturer Z. Machine A costs $18 000 and will last 15 years and will have salvage value of $2400 at that time. The cost of maintenance is $1500 a year. Machine Z costs $30 000, will last 20 years and will have salvage value of $2000 at that time. The annual maintenance cost is $1200. If money is worth $j_1 = 15\%$, which machine should be purchased?

5. Ontario Hydro uses poles costing $20 each. These poles last 15 years. How much per pole would Ontario Hydro be justified in spending on a preservative to lengthen the life of the pole to 20 years? Assume that the annual maintenance costs are equal, and that money is worth $j_1 = 8\%$.

6. A town is putting a new roof on its arena. One type of roof costs $60 000 and has an expected lifetime of 20 years with no salvage value. Another type costs $70 000 but will last 30 years with no salvage value. Maintenance costs are equal. If money is worth $j_1 = 17\%$, how much can be saved each year by purchasing the most economical roof?

7. A new car can be purchased for $6000. If it is kept for 4 years its trade-in value will be $1200. What should the trade-in value be at the end of 3 years so that trading would be economically equivalent to keeping it 4 years if money is worth $j_1 = 18\%$?

8. Machine 1 sells for $100 000, has an annual maintenance expense of $2000 and an estimated lifetime of 25 years with a salvage value of $5000. Machine 2 has an annual maintenance expense of $4000 and an estimated lifetime of 20 years with no salvage value. Machine 2 produces output twice as fast as Machine 1. If money is worth $j_1 = 16\%$, find the price of Machine 2 so that it would be economically equivalent to Machine 1.

9. A machine costing $40 000 has a scrap value of $5000 after 10 years. It produces 2000 units of output per year. The annual maintenance cost is $1500. How much can be spent on increasing its productivity to 3000 units per year if its period of service, scrap value, and maintenance cost remain unchanged. Assume money is worth $j_1 = 17\%$.

Part B

1. A company is thinking of buying a machine that will replace five skilled workmen. These workmen are paid $1200 each at the end of each month. The machine costs $800 a month to maintain, will last 20 years and will have no

scrap value at that time. If money is worth $j_1 = 8\%$, what is the largest amount (in thousands of dollars) that can be spent for the machine and still be profitable?

2. Show that the capitalized cost K of an asset with zero salvage value is

$$K = \frac{1}{i}\left[\frac{C}{a_{\overline{n}|i}} + M\right]$$

3. An asset that costs C dollars when new has a service life of n years. At the rate of interest i per year, show that the maximum amount to be spent to extend the life of this asset by an additional m years, given $S = 0$, is:

$$\frac{C\, a_{\overline{m}|i}}{s_{\overline{n}|i}} \text{ dollars}$$

4. A machine that costs $8000 when new has a salvage value of $1000 after 5 years of service. How much could be spent on increasing its output by 40% and extending its service life by 20%? Assume that the salvage value remains the same and that money is worth $j_1 = 15\%$.

8.9 Review Exercises

1. An asset with an initial value of $10 000 has a salvage value of $1000 after 10 years. Find the difference between the depreciation expense entered in the books in the seventh year under the sinking-fund method using $j_1 = 9\%$ and under the constant-percentage method.

2. a) An asset is being depreciated over an expected lifetime of 10 years at which time it will have no salvage value ($S = 0$). If the depreciation expense in the third year is $2000, find the depreciation expense in the eighth year
    i) by the straight-line method
    ii) by the sum-of-digits method
    iii) by the sinking-fund method where $j_1 = 10\%$.
   b) Find the original value of the asset, C, in each of the above three cases.

3. A $9000 car will have a scrap value of $1000 six years from now. Prepare a complete depreciation schedule using
   a) the straight-line method
   b) the constant-percentage method
   c) the physical use method given the following mileages.

Year	Miles Driven
1	12 500
2	14 700
3	11 800
4	16 200
5	13 800
6	11 000

4. A gravel pit is purchased for $150 000 and has expected usable gravel equal to 30 000 truck loads. After excavation is completed the land will be worth $25 000. Given the following shipments, produce a depletion schedule for the gravel pit.

Year	Truck Loads of Gravel
1	8000
2	9100
3	7300
4	5600

5. A machine sells for $100 000 and is expected to have a salvage value of $10 000 after 5 years. The maintenance expense of the machine is estimated to be $2000 per year payable at the end of each year.
   a) Construct a depreciation schedule using the sinking-fund method and $j_1 = 10\%$.
   b) Determine the capitalized cost of the asset.

6. A company is considering buying a certain machine. One machine costs $6000, will last 15 years and have a scrap value of $800 at that time. The cost of maintenance is $500 a year. The second machine costs $10 000, will last 25 years and will have scrap value of $1000 at that time. The cost of maintenance is $800 a year. If money is worth $j_1 = 11\%$ which machine should be purchased?

7. A machine costing $20 000 has, after 10 years of service, a scrap value of $2500. It produces 1000 units of output a year. The annual maintenance cost is $750. How much can be spent to double its output if its scrap value, lifetime, and maintenance costs remain the same. Assume $j_1 = 13\%$.

9

Contingent Payments

9.1 Introduction

In Question B3 of Exercise 7.8 we set up a comparison of a bond issued from an imaginary XYZ corporation and a bond issued by Algoma Steel. The implication of the exercise was that two bonds that were identical with respect to face value, coupons, and maturity date could still trade at different prices.

In real life, that is often the case. For example, if Massey-Ferguson and Ontario Hydro were to issue identical bonds today, the prices paid for these bonds would differ significantly. That is because, at the time the book was written, Massey-Ferguson was working very hard to prevent itself from slipping into bankruptcy. Ontario Hydro, on the other hand, was financially strong and was backed by the tax-collecting power of the Ontario government.

In fact, there is a rating system provided for corporations issuing bonds. Some companies are rated "Triple A" or AAA. This means they are financially sound and that there is little risk that the company issuing the bonds will default on any of the payments. Thus, the investor can determine the purchase price as outlined in chapter seven.

Ratings of Double A, Single A, or B imply lower levels of security or higher levels of risk, so that an investor may want to discount the purchase price even further to account for the fact that he may not receive all of the money he has been promised by the bond issuer. It is worth pointing out here that, in the case of bankruptcy, debts in the form of bonds are paid off first, followed by preferred stocks and, finally, common stocks. Thus, bonds are the least risky of the investment vehicles.

9.2 Probability

Benjamin Franklin once noted jokingly that "nothing is certain except death and taxes." To all other events, it is possible to assign a probability value.

We are now used to the weatherman telling us that there is a "20% chance of rain" for example. What does this and similar phrases mean?

Some probabilities are easily determined. For example, we know that the probability of tossing a head with a balanced coin is $\frac{1}{2}$ or 50%. Similarly, the probability of rolling a "2" with a fair die is 1/6. These probabilities can be determined before the event occurs and allow the following definition:

If an event can happen in h ways, and fail to happen in f ways, all of which are equally likely, the probability p of the occurrence of the event is:

$$p = \frac{h}{h + f}$$

and the probability the event will fail to occur is:

$$q = \frac{f}{h + f}$$

We can see that:

$$p + q = \frac{h}{h + f} + \frac{f}{h + f} = \frac{h + f}{h + f} = 1$$

That is, any event either occurs or fails to occur. Furthermore when $f = 0$, $p = 1$ and when $h = 0$, $q = 1$. That is, if an event is certain to occur, the probability of its occurrence is unity. Finally, if an event occurs with probability p, the probability that the event will not occur is $q = 1 - p$.

Events are said to be **mutually exclusive** if the occurrence of one event precludes the occurrence of any other events. For example, in flipping a coin, the two possible outcomes are heads and tails. Since the occurrence of a head precludes any possibility of a tail (and vice-versa) these events are said to be mutually exclusive.

Given n mutually exclusive events $E_1, E_2, \ldots, E_n$, the probability of occurrence of any one of the n events (i.e., E_1 or $E_2 \ldots$ or $\ldots E_n$) is the sum of the respective probabilities of the individual events. That is:

$$P(E_1 \text{ or } E_2 \text{ or } E_3 \ldots \text{ or } E_n) = P(E_1) + P(E_2) + \ldots + P(E_n) \qquad (36)$$

Events are said to be **independent** if the occurrence of one event has no effect on the occurrence of any other event. Successive flips of a fair coin are an example of independent events. The occurrence of a head or tail on any one toss has no effect on the occurrence of a head or tail on any other toss. Life insurance companies assume that policyholders' deaths are independent events. That is, it is assumed that the time when one policyholder dies will not affect the time when another policyholder dies. In some situations (e.g. a husband and wife) this assumption may not be completely valid, but it is made nevertheless.

The probability of the occurrence of all of a set of independent events E_1, $E_2, \ldots , E_n$, is the product of the respective probabilities of the individual events.

That is:

$$P(E_1 \text{ and } E_2 \text{ and} \ldots \text{ and } E_n) = P(E_1) \cdot P(E_2) \cdot \ldots \cdot P(E_n) \qquad (37)$$

For more difficult problems where the answer cannot be determined intuitively, a useful device is a **probability tree**. This device will be illustrated in example 2 that follows.

Example 1 Find the probability in drawing one card from a standard deck of 52 cards, that I get *either* an ace *or* a king.
Solution There are four aces and four kings in a standard deck. Thus, there are eight cards that qualify here, and 44 that don't so the solution is:

$$p = \frac{h}{h + f} = \frac{8}{8 + 44} = \frac{8}{52} = \frac{2}{13}$$

Equivalently, we can see that the probability of drawing an ace is $\frac{1}{13}$ and of drawing a king is $\frac{1}{13}$ so from formula (36)

$$P(\text{ace or king}) = P(\text{ace}) + P(\text{king}) = \frac{1}{13} + \frac{1}{13} = \frac{2}{13}$$

Example 2 Find the probability in drawing two cards from a standard deck of 52 cards, that I get an ace *and* a king.
Solution It is helpful here to draw what is referred to as a probability tree.

Stage I

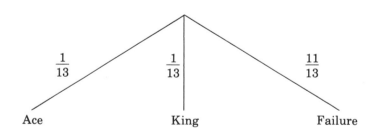

Stage II

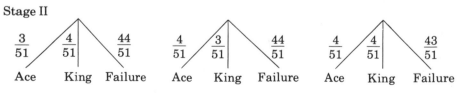

We can draw an ace first followed by a king with probability

$$P(E_1) = \frac{1}{13} \times \frac{4}{51} = \frac{4}{663}$$

OR we can draw a king first followed by an ace with probability

$$P(E_2) = \frac{1}{13} \times \frac{4}{51} = \frac{4}{663}$$

The total probability is $P(E_1 \text{ or } E_2) = P(E_1) + P(E_2) = \frac{4}{663} + \frac{4}{663} = \frac{8}{663}$

Note   In our tree diagram, we first compute the probability of each path in the event by multiplying together the probabilities of each branch in the path. Then we add the probabilities of each path in the event together to get the total probability of the event. Example 1 fits these general rules given that it was a one stage event.

Example 3   A bag contains five white, three black and four red balls. Determine the following probabilities

   a) Drawing a red ball;
   b) Drawing a white or a black ball;
   c) Drawing two white balls (no replacement);
   d) Drawing a black ball twice (with replacement);
   e) Drawing a white ball followed by a red ball (no replacement);
   f) Drawing a red ball followed by a black ball (with replacement).

Solution

   a) Probability $= \frac{4}{12} = \frac{1}{3}$

     Since there are 4 red balls and 12 balls in total.

   b) Probability of white $= \frac{5}{12}$

     Probability of black $= \frac{3}{12}$

     Then from formula (42), probability of white or black $= \frac{5}{12} + \frac{3}{12} = \frac{8}{12} = \frac{2}{3}$

   c) Probability of 1st white ball $= \frac{5}{12}$

     Probability of 2nd white ball $= \frac{4}{11}$

     Probability of two white balls with no replacement $= \frac{5}{12} \times \frac{4}{11} = \frac{5}{33}$

   d) Probability of 1st black ball $= \frac{3}{12} = \frac{1}{4}$

     Probability of 2nd black ball $= \frac{1}{4}$ (replacement)

     Probability of drawing black twice $= \frac{1}{4} \times \frac{1}{4} = \frac{1}{16}$

   e) Probability of white 1st $= \frac{5}{12}$

     Probability of red 2nd $= \frac{4}{11}$

     Then, probability $= \frac{5}{12} \times \frac{4}{11} = \frac{5}{33}$

   f) Using same reasoning as above,

     probability $= \frac{4}{12} \times \frac{3}{12} = \frac{1}{12}$

    Not all events allow for *a priori* ("before the fact") calculation of probability. For example, if a community has 1000 birth events per year how many of these will be multiple births (twins, triplets).

Similarly, we could ask "What is the probability of rolling a '2' with a loaded or unfair die?"

The only method of solution here is to observe a large number of occurrences and to develop empirically, and after the fact, an estimate of the true underlying probability.

For example, we could roll our unfair die 100 times. If we count sixteen 2's, then an approximation to the true underlying probability of rolling a '2' is .16. If we roll the same die 10 000 times and observe 1715 '2's, then we would refine our previous estimate and say that the "probability" of rolling a 2 is .1715.

Most real life situations, including all insurance situations, require this type of estimated probability. It is important to note that this value for the probability is determined from past experience and its use for prediction of future events involves the assumption that the future can be predicted by events in the past.

Also, if we say that the probability of an event occurring is 2/3, this does not mean that in 60 trials, there will be exactly 40 occurrences. Rather it means that as the number of trials is increased, the ratio of occurrences will approach 2/3. This is known as the Law of Large Numbers. Formally it states that: as the number of trials n increases, the probability, that the average proportion of successes deviates from the true underlying number p, tends toward zero.

In real life, however, we are usually forced to use the "best estimate," based on a relatively small number of observations, to predict future events.

Example 4   According to statistics gathered in the Province of Ontario, in 1982 there were 200 000 births of which 2087 were multiple births (i.e., twins, triplets etc.). If there were 24 000 births in Alberta in 1982, estimate the number of multiple births.

Solution   We are forced to use Ontario data to predict an event in Alberta.
Based on the Ontario data, the probability of having a multiple birth is:
$$\frac{2087}{200\ 000} = 0.010\ 435$$
Therefore, our best estimate for the number of multiple births in Alberta is:
$$24\ 000(0.010\ 435) = 250$$

Example 5   Based on the data of a large life insurance company, we are told that the probability of surviving ten years is 0.8, 0.7, and 0.6 for persons aged 40, 50, and 60 respectively. Determine the following probabilities:
a) The probability of dying in the next 10 years for each group.
b) The probability that a 40 year-old lives to age 70.
c) The probability that a 40 year-old dies between ages 60 and 70.

Solution   In answering these questions, we are forced to assume that these probabilities will remain constant and that the mortality rates derived from past events can be used to predict future probabilities of death.

The following tree diagram will assist us.

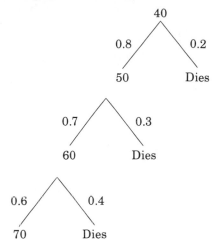

a) For each age group, the event of dying is just the complement of the event of living. Therefore
   Prob (age 40 dies in next 10 years) = 1 − 0.8 = 0.2
   Prob (age 50 dies in next 10 years) = 1 − 0.7 = 0.3
   Prob (age 60 dies in next 10 years) = 1 − 0.6 = 0.4

b) To survive to age 70 requires survival through each of the age groups. Therefore, using the tree diagram
   Prob (40 survives to 70) = 0.8 × 0.7 × 0.6 = 0.336

c) For someone aged 40 to die between 60 and 70 requires that he lives to age 60 and then dies in the next 10 years. Therefore, using the tree diagram
   Prob (40 dies between 60 and 70) = 0.8 × 0.7 × 0.4 = 0.224

Exercise 9.2
Part A

1. A jar contains 4 white marbles, 2 blue marbles, and 1 red marble. Find the following probabilities: (for multiple drawings, assume no replacement).

   a) You draw out one marble and it is blue;
   b) You draw a blue or red marble;
   c) You draw out two marbles which are white;
   d) You draw two marbles; the first is red and the second is blue;
   e) You draw two marbles; the first is white and the second one is blue;
   f) You draw out two marbles of the same colour.

2. Given a normal deck of 52 cards, determine the following probabilities

   a) Drawing the ace of spades;
   b) Drawing an ace or a king;
   c) Drawing the ace of spades in two draws with no replacement;
   d) Drawing the ace of spades in two draws given replacement of the first draw;
   e) Drawing the ace of spades on the second draw with no replacement;
   f) Drawing a 2, then a 3, then a 4 if there is no replacement.

3. Given a fair die, determine the following probabilities
   a) Rolling a 2;
   b) Rolling an even number;
   c) Rolling a prime number;
   d) In two rolls, rolling numbers whose sum equals 9;
   e) In two rolls, rolling numbers whose sum exceeds 5.

4. Given two fair dice, determine the following probabilities
   a) Rolling a total equal to 3;
   b) Rolling a total equal to 9;
   c) Rolling a total which exceeds 5;
   d) Rolling an even number, in total;
   e) Rolling a prime number, in total;
   f) In two rolls, getting an overall total equal to 23.

5. Given a fair coin, determine the following probabilities
   a) The probability of 2 heads in three tosses;
   b) The probability of all heads in four tosses;
   c) The probability of 2 heads and then a tail;
   d) The probability of a tail and then two heads.

6. Given that the probability of having a male baby is equal to the probability of having a female baby, determine the following probabilities
   a) The probability of having 2 boys in a family of three children;
   b) The probability of all boys in a family of four children;
   c) The probability of 2 boys and then a girl;
   d) The probability of a girl and then two boys.

7. A businessman must change planes three times in a long trip. If the probability of making any one connection successful is 4/5, what is the probability
   a) That he completes his trip successfully;
   b) He does not complete his trip successfully.
   (Assume the changes are independent events).

8. The probability of team A winning a game is 3/5. (i.e., they presently have a .600 record). They are just starting a three game series. What is the probability
   a) That they win the first two, but lose the third game?
   b) That they win two of three?
   c) That they win at least one game?
   (Assume the games are independent events).

9. The probabilities of A, B, C, and D surviving a certain period are 3/4, 4/5, 5/8, and 9/10 respectively. What is the probability that
   a) All four die in the period?
   b) All four survive the period?
   c) At least one survives the period?
   d) At least one dies in the period?
   (Assume the deaths are independent events).

10. We have the following data.

Age	Probability of Surviving 10 Years
50	0.75
60	0.60
70	0.50

Determine the following probabilities

a) Someone aged 50 lives to age 80.

b) Someone aged 50 dies between ages 70 and 80.

11. The probability of a 40 year old surviving to age 80 is 1/4. The probability of a 40 year old dying between age 65 and 80 is 1/10. Find the probability of a 40 year old surviving to age 65.

Part B

1. What is the probability that a 3-card hand, drawn at random, and without replacement from an ordinary deck, consists entirely of black cards?

2. An unbiased die is thrown twice. Given that the first throw resulted in an even number, what is the probability that the sum obtained is 8?

3. A bowl contains three red chips numbered 1, 2, 3 and three blue chips numbered 1, 2, 3. What is the probability that two chips drawn at random without replacement match *either* as to colour *or* as to number?

9.3 Mathematical Expectation

A term that most students are familiar with is "average." If you take six courses, your average mark is found by taking your total mark and dividing by six. If there are 34 students in your class, the class average can be found by totalling all marks and dividing by 34.

We can look at the latter problem in another manner. Let's say the mark distribution was as follows:

Mark	# of Students
40	4
50	6
60	8
70	10
80	4
90	2

Thus the teacher could find the class average using the following formula:

$$40\left(\frac{4}{34}\right) + 50\left(\frac{6}{34}\right) + 60\left(\frac{8}{34}\right) + 70\left(\frac{10}{34}\right) + 80\left(\frac{4}{34}\right) + 90\left(\frac{2}{34}\right) = 62.94$$

It should not trouble us that the class average was a mark that was not achieved by anyone and, in fact, could not have been achieved by anyone.

In statistics, the class average would be called the mean of the distribution of marks. This can also be called the expected value or mathematical expectation. Formally, we say that:

If X represents possible numerical outcomes of an experiment which can take the values x_1, x_2,... with corresponding probabilities $f(x_1)$, $f(x_2)$,... the **mathematical expectation** or **expected value** or **mean value** of X is defined by

$$E(X) = x_1 f(x_1) + x_2 f(x_2) + x_3 f(x_3) + ...$$

Example 1 If, in a dice game, one wins a number of dollars equal to the number showing on the die's upward face, what is the mathematical expectation of any participant?

Solution You can win $1, $2, $3 ... up to $6 each with probability 1/6 (assuming a fair die). Therefore

$$E(X) = 1(1/6) + 2(1/6) + \ldots + 6(1/6) = 21/6 = \$3.50$$

Again, it should not trouble us that the expected value is an amount that cannot be won on any throw during the game.

Example 2 Two players participate in the game described in example 1. Player A wins ($1, $2, or $3) if the face showing is 1, 2, or 3; and player B wins ($4, $5, or $6) if the face showing is 4, 5, or 6. How much should each player place in the pot (i.e., wager) if the game is to be fair?

Solution If each player in this game wagers exactly his expectation with respect to winnings, then the game will be fair. That is, in the long run, in this game, the players should expect to neither win nor lose. Thus, we find each player's expectation of winnings.

$$E(A) = \$1(1/6) + \$2(1/6) + \$3(1/6) = \$1$$
$$E(B) = \$4(1/6) + \$5(1/6) + \$6(1/6) = \$2.50$$

Therefore, if A wagers $1, and B wagers $2.50 this game will be fair.

Example 3 In the Wintario Lottery, sponsored by the Province of Ontario, 5 million $1 tickets are sold each week. The cash prizes awarded are listed below. Also 250 000 people can win "Win Fall" Prizes which entitled them to 5 tickets in the next draw. These 1 250 000 free tickets will have the same mathematical expectation as the ticket you purchase. Find the expected value of a $1 Wintario ticket.

Prize	No. Awarded	Probability
$100 000	5	$\dfrac{1}{1\,000\,000}$
$25 000	20	$\dfrac{1}{250\,000}$
$5 000	45	$\dfrac{9}{1\,000\,000}$
$1 000	100	$\dfrac{1}{50\,000}$
$100	1 950	$\dfrac{39}{100\,000}$
$10	24 500	$\dfrac{49}{10\,000}$

Solution Let X be the value of a Wintario ticket.

$$E(X) = \$100\,000\left(\frac{1}{1\,000\,000}\right) + \$25\,000\left(\frac{1}{250\,000}\right) + \$5\,000\left(\frac{9}{1\,000\,000}\right)$$
$$+ \$1000\left(\frac{1}{50\,000}\right) + \$100\left(\frac{39}{100\,000}\right) + \$10\left(\frac{49}{10\,000}\right) + E(X)\left(\frac{1\,250\,000}{5\,000\,000}\right)$$

Solving for $E(X)$ we obtain $E(X) \doteq 47$¢.

That means that a $1 Wintario ticket has an expected value of 47¢.

In general, lotteries in Canada have an expected return of 42¢ to 49¢ on the dollar. This compares to an expected return of 87¢ on the dollar at the horse races and a 93¢ to 95¢ expected return on the dollar at Las Vegas.

Example 4 Mr. A pays $1 to enter a betting game. If Mr. A can get three heads in a row by flipping a fair coin, he wins $5. Otherwise, he loses his $1. What is his expectation?

Solution Probability of winning = 1/8

          Probability of losing = 7/8

Therefore, expectation = $5(1/8) − $1(7/8) = −25¢

Exercise 9.3
Part A

1. Allan is willing to bet $1 that he can flip a coin 3 times and not get any heads. How much should Bob wager to make the game fair?

2. A box contains four $10 bills, six $5 bills, and two $1 bills. You are allowed to pull two bills at random from the box. If both bills are of the same denomination, you can keep them. What is the maximum amount you can afford to pay to take part in this game without expecting to lose some money?

3. On a T.V. Game show, a contestant has won a boat and motor valued at $2600. He can continue to play by relinquishing his prize. If so, he can choose curtain A or B. Behind one curtain is a gag prize worth nothing. Behind curtain B is a car valued at $7000. What should he do to maximize his mathematical expectation?

4. Students who take driver education have probability .03 of having an accident in one year. Students without driver education have probability 0.08 of having an accident in one year. Statistics show that the cost of any one accident averages $1500. If car insurance were not available, should a student pay $70 for a driver education course? (Assume no one has two accidents in one year.)

5. A and B play a dice game. A wins if, when the dice are thrown, the two faces showing are identical. Otherwise, B wins. If A wagers $15, how much should B wager to make the game fair?

6. For $1 a Lottery offers the following prizes

        1 prize of $25 000

       20 prizes of $1 000

    168 prizes of $25

  and 1701 prizes of 5 free tickets.

  If 100 000 tickets are sold, find the expectation per ticket.

7. A 25-year old man wants to buy insurance on his life for one year worth $10 000 in the event of his death. Ignoring any effect of compound interest and expenses, what is a fair price for this coverage if, on the average, 158 men out of each 100 000 die at age 25?

8. A rock concert promoter wants to insure his next outdoor concert against the possibility of bad weather. He estimates that if it doesn't rain, 10 000 people will pay $5 each to attend the concert. If it does rain, only 5000 people will attend. Based on weather statistics over several past years for the day of the event, it is determined that there is a 12% chance of rain. Ignoring any effect of compound interest and expenses, what is a fair price for the insurance?

Part B

1. When P plays Q, P wins, on the average, 1 out of 3 games. If P and Q agree to play until Q wins, but no more than 3 games, and if at the close of each game the loser pays the winner $1, what are Q's expected winnings?

2. A current quiz program gives the contestant six true and false statements and awards five dollars for each correct answer. If he answers all six correctly, he gets $1000 extra. What is the value of his expectation assuming he guesses every answer?

3. A man wins a dollar if he tosses a head, and loses a dollar if he tosses a tail. He tosses once and quits if he wins, but tries only once more if he loses. What is his expectation?

4. A perishable product is purchased by a retailer for $6 and is sold for $8. Based on past experience, the following probability table has been derived. If an item is not sold on the first day, the retailer absorbs a $6 loss. Find the number of units the retailer should purchase to maximize his daily profit.

Daily Demand	Probability
20	0.12
21	0.30
22	0.25
23	0.18
24	0.15

5. A manager of an insurance agency is interested in trying to develop a strategy for next year. He can take three possible courses of action:
   I   stay with his present sales staff.
   II   hire additional agents, all untrained.
   III hire additional agents, all trained.

The net payoffs for these actions are:

Next year's sales	Same Staff	Agents Hire Untrained	Agents Hire Trained
No change	0	−40 000	−65 000
Moderate increase	25 000	40 000	70 000
Large increase	70 000	110 000	150 000

The probability predicted for next year's sales are
   same as this year   0.60
   moderate increase   0.25
   large increase   0.15
What should he do?

9.4 Contingent Payments with Time Value

We started this chapter by pointing out that two bonds that are identical, with respect to face value, coupon rate, maturity date etc., may sell for very different prices. This is because the potential investors do not place the same probability on their actually receiving payment in full.

We are now in a position to mathematically analyze such situations, which can be referred to as contingent payments. All that is required is a combination of compound interest theory and the theory of mathematical expectation.

If p is the probability of receiving a sum S, then pS is the expected value of S or the expectation of S. This is a special case of $E(X)$ as defined in Section 9.3. In this case, we have two possible outcomes: x_1 where we receive S with probability $f(x_1) = p$ and x_2 where we receive 0 with probability $f(x_2) = 1 - p$.

$$E(X) = x_1 f(x_1) + x_2 f(x_2) = Sp + 0(1 - p) = pS$$

The **discounted value** or the **present value of the expectation pS** to be received n periods from today assuming money is worth i per period is:

$$pS(1 + i)^{-n} \tag{38}$$

Example 1   Mr. Smith goes to a finance company and borrows $1000 for 1 year. If repayment were certain, the finance company would charge Mr. Smith 18% per annum. After doing a credit check on Mr. Smith, they determine that there is a 10% chance of default in which case no money will be repaid at all.

   a) How much should he repay?
   b) What rate of interest should the finance company charge Mr. Smith?

Solution a   If repayment were certain, the finance company would charge 18% and Mr. Smith would repay $1180. But, the finance company places a 90% probability of repayment. (That is, if 100 such loans are made, 90 will be repaid and 10 will not).

Let the amount to be repaid be X. The expected value of repayment is $X(0.90)$. The present value of this is $X(0.90)(1.18)^{-1}$.
To find X then: $X(0.90)(1.18)^{-1} = \$1000$
$$X = \$1311.11$$

Solution b   If Mr. Smith does repay the loan, the rate of interest he pays is i such that

$$1000 = \$1311.11(1 + i)^{-1}$$
$$(1 + i) = 1.3111$$
$$i = 31.11\%$$

While Mr. Smith experiences a very high rate of interest, if the finance company lends $1000 to 100 people and only 90 repay the loan, they make only 18% on their total investment.

In the above example, we assumed that if the borrower defaults at some time, the lender gets nothing at all from the time of default. This is seldom true in reality, but is a necessary assumption for ease of analysis.

Example 2   Mr. Adams is approached by an agent selling a special university scholarship award. If Mr. Adams' newborn daughter survives to age 18, qualifies for and enters a Canadian University, she will be awarded a $5000 scholarship on her 18th birthday. The cost for this plan is $250.

Mr. Adams realizes that he can make 15% per annum on his investments. He also determines from statistical tables that the probability of a new-born female surviving to age 18 is 0.9767. What probability must Mr. Adams attach to his daughter entering university before the scheme is worthwhile?

Solution   Let the unknown probability be p. The scheme will be worthwhile if the discounted value of Mr. Adam's expectation is at least $250.

$$250 = 5000(1.15)^{-18}(0.9767)p$$
$$p = 0.6335$$

If the probability exceeds 63.35%, the plan would be worthwhile.

Example 3   An insurance company issues a one-year insurance policy which pays $100 000 at the *end* of the year if the policyholder dies during the year. If the probability that a 35-year-old female dies in the next year is 0.000 86, what is a fair price for this policy ignoring expenses and assuming $j_1 = 10\%$?

Solution   Price = $100\,000(0.000\,86)(1.10)^{-1} = \$78.18$

Example 4   Mr. Brown, who is in very poor health, is to receive $1000 at the end of each year as long as he is alive. The probability he will live n years is given in the following table.

n	Probability of Surviving n years
1	0.80
2	0.45
3	0.00

If $j_1 = 15\%$, what value should Mr. Brown place on these series of payments now?

Solution

The solution follows directly from the data given, and can be derived by using the following time diagram:

Probability→   (0.8)   (0.45)   (0)
                        $1000 $1000 $1000
        |----------------|------------|------------|
        0   1   2   3
        ↓
      X = ?

The discounted value of the expected payment is

$X = 1000\,(0.8)(1.15)^{-1} + 1000\,(0.45)(1.15)^{-2} + 1000\,(0)\,(1.15)^{-3} = \$1035.92$

Example 5   How much would you lend a person today if he promises to repay $1000 at the end of each year for 10 years but there is a 10% chance of default in any year and $j_1 = 12\%$. If default occurs, no money will be received beyond the time of default.

Solution   The fact that there is a 10% chance of default in any year means that there is a 90% probability of receiving the first payment, an 81% chance, $(0.9)^2$, of receiving the second payment, a 72.9% chance, $(0.9)^3$, of receiving the third payment, and so on.

In Example 1, Section 4.5 of Chapter 4, we found the present value of an annuity where payments varied to cover the rate of inflation. The two methods used to solve that example in Chapter 4 can be used here to solve this contingent payment problem. Students are encouraged to review Section 4.5, Example 1 before going on.

One method of solution is to sum the following geometric series (as outlined in Appendix 2). The discounted value of the expected series of payments is

$1000(1.12)^{-1}(0.9) + 1000(1.12)^{-2}(0.9)^2 + \ldots + 1000(1.12)^{-10}(0.9)^{10}$

An easier method of solution, as in Section 4.5, is to determine a new rate of interest, j_1, that covers both the standard rate of interest and the probability of default. That is

$$1 + j_1 = \frac{1.12}{0.9}$$
$$1 + j_1 = 1.244\dot{4}$$
$$j_1 = 24.4\dot{4}\%$$

Now we calculate the discounted value of a simple annuity of $1000 a year for 10 years at $j_1 = 24.44\%$

$$1000 \, a \, \overline{_{10}}.2444 = 1000 \frac{1 - (1.2444)^{-10}}{0.2444} = \$3631.64$$

Example 6   A 20-year $1000 bond is offered for sale January 1, 1983. The bond interest is $j_2 = 12\%$ and the bond matures at par.

a) Find the purchase price to yield $j_2 = 14\%$.
b) Find the purchase price to yield $j_2 = 14\%$ if the probability of default in *any* six-month period is 5%.

Solution

a) $P = Fr \, a_{\overline{n}i} + C(1 + i)^{-n}$
   $= 60 \, a_{\overline{40}.07} + 1000(1.07)^{-40} = 799.90 + 66.78 = \$866.68$

b) First we find a new interest rate, i per half year, that automatically includes the probability of default.

$$(1 + i) = \frac{1.07}{0.95}$$
$$1 + i = 1.126\,315\,79$$
$$i = 0.126\,315\,79$$

and then calculate the purchase price

$P = Fr \, a_{\overline{n}i} + C(1 + i)^{-n} = 60 \, a_{\overline{40}i} + 1000(1 + i)^{-40}$
$= 470.92 + 8.58 = \$479.50$

While it appears that a relatively small probability of default leads to a large difference in price, a 5% default probability each half-year for 20 years gives only a 12.9% chance of full repayment of the debt. Further, we have assumed there is no value at all beyond the point of default.

Exercise 9.4

Part A

1. The Friendly Finance Company could lend out their money at 18% per annum if everyone repaid their loans in full. From past experience, however, 5% of all loans are not repaid. What rate of interest, j_1, should the Friendly Finance Company charge for one year loans?

2. Mr. Jones wants to borrow some money. He can repay the loan with a single payment of $2000 in one year's time. The lending institution determines that there is a 10% chance that Mr. Jones will not repay the loan. The normal lending rate at that time is $j_1 = 15\%$. How much will they lend Mr. Jones? If he repays the loan in full, what rate of interest was realized?

3. Mrs. Adams wants to borrow $4000. She will repay the loan with one single payment at the end of one year's time. The lending agency estimates that there is a 5% chance of default on this loan in which case they receive nothing at all. How much will they ask Mrs. Adams to repay if their "risk-free" rate of interest is a) $j_1 = 21\%$, b) $j_2 = 21\%$?

4. For loans repayable with single payments at the end of one year if repayment is assured, $j_1 = 15\%$. If the XYZ Finance Company charges $j_1 = 20\%$ for the same loan, what is their expected default rate?

5. Mr. Jones dies and leaves an estate valued at $500\,000 in a bank account earning 8% per annum. He has two children: Robert aged 8, and Tammy aged 3.

The estate will be divided amongst the survivors 18 years from now when Tammy turns 21. Find the expected value of the inheritance for each child given the probability an 8-year-old boy survives for 18 years is 0.95 and the probability a 3-year-old girl survives 18 years is 0.97, and assuming independence of events. Why is your total not $500\,000(1.08)^{18}$?

6. How much would you lend a person today if she promises to repay $5000 at the end of each year for 5 years and there is a 5% chance of default in any year? Assume $j_1 = 15\%$ when payment is assured.

7. An insurance company sells an annuity to a person who has the following probability of survival in the future

Year	Probability of Survival
1	0.85
2	0.65
3	0.35
4	0

If $j_1 = 12\%$, and we ignore expenses, what is a fair price for an annuity paying $2000 at the end of each year?

8. A 20-year $1000 bond is offered for sale. The bond interest is $j_2 = 10\%$ and the bond matures for $1050. Find the purchase price to yield $j_2 = 15\%$ if the probability of default in any six-month period is 1%.

9. A $1000 bond with coupons at $j_2 = 12\%$ and redeemable at par has exactly 10 years left to run. Find its price if the probability of default in any six-month period is 2% and the desired yield rate is $j_2 = 10\%$.

Part B

1. Mr. X buys a $1000, 20-year bond with coupons at $j_2 = 12\%$ redeemable at par. He determines his purchase price to yield $j_2 = 14\%$ and to allow for a semi-annual default probability of 2%. Exactly 5 years later Mr. X sells the bond to Mrs. Y who determines her purchase price to yield $j_2 = 10\%$ but to allow for a semi-annual default probability of 3% in the remaining period. Find
   a) the original purchase price,
   b) the selling price;
   c) the yield, j_2, to Mr. X.

2. The XYZ finance company experiences a 90% repayment rate (a 10% default rate) on one year loans. The ABC Bank across the street experiences a 95% repayment rate (a 5% default rate) on its one year loans. If the ABC Bank charges $j_1 = 15\%$ on loans, what rate j_1 should the XYZ finance company charge to have the same return on loans?

3. Mrs. Brown dies and leaves an estate valued at $50\,000 in a bank account earning interest at rate $j_{12} = 9\%$. She has three children: Jim aged 7, Fred aged 5, and Sandra aged 4. The estate will be divided amongst the survivors 14 years from now when Sandra turns 18. Find the expected value of the inheritance for each child given the following, and assuming independence.

Age Today	Probability of Survival for 14 Years
7	0.95
5	0.97
4	0.98

4. Mr. Jones pays $880 for a $1000 bond paying bond interest at $j_2 = 9\%$ and redeemable at $1000 in 20 years. If his desired yield was $j_2 = 8\%$, what semi-annual probability of default did he expect?

5. Mr. Smith wants to borrow some money and repay the loan with a single payment at the end of one year. Based on past experience, the bank has the following probability distribution of repayments.

Proportion of Total Debt Repaid	Probability
0%	5%
50%	5%
75%	10%
90%	10%
100%	70%

If the "risk-free" rate of interest the bank uses is $j_1 = 20\%$, what rate of interest will they charge Mr. Smith?

9.5 Review Exercises

1. A card is drawn at random from a well-shuffled deck. What is the probability that the card will be

   a) an ace or a king;
   b) a red face card (jack, queen, or king)?

2. On a particular assembly line, 8 parts in 1000 are defective. Assuming statistical independence determine the probability that

   a) out of 100 parts none are defective;
   b) two parts in succession are defective;
   c) the first two parts are not defective but the third is.

3. A coin is weighted such that the probability of a head is 2/3 and the probability of a tail is 1/3. Determine

   a) the probability of 3 heads in a row;
   b) the probability of no heads in two tosses;
   c) the probability of a head followed by two tails.

4. Three cards are drawn from a deck of 52. If these cards are not replaced what is the probability of a queen followed by a king followed by an ace?

5. A consumers association tests batteries to see how long certain brands will last. Compare brand X and brand Y below by looking at their expected lifetimes.

Time (hours)	Brand X	Brand Y
	(# having failed)	
3	5	6
4	15	18
5	30	22
6	20	35
7	20	12
8	10	7

6. A gambling game is played whereby a single card is pulled from a deck of 52. For the cards 2 to 10 one wins the face value of the card (i.e., $2 to $10). For a Jack, Queen, or King, one wins $20 and for an ace one wins $25. How much would one be expected to place in the pot to make this a fair game?

7. Perishable goods are purchased by a retailer for $10 each and sold for $15 each. These goods last only one day. Given the following table determined from past experience, how many items of this good should the producer purchase to maximize his profit? What is his expected profit given that purchase?

Daily Demand	Probability
70	0.05
71	0.35
72	0.40
73	0.15
74	0.05

8. Miss Jones goes to the "Family Trust Company" to borrow some money. Family Trust charges 16% per annum for customers with an established credit rating. Otherwise they assume a 5% probability of default (in which case they get nothing). For a loan to be repaid with one payment at the end of one year, what interest rate should they charge Miss Jones who has no credit rating?

9. An insurance company issues a special retirement savings policy whereby they will pay the policyholder $10 000 on his 65th birthday if he is then alive. If the probability that a 40-year old male lives to age 65 is 0.810 and if $j_1 = 10\%$, what is a fair price for this policy ignoring expenses?

10. How much would you lend a person today if he promises to repay $1000 at the end of each year for 10 years, there is a 5% chance of default in any year, and $j_1 = 14\%$? (If default occurs, no payment will be made beyond the time of default.)

11. A 20-year $1000 par value bond with semi-annual coupons at $j_2 = 11\%$ is issued by a company that is not strong financially. In fact, the probability of bankruptcy is 5% in any six-month period with no value if that happens. Find the purchase price of this bond if $j_2 = 15\%$ with no default.

10

Life Annuities and Life Insurance

10.1 Introduction

If you review carefully the examples done in Chapter 9, you will see that we have already done several questions involving life annuities and life insurance. In fact, life annuities and life insurance are nothing more than contingent payments with time value and no new theory is needed in this chapter. Rather, we will present a mortality table that could be used in Canada for such policies and then present some of the notation familiar to Canadian actuaries working with life annuities and life insurance on a day-to-day basis.

10.2 Mortality Tables

Many organizations collect mortality data in Canada. For example, any time a person dies, information on that death, including age at death and cause of death is sent to the Provincial government. These "vital statistics" are compiled by Statistics Canada and analyzed every five years (just after each census). These statistics provide us with mortality tables showing the probability of death at each age separately for Canadian males and females.

Insurance companies also collect data on age at death, but only for their policyholders. These statistics are compiled and analyzed by a committee of the Canadian Institute of Actuaries which, from time to time, will issue mortality tables showing the probability of death at each age. These tables are done separately for females and males and are also done separately for annuity-holders versus insurance-holders. In general, the people who buy annuities from insurance companies are in above-average health. Thus to determine the value of an annuity, the actuary will use a mortality table based on annuitant's experience. Consequently, to determine the value of an insurance contract, the actuary will use a mortality table based on the experience of insured lives.

In Table II, at the back of this text, we have presented the Canadian Institute of Actuaries 1969-1975 Mortality Table. This table was derived using the experience of insured lives who died in the period 1969 to 1975. This table is used widely in Canada to determine the premiums for life insurance policies. Note that by using this table, the actuary is forced to assume that experience from the past will accurately predict events in the future. We have presented both the male and female tables.

Canadian Institute of Actuaries
1969-75
Ultimate Female Mortality Table
Commutation Functions at 4%

Age	ℓ_x	d_x	$1000q_x$	D_x	N_x	M_x
0	10 000 000	1 6200	1.62	10 000 000.00	245 297 221.97	565 491.43
1	9 983 800	7787	.78	9 599 807.69	235 297 221.97	549 914.51
2	9 976 013	4788	.48	9 223 384.80	225 697 414.28	542 714.99
3	9 971 225	3789	.38	8 864 382.72	216 474 029.48	538 458.48

Part of the female table has been reproduced above. You will see column 3 headed "1000 q_x." In particular at age 0, 1000 q_x = 1.62, and at age 1, 1000 q_x = 0.78. This column lists the probability of death at each age. That is:

$q_x \equiv$ the probability someone aged x dies before age $x + 1$.

Thus we can see that for a female at age 0, the probability of dying in one year is 0.00162.

Columns 1 and 2 of this mortality table are derived from column 3. Column 1, headed "ℓ_x," represents a hypothetical group of lives or population. This column starts with an arbitrary constant, ℓ_0, called the radix. In our tables ℓ_0 has been arbitrarily assigned the value 10 000 000.

Column 2, headed "d_x," represents the number of deaths that would occur in our hypothetical population given the probability of death at each age, q_x. Thus

$$d_0 = l_0 \cdot q_0 = 10\ 000\ 000 \times .00162 = 16\ 200.$$

Then $l_1 = l_0 - d_0$.

In general:

$\qquad l_x \equiv$ the number of lives who survive to age x
$\qquad d_x \equiv$ the number of lives who die between age x and $x+1$
$\qquad l_{x+1} = l_x - d_x$
$\qquad d_x = l_x \cdot q_x$

Thus, given a vector of probabilities of death, q_x, and an arbitrary starting point, l_0, we can form the entire mortality table.

In reality, there is no age where the probability of death is 1. In practice, however, the actuary will choose a termination age for his table and (again arbitrarily) set $q_x = 1$ at this age. In our table, the termination age was set at 105.

Example 1   A scientist studies the mortality patterns of laboratory rats and establishes the following probabilities of death.

Age	Probability of Death
0	0.20
1	0.20
2	0.30
3	1.00

Starting with an arbitrary radix $l_0 = 100$, do a complete mortality table for this population.

Solution

Age	l_x	d_x	q_x
0	100	20	0.20
1	80	16	0.20
2	64	19	0.30
3	45	45	1.00

Notice at age 2 we rounded the computed answer of 19.2 deaths to the nearest integer. Also notice that at any age, the total of future deaths equals the number of survivors alive today.

That is: $l_x = \displaystyle\sum_{t=0}^{\infty} d_{x+t}$

Using the C.I.A. 1969-75 mortality table, we can estimate other probabilities of death or survival.

Example 2   Using the C.I.A. 1969-75 mortality table, estimate the probability that an 18-year-old survives to age 65.

Solution   First we must realize that the answer will differ depending upon whether the person is male or female. In either case, however, the answer is given by the ratio $\frac{\ell_{65}}{\ell_{18}}$. That is, by looking at how many people out of the ℓ_{18} group of lives survive to age 65, we can determine an estimate for the probability of survival for any individual aged 18.

For a male, the probability of survival is:

$$\frac{\ell_{65}}{\ell_{18}} = \frac{7\ 763\ 555}{9\ 885\ 501} = 0.7853$$

For a female, the probability of survival is:

$$\frac{\ell_{65}}{\ell_{18}} = \frac{8\ 633\ 792}{9\ 927\ 840} = 0.8697$$

It is interesting to note that the probability of survival to age 65 is quite large and that the female probability is greater than the male probability.

This probability of survival is denoted $_np_x$ (in our example $_{47}p_{18}$).

In general

$_np_x \equiv$ the probability that an individual aged x will survive for at least n years.

$$_np_x = 1 - {_nq_x} = \frac{\ell_{x+n}}{\ell_x} \tag{39}$$

$p_x \equiv$ the probability that an individual aged x will survive for at least one year.

$$p_x = 1 - q_x = \frac{\ell_{x+1}}{\ell_x}$$

$_nq_x \equiv$ the probability that an individual alive at age x will die before age $x+n$.

$$_nq_x = 1 - {_np_x} = \frac{\ell_x - \ell_{x+n}}{\ell_x} \tag{40}$$

$q_x \equiv$ the probability that an individual aged x will die before age $x+1$

$$q_x = 1 - p_x = \frac{\ell_x - \ell_{x+1}}{\ell_x}$$

Example 3   From the C.I.A. 1969-75 male mortality table determine the following probabilities

a) a life aged 25 survives to age 42;
b) a life aged 42 dies before age 60;
c) a life aged 25 dies between age 42 and age 60.

Solution a $_{17}p_{25} = \frac{\ell_{42}}{\ell_{25}} = \frac{9\ 547\ 634}{9\ 785\ 599} = 0.9757$

Solution b $_{18}q_{42} = \frac{\ell_{42} - \ell_{60}}{\ell_{42}} = \frac{9\ 547\ 634 - 8\ 494\ 711}{9\ 547\ 634} = 0.1103$

Solution c   You must live to age 42 and then die between age 42 and age 60.

$$\text{Probability} = {_{17}p_{25}} \cdot {_{18}q_{42}} = \frac{\ell_{42}}{\ell_{25}} \cdot \frac{\ell_{42} - \ell_{60}}{\ell_{42}} = \frac{\ell_{42} - \ell_{60}}{\ell_{25}}$$

$$= \frac{9\ 547\ 634 - 8\ 494\ 711}{9\ 785\ 599} = 0.1076$$

Exercise 10.2

Part A

1. The following mortality probabilities have been established for a type of bird.

Age	Probability of Death
0	0.20
1	0.15
2	0.45
3	1.00

Starting with $l_0 = 10\,000$ do a complete mortality table for this population.

2. Using the 1969-75 C.I.A. mortality table, estimate the following probabilities
   a) a 41-year old male survives to age 60;
   b) a 19-year old female survives to age 80;
   c) a 20-year old female dies before age 65;
   d) a 25-year old male dies between age 30 and age 60;
   e) a 30-year old female dies between age 65 and age 80;
   f) a 25-year old female dies at age 50.
3. Using the 1969-75 C.I.A. mortality table, determine
   a) for a group of males the age at which

$$l_x \cong \tfrac{1}{2}l_{20}$$

   b) for a group of females, the age at which the probability of dying is the least;
   c) for a group of females, the age at which

$$l_x \cong \tfrac{1}{2}l_0$$

4. Using the 1969-75 C.I.A. mortality table determine how many male students out of 1000 who enter a four-year university program at age 18 will live to attend their 50th year *graduation* reunion?

Part B

1. Show that
   a) $l_x - l_{x+n} = d_x + d_{x+1} + d_{x+2} + \ldots + d_{x+n-1}$
   b) $l_x = d_x + d_{x+1} + d_{x+2} + \ldots$
   c) $l_{x+n} = l_x \cdot p_x \cdot p_{x+1} \cdot \ldots \cdot p_{x+n-1}$

2. Given $l_x = 1000\left(1 - \dfrac{x}{110}\right)$ determine

   a) l_0
   b) l_{65}
   c) d_{18}
   d) $_{20}p_{25}$
   e) $_{10}q_{21}$
   f) the probability that a 22 year old dies between age 44 and 66.

3. Prove that
   a) $_{m+n}p_x = {}_mp_x \cdot {}_np_{x+m} = {}_np_x \cdot {}_mp_{x+n}$

   b) $_np_x = \dfrac{_np_x - {}_{n+1}p_x}{q_{x+n}}$

   c) $q_x + p_x \cdot q_{x+1} + {}_2p_x \cdot q_{x+2} + {}_3p_x \cdot q_{x+3} + \ldots = 1$

4. If $l_x = l_0\dfrac{(100-x)}{100}$ find formulae for

   a) d_x
   b) p_x
   c) q_x

5. Using the 1969-75 C.I.A. Table plot the values of q_x on a graph. Compare the graph for a male versus a female to age 55.

6. Complete the following table.

x	l_x	d_x	p_x	q_x
100	1200	200		
101				
102	800		$\frac{3}{4}$	
103				
104	400			$\frac{1}{2}$
105				
106	0			

10.3 Pure Endowments

A contract that promises to pay a person aged x today $1 if and when he reaches age $x+n$ is called an **n-year pure endowment** and is denoted $_nE_x$. Pure endowment contracts are not actually sold today, but are of theoretical importance.

   We wish to determine a value for $_nE_x$ given a mortality table and some rate of interest.

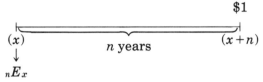

Using the theory developed in Chapter 9, for an individual aged x today, the value of this contract is:

$$_nE_x = (1+i)^{-n}\,_np_x.$$

This value can be derived in another way. Assume that l_x people buy this contract and each one pays $\$_nE_x$ for the contract. This money can be placed in a fund earning interest at rate i for n years for a total accumulated value of $\$l_x \cdot _nE_x \cdot (1+i)^n$. The fund will then be divided equally among the l_{x+n} survivors so that each survivor's share is:

$$\frac{l_x \cdot _nE_x \cdot (1+i)^n}{l_{x+n}}$$

But we know that each survivor is to get $1.

Thus $$\frac{\ell_x \cdot {}_nE_x \cdot (1+i)^n}{\ell_{x+n}} = 1, \text{ and}$$

$${}_nE_x = (1+i)^{-n} \cdot \frac{\ell_{x+n}}{\ell_x} = (1+i)^{-n} {}_np_x \qquad (41)$$

${}_nE_x$ is sometimes called the **net single premium for a n-year pure endowment contract**. We refer to it as a net premium since expenses have been ignored.

There is one other widely used formula for determining ${}_nE_x$ which can be derived as follows

$${}_nE_x = (1+i)^{-n} \frac{\ell_{x+n}}{\ell_x} = \frac{(1+i)^{-(x+n)}\ell_{x+n}}{(1+i)^{-x}\ell_x}$$

If we define a new symbol $D_x = (1+i)^{-x}\ell_x$ then

$${}_nE_x = \frac{D_{x+n}}{D_x} \qquad (42)$$

In column 4 of the C.I.A. 1969-75 mortality table we present values of D_x assuming $j_1 = 4\%$. These values often prove helpful in solving numerical problems. "D_x" is called a "commutation symbol" and is used as a computational aid.

Example 1   Mr. Jones works for the Acme Manufacturing Company. The company has a retirement plan paid for by the employer which provides each retiring employee with $10 000 at age 65. Mr. Jones is age 49 today and wants to change jobs. The Acme Manufacturing company will allow him to transfer the present value of the $10 000 to his new employer's retirement scheme. How much money will be transferred if

  a) $j_1 = 4\%$;
  b) $j_1 = 9\%$?

Solution a   We will do this using both formula (41) and (42).
Using formula (41)

$$10\ 000\ {}_{16}E_{49} = 10\ 000(1+i)^{-16}\ {}_{16}p_{49} = 10\ 000(1.04)^{-16}\frac{\ell_{65}}{\ell_{49}} = \$4441.67$$

Using formula (42)

$$10\ 000\ {}_{16}E_{49} = 10\ 000\ \frac{D_{65}}{D_{49}} = 10\ 000\left(\frac{606\ 587.67}{1\ 365\ 676.11}\right) = \$4441.67$$

Solution b   We can only use formula (41) here.

$$10\ 000\ {}_{16}E_{49} = 10\ 000(1+i)^{-16}\ {}_{16}p_{49} = 10\ 000(1.09)^{-16}\frac{\ell_{65}}{\ell_{49}} = \$2095.34$$

Example 2   Find the net single premium for a 20-year pure endowment of $5000 sold to a male and a female aged 25 if

  a) $j_1 = 4\%$;
  b) $j_1 = 11\%$.

Solution a   Using formula (42), in both cases the answer is:

$$5000\ {}_{20}E_{25} = 5000\ \frac{D_{45}}{D_{25}}$$

For the male this cost is \$2209.17. For the female this cost is \$2235.89. The reason the cost is higher for the female is because the probability is greater that she will survive the 20-year period.

Solution b   Using formula (41), in both cases the answer is:

$$5000 \; _{20}E_{25} = 5000(1.11)^{-20} \frac{\ell_{45}}{\ell_{25}}$$

For the male the cost is \$600.39. For the female the cost is \$607.66.

Exercise 10.3

Part A

1. Jamie Smith, aged 5 today, wins first prize in a Lottery. He can have \$100 000 on his 21st birthday or \$x today. What would x equal if
   a) $j_1 = 4\%$;
   b) $j_1 = 11\%$.

2. The Browns want to place some money in a fund to provide tuition fee expenses for their daughter now aged 1. They want the fund to pay out \$6000 to their daughter on her 18th birthday if she is still alive. How much must be placed in the fund today if
   a) $j_1 = 4\%$;
   b) $j_1 = 8\%$.

3. Find the net single premium for a 20-year pure endowment of \$10 000 sold to a female aged 45 if
   a) $j_1 = 4\%$;
   b) $j_1 = 10\%$.

4. Find the present value of \$5000 due in 15 years' time at $j_1 = 4\%$ if
   a) the payment is certain to be made;
   b) the payment is contingent upon a 35-year-old male surviving to age 50.

5. How large a pure endowment, payable at age 65, can a female aged 40 buy with \$1000 cash if
   a) $j_1 = 4\%$;
   b) $j_1 = 12\%$?

Part B

1. Given $\ell_x = \ell_0 \left(1 - \dfrac{x}{105} \right)$ find the net single premium for a pure endowment of \$1000 due in 20 years if purchased by a 21 year old male if $j_1 = 11\%$.

2. Show that
   a) $_mE_x \cdot {_nE_{x+m}} = {_{m+n}E_x}$
   b) $_nE_x = {_1E_x} \cdot {_1E_{x+1}} \cdot {_1E_{x+2}} \cdot \ldots \cdot {_1E_{x+n-1}}$

3. Prove that $D_{x+1} = (1 + i)^{-1} \, p_x \, D_x$

10.4 Life Annuities

A **life annuity** is a level series of payments made to a policyholder aged x, called an **annuitant**, as long as the annuitant is alive. If not otherwise specified, a life annuity has its first payment at the end of the first year, i.e., an **ordinary life annuity**.

Life annuities can be paid more frequently than annually, but we will present formulas only for annual payment schemes. We will continue to use the C.I.A. 1969-75 mortality table despite the fact that, strictly speaking, it is used for insurance policies and not annuities. The formula and methodology are not affected.

To determine the discounted value of a $1 ordinary life annuity issued to someone aged x, denoted a_x, we can return to the methodology of Chapter 9 and see that

$$a_x = (1+i)^{-1}p_x + (1+i)^{-2} {}_2p_x + (1+i)^{-3} {}_3p_x + \ldots = \sum_{t=1}^{\infty}(1+i)^{-t}{}_tp_x$$

The upper bound on the summation is given as infinity, but in reality we need proceed no further than age 105.

If we had access to a computer, this would be an easy expression to evaluate. However, this is not a suitable methodology given only a pocket calculator.

Another way of looking at life annuities is to perceive the payments made as a series of pure endowments. Using (41) we obtain

$$a_x = \sum_{t=1}^{\infty} {}_tE_x$$

Using the commutation symbol D_x, we can write this as

$$a_x = \frac{D_{x+1} + D_{x+2} + \ldots \text{ to the end of the table}}{D_x}$$

We now define a new commutation symbol "N_x."

$$N_x = \sum_{t=0}^{\infty} D_{x+t} = D_x + D_{x+1} + D_{x+2} + \ldots \text{ to the end of the table.}$$

Values of N_x are presented in column 5 of the C.I.A. Table. We can now write a simplified expression for a_x, namely:

$$a_x = \frac{D_{x+1} + D_{x+2} + \ldots}{D_x} = \frac{N_{x+1}}{D_x} \tag{43}$$

Example 1 Find the cost of a life annuity issued to a male aged 65 paying $1000 a year (first payment at age 66) if $j_1 = 4\%$.

Solution Using formula (43), the cost of the annuity is

$$1000\,a_{65} = 1000\,\frac{N_{66}}{D_{65}} = 1000\left(\frac{6\,109\,899.17}{606\,587.67}\right) = \$10\,072.57$$

It is interesting to note that the cost to a female for the same annuity would be

$$1000\,a_{65} = 1000\,\frac{N_{66}}{D_{65}} = 1000\left(\frac{8\,073\,510.16}{674\,581.66}\right) = \$11\,968.17$$

The extra cost is due to the fact that women, as a group, live significantly longer than do men.

This cost is referred to as a **net single premium**. It is a net premium instead of a gross premium since we have ignored expenses.

In Chapter 4, we looked at other simple annuities; for example, annuities due, and deferred annuities. **Life annuities due** are used a great deal by life insurance companies.

A \$1 life annuity due has the first payment now. Therefore, the discounted value of a \$1 life annuity due, denoted $\ddot{a}_x$, is given by

$$\ddot{a}_x = \frac{D_x + D_{x+1} + D_{x+2} + D_{x+3} + \dots}{D_x} = \frac{N_x}{D_x} \tag{44}$$

We can also show that $\ddot{a}_x = a_x + 1$. The proof is left to the student as an exercise.

Example 2 Find the cost of a life annuity due issued to a male aged 65 that pays \$1000 a year if $j_1 = 4\%$.

Solution   Using formula (44)

$$1000 \, \ddot{a}_{65} = 1000 \, \frac{N_{65}}{D_{65}} = 1000 \left(\frac{6\,716\,486.84}{606\,587.67} \right) = \$11\,072.57$$

Example 3 Determine the cost to a male aged 34 of a life annuity of \$1000 a year where payments start at age 65 if $j_1 = 4\%$.

Solution   Let P denote the cost of the annuity as shown.

```
                          1000      1000      1000
     |————————————...————————+————————+————————+————...
     34                      65       66       67
     ↓
     P?
```

$$P = 1000(_{31}E_{34} + _{32}E_{34} + _{33}E_{34} + \dots) = 1000 \left(\frac{D_{65} + D_{66} + D_{67} + \dots}{D_{34}} \right)$$

$$= 1000 \, \frac{N_{65}}{D_{34}} = 1000 \left(\frac{6\,716\,486.84}{2\,549\,762.89} \right) = \$2634.16$$

Example 3 illustrates what is known as a **deferred life annuity**. The notation used is $_n| a_x$ for the discounted value of a \$1 ordinary deferred life annuity and $_n| \ddot{a}_x$ for the discounted value of a \$1 deferred life annuity due.

In general

$$_n| a_x = \frac{N_{x+n+1}}{D_x} \tag{45}$$

$$_n| \ddot{a}_x = \frac{N_{x+n}}{D_x} \tag{46}$$

Example 4 Determine the net single premium P for a life annuity of \$500 a year payable for a maximum of 5 years, issued to a female aged 40 if

a) $j_1 = 4\%$;
b) $j_1 = 12\%$.

Solution a   The following time diagram illustrates the payments.

```
              500      500      500      500      500
     |————————+————————+————————+————————+————————+
     40       41       42       43       44       45
     ↓
     P?
```

From the diagram, we see that our payments start at age 41 and end at age 45. These payments will be valued at age 40. Thus:

$$P = 500 \, \frac{N_{41} - N_{46}}{D_{40}} = 500 \left(\frac{38\,839\,716.83 - 29\,817\,811.66}{2\,036\,104.35} \right) = \$2215.48$$

Solution b   Since $j_1 = 12\%$, we cannot use the commutation symbols provided in Table II. If we were to return to the beginning of this section, we would remember that:

$$a_x = (1+i)^{-1}p_x + (1+i)^{-2}{}_2p_x + (1+i)^{-3}{}_3p_x + \ldots \ = \sum_{t=1}^{\infty}(1+i)^{-t}{}_tp_x$$

In this case, we need only evaluate five terms, to get

$$P = 500\left[(1.12)^{-1}p_{40} + (1.12)^{-2}{}_2p_{40} + (1.12)^{-3}{}_3p_{40} + (1.12)^{-4}{}_4p_{40} + (1.12)^{-5}{}_5p_{40}\right]$$

Using ${}_np_x = \dfrac{\ell_{x+n}}{\ell_x}$ and the 1969-75 C.I.A. Table we get $P = \$1794.41$

Example 4 illustrates what is known, as a **temporary life annuity**. The notation for the discounted value of a \$1 temporary life annuity is $a_{x:\overline{n}|}$ and $\ddot{a}_{x:\overline{n}|}$ for the discounted value of a \$1 temporary life annuity due.

In general

$$a_{x:\overline{n}|} = \frac{N_{x+1} - N_{x+n+1}}{D_x} \qquad (47)$$

$$\ddot{a}_{x:\overline{n}|} = \frac{N_x - N_{x+n}}{D_x} \qquad (48)$$

Note: In formulae (43) through (48), the numerator represents the payments to be made, the denominator tells us the age at which the life annuity is evaluated.

Exercise 10.4

Part A

1. Prove that $\ddot{a}_x = a_x + 1$.
2. In Example 4 we showed that for a female aged 40, the net single premium for a 5-year temporary annuity of \$500 a year was \$2215.48. From Chapter 3, we know that the cost of a 5-year annuity certain of \$500 a year at $j_1 = 4\%$ is $500\, a_{\overline{5}|.04} = \$2225.91$. Explain why a temporary life annuity costs less than an annuity certain of the same duration.
3. Find the net single premium for a life annuity issued to a female aged 40 paying \$600 a year (first payment at age 41) if $j_1 = 4\%$.
4. Find the cost of a life annuity due of \$2000 a year payable to a male aged 60 if $j_1 = 4\%$.
5. Determine the net single premium for a female aged 40 of an annuity of \$6000 a year where the first payment will be at age 60 if $j_1 = 4\%$.
6. Determine the cost of a temporary life annuity of \$1500 a year payable for 5-years issued to a male aged 25 if
   a) $j_1 = 4\%$;
   b) $j_1 = 9\%$.
7. Determine the net single premium for a 10-year temporary life annuity due issued to a female aged 40 which pays \$900 per annum if $j_1 = 4\%$.
8. Mrs. Anderson, aged 37, inherits \$10 000 and uses this money to buy a life annuity at $j_1 = 4\%$. What annual payments will she receive from the annuity if
   a) the first payment is now;
   b) the first payment is at age 38?

9. Robbie Smith, aged 7, wins \$50 000 in a lottery. The money is left to accumulate at $j_1 = 4\%$ and will be paid to him in the form of a 5-year temporary life annuity first payment at age 21 if he is then alive. Find the size of each payment.

10. A 25-year old male earning \$22 000 a year is left paralyzed as the result of an industrial accident. He sues the company for the present value of his lost income through to age 65. Find the value of the lawsuit, if successful, if we assume his salary is paid at the end of each year, and if rates of investment returns are expected to exceed salary increases in the future by the rate of $j_1 = 4\%$.

11. A 25-year old female takes out a life insurance policy on which premiums are \$300 a year (at the beginning of each year) for life. Find the present value of these payments if $j_1 = 4\%$.

12. A male and female worker both working for the same period of employment with the same company at the same past salary both retire at age 65. The employer has built up a fund of \$100 000 for each of them to buy them a life annuity (first payment due at age 65) at $j_1 = 4\%$. What annual income will each worker receive?

13. A five-year-old girl inherits \$100 000. The money is set aside in a fund to provide 5 annual payments to her, first payment at age 21, as long as she is alive. Find the size of each payment she will receive assuming
   a) $j_1 = 4\%$ throughout;
   b) $j_1 = 11\%$ throughout.

Part B

1. Show that $\ddot{a}_x = \ddot{a}_{x:\overline{n}|} + {}_n|\ddot{a}_x = \ddot{a}_{x:\overline{n}|} + {}_nE_x \cdot \ddot{a}_{x+n}$

2. Mr. Smith, aged 65, buys a retirement annuity with the first payment made one year hence with annual payments of \$4500 each. Payments in the first ten years are guaranteed. After that, payments are made contingent upon Mr. Smith being alive. Find the value of this annuity at age 65 if $j_1 = 4\%$.

3. Show that
   a) $\ddot{a}_x = 1 + (1+i)^{-1} \cdot p_x \cdot \ddot{a}_{x+1}$
   b) $a_x = (1+i)^{-1}p_x + (1+i)^{-2} \cdot {}_2p_x \cdot \ddot{a}_{x+2}$

4. Show that
   a) $\ddot{a}_{x:\overline{n}|} = 1 + a_{x:\overline{n-1}|}$
   b) $\ddot{a}_{x:\overline{n}|} = a_{x:\overline{n}|} + 1 - {}_nE_x$

5. Given $\ell_x = \ell_0\left(1 - \dfrac{x}{105}\right)$ calculate $\ddot{a}_{20:\overline{5}|}$ if interest is 9% per annum.

10.5 Life Insurance

People buy life insurance to protect their dependents from the financial consequences of their untimely death.

The principal types of life insurance are:
a) **Whole life insurance** where the insurance company pays the face value of the policy to the beneficiary upon the death of the insured, whenever that occurs.

b) ***n*-year term insurance** where the insurance company pays the face value of the policy to the beneficiary upon the death of the insured but only if the insured dies within the n-year period defined.

c) ***n*-year endowment insurance** where the insurance company pays the face value of the policy to the beneficiary upon the death of the insured if the insured dies within the n-year period defined or pays the face value of the policy to the insured at the end of the n-year period if the policyholder is still alive. That is, an n-year endowment insurance policy combines the features of an n-year term insurance policy and an n-year pure endowment.

In Example 3 of Section 9.4, we solved a problem involving a one-year term insurance policy. We will now return to a similar problem and formalize the methodology used to determine the cost of certain insurance policies. While in reality death benefits are paid as soon as proof of death is given to the insurance company, we will be assuming that all death benefits are paid at the end of the year of death. This assumption is necessary to allow for ease of calculation.

Example 1   Find the net single premium for a $10 000 one year term insurance policy issued to a male aged 31 if $j_1 = 11\%$.

Solution   As in Example 3 of Section 9.4, the premium P is:

$$P = 10\ 000(1.11)^{-1} \cdot q_{31}$$

Using q_{31} from the 1969-75 C.I.A. Table we get $P = \$11.08$

From here, we can build up the formulae for the other insurance contracts commonly offered.

Example 2   Find the net single premium for a $5000, 5-year term insurance issued to a female aged 27 if

a) $j_1 = 12\%$;

b) $j_1 = 4\%$.

Solution a   The data presented in the 1969-75 C.I.A. Table provides us with the probability of dying in any one year. We are assuming that the death benefit is paid at the end of the year of death. Hence, the net single premium P can be determined as follows:

$$P = 5000\big[(1.12)^{-1}q_{27} + (1.12)^{-2} \cdot p_{27} \cdot q_{28} + (1.12)^{-3} \cdot {}_2p_{27} \cdot q_{29}$$
$$+ (1.12)^{-4}{}_3p_{27} \cdot q_{30} + (1.12)^{-5} \cdot {}_4p_{27} \cdot q_{31}\big]$$

$$= 5000\Big[(1.12)^{-1} \frac{d_{27}}{\ell_{27}} + (1.12)^{-2} \frac{\ell_{28}}{\ell_{27}} \cdot \frac{d_{28}}{\ell_{28}} + (1.12)^{-3} \frac{\ell_{29}}{\ell_{27}} \cdot \frac{d_{29}}{\ell_{29}}$$

$$+ (1.12)^{-4} \frac{\ell_{30}}{\ell_{27}} \cdot \frac{d_{30}}{\ell_{30}} + (1.12)^{-5} \frac{\ell_{31}}{\ell_{27}} \cdot \frac{d_{31}}{\ell_{31}}\Big]$$

$$= \frac{5000}{\ell_{27}}\big[(1.12)^{-1}d_{27} + (1.12)^{-2}d_{28} + (1.12)^{-3}d_{29} + (1.12)^{-4}d_{30} + (1.12)^{-5}d_{31}\big]$$

$$= \$11.52$$

This formula can be explained by looking at it from the insurance company's point of view. ℓ_{27} people will buy this policy and pay premium P. Every time someone dies, they will pay out a benefit of $5000.

Thus: $\ell_{27}P = 5000((1.12)^{-1}d_{27} + (1.12)^{-2}d_{28} + \ldots + (1.12)^{-5}d_{31})$.

Solution b   From part a), we can see that the answer is:

$$P = \frac{5000}{\ell_{27}}\big[(1.04)^{-1}d_{27} + (1.04)^{-2}d_{28} + (1.04)^{-3}d_{29} + (1.04)^{-4}d_{30} + (1.04)^{-5}d_{31}\big]$$

This could be re-written as:

$$P = \frac{5000}{(1.04)^{-27}l_{27}} \left[(1.04)^{-28}d_{27} + (1.04)^{-29}d_{28} + (1.04)^{-30}d_{29} + (1.04)^{-31}d_{30} \right.$$
$$\left. + (1.04)^{-32}d_{31} \right]$$

We now define a new commutation symbol

$$C_x = (1+i)^{-(x+1)}d_x$$

Using this and remembering that $D_x = (1+i)^{-x}l_x$ we get:

$$P = \frac{5000}{D_{27}} (C_{27} + C_{28} + C_{29} + C_{30} + C_{31})$$

We now define yet another commutation symbol

$$M_x = \sum_{t=0}^{\infty} C_{x+t} = C_x + C_{x+1} + C_{x+2} + \ldots \text{ to the end of the table}$$

and we can see that

$$P = 5000 \frac{(M_{27} - M_{32})}{D_{27}}$$

using the values of M_x and D_x from the 1969-75 C.I.A. Table at $j_1 = 4\%$, we get

$$P = 5000 \left(\frac{491\ 179.36 - 481\ 368.36}{3\ 426\ 921.58} \right) = \$14.31$$

In general, the symbol for the **net single premium for a \$1, _n_-year term insurance policy** is $A^1_{x:\overline{n}|}$ and

$$A^1_{x:\overline{n}|} = \frac{M_x - M_{x+n}}{D_x} \tag{49}$$

The "1" over the x signifies that the event that causes a payment to be made is the death of x before the passage of n years of time.

In Example 1, the one-year term insurance policy, could be denoted $10\ 000\ A^1_{x:\overline{1}|}$.

Example 3 Find the net single premium for a whole life policy for \$50 000 issued to a male aged 36 if $j_1 = 4\%$.

Solution As stated before, this policy provides coverage for the whole of life and will pay the benefit at the end of the year of death whenever death occurs. This is just term insurance that proceeds to the end of the table. That is:

$$P = \frac{50\ 000}{l_{36}} \left[(1.04)^{-1}d_{36} + (1.04)^{-2}d_{37} + \ldots \text{ to the end of the table} \right]$$
$$= \frac{50\ 000}{D_{36}} (C_{36} + C_{37} + \ldots \text{ to the end of the table})$$
$$= 50\ 000 \left(\frac{M_{36}}{D_{36}} \right) = 50\ 000 \left(\frac{560\ 182.46}{2\ 351\ 085.42} \right) = \$11\ 913.27$$

In general, the notation for the **net single premium for a \$1 whole life insurance policy** is A_x and

$$A_x = \frac{M_x}{D_x} \tag{50}$$

Example 4 Mary Smith decides to buy a \$4000 20-year endowment insurance policy for her niece on her first birthday. Find the net single premium for this policy if $j_1 = 4\%$.

Solution   This policy provides term insurance of $4000 for 20 years and, if the policyholder is then alive, it pays out a pure endowment of $4000. That is, the net single premium

$$P = 4000(A^1_{1:\overline{20}} + {}_{20}E_1) = 4000\left(\frac{M_1 - M_{21}}{D_1} + \frac{D_{21}}{D_1}\right) = 4000\left(\frac{M_1 - M_{21} + D_{21}}{D_1}\right)$$

$$= 4000\left(\frac{549\ 914.51 - 502\ 676.73 + 4\ 349\ 310.99}{9\ 599\ 807.69}\right) = \$1831.93$$

Out of this cost, $19.68 is for the term insurance and $1812.25 is for the pure endowment.

In general, the notation for the **net single premium for a $1, n-year endowment insurance policy** is $A_{x:\overline{n}}$ and

$$A_{x:\overline{n}} = \frac{M_x - M_{x+n} + D_{x+n}}{D_x} \tag{51}$$

Exercise 10.5

Part A

1. Find the net single premium for a $30 000 one-year term insurance policy issued to a female aged 29 if
   a) $j_1 = 12\%$;
   b) $j_1 = 4\%$.

2. Find the net cost of a $50 000 5-year term insurance policy issued to a male aged 36 if
   a) $j_1 = 4\%$;
   b) $j_1 = 10\%$.

3. Find the net cost of a whole life policy for $40 000 issued to a female aged 33 if $j_1 = 4\%$.

4. Determine the net single premium for a $10 000 20-year endowment insurance policy issued to a female aged 2 if $j_1 = 4\%$.

5. Compare the cost of a $100 000 whole life policy issued to a male and a female aged 40 if $j_1 = 4\%$.

6. How much whole life insurance can a female aged 31 buy with $3000 if $j_1 = 4\%$?

Part B

1. The XYZ Insurance Company issues a "Jumping Juvenile" Insurance Plan that offers $2000 of insurance coverage on the policyholder until age 21 when the coverage jumps to $10 000. Find the net single premium for this policy if issued to a male aged 5 and $j_1 = 4\%$.

2. Prove that $A_x = (1+i)^{-1}(q_x + p_x \cdot A_{x+1})$

3. Show that
   a) $C_x = (1+i)^{-1}D_x - D_{x+1}$
   b) $M_x = (1+i)^{-1}N_x - N_{x+1}$
   c) $A_x = (1+i)^{-1}\ddot{a}_x - a_x$
   d) $A^1_{x:\overline{n}} = (1+i)^{-1}\ddot{a}_{x:\overline{n}} - a_{x:\overline{n}}$

4. Given $\ddot{a}_x = 14.260$ and $A_x = 0.192\ 83$, find i.

5. Given $A_x = .021$ and $i = 4\%$, find $\ddot{a}_x$.

6. Given $\ell_x = \ell_0\left(1 - \frac{x}{105}\right)$ calculate $A^1_{21:\overline{5}}$ if $j_1 = 10\%$.

10.6 Annual Premium Policies

While it is possible to buy either an annuity or an insurance contract by paying a single premium, this is seldom done. Looking at the cost of some of the policies in section 10.5 provides one obvious reason. Instead, individuals usually pay a periodic premium to the insurance company to pay for the contract benefits that they desire. While premiums may be paid in a variety of patterns (e.g. weekly, monthly) we will assume that all premiums are paid annually, and at the beginning of each year.

To determine the fair value of the net annual premium P for an annuity or an insurance contract, we must use the theory of mathematical expectation. In particular, we can say that a fair price will be determined if:

$$\begin{matrix} \text{Mathematical Expectation} \\ \text{of Premium Income} \end{matrix} = \begin{matrix} \text{Mathematical Expectation} \\ \text{of Benefits to be paid} \end{matrix}$$

These values are now easily determined. The mathematical expectation of the premium income will always be of the form $P \cdot \ddot{a}_x$ since premiums are paid at the beginning of each year, but only if the annuitant is alive. The mathematical expectation of the benefits to be paid is just the particular net single premium for the policy in question. These values have been derived in sections 10.3, 10.4, and 10.5 depending on the contract. Thus, no new theory is required as the following examples will illustrate.

Example 1   Mr. Smith aged 37 decides to set up a retirement fund. He wishes to retire at age 65 and receive $5000 a year for life from the fund with the first payment at age 65. What premium deposit is required at the beginning of each year up to age 64 inclusive if $j_1 = 4\%$?

Solution   We want the mathematical expectation of premium income to equal the mathematical expectation of benefits to be paid as evaluated at age 37.

Thus
$$P\left(\frac{N_{37} - N_{65}}{D_{37}}\right) = 5000\left(\frac{N_{65}}{D_{37}}\right)$$

and $\quad P = \dfrac{5000\,N_{65}}{N_{37} - N_{65}} = \dfrac{5000(6\ 716\ 486.84)}{44\ 212\ 390.99 - 6\ 716\ 486.84} = \$895.63$

Example 2   Find the net annual premium for a $25\ 000 whole life policy issued to a female aged 31 if $j_1 = 4\%$.

Solution

We have
$$P\ddot{a}_{31} = 25\ 000A_{31}$$

$$P\left(\frac{N_{31}}{D_{31}}\right) = 25\ 000\left(\frac{M_{31}}{D_{31}}\right)$$

and $\quad P = 25\ 000\left(\dfrac{M_{31}}{N_{31}}\right) = 25\ 000\left(\dfrac{483\ 334.97}{63\ 403\ 796.44}\right) = \$190.58$

In general, the notation for the **net annual premium for a \$1 whole life insurance policy** is P_x and

$$P_x = \frac{M_x}{N_x} \tag{52}$$

Example 3   Find the net annual premium for a $40 000, 20-pay life policy issued to a male aged 29 if $j_1 = 4\%$.

Solution   Premiums are payable for 20 years, but the insurance coverage is whole life.

We have
$$P\ddot{a}_{29:\overline{20|}} = 40\ 000A_{29}$$

$$P\left(\frac{N_{29}-N_{49}}{D_{29}}\right) = 40\ 000\left(\frac{M_{29}}{D_{29}}\right)$$

and $P = 40\ 000\left(\dfrac{M_{29}}{N_{29}-N_{49}}\right) = \dfrac{40\ 000(583\ 741.37)}{65\ 979\ 618.51-22\ 407\ 747.21} = \$535.89$

In general, the notation for the **net annual premium for a \$1, n-pay life insurance policy** is $_nP_x$ and

$$_nP_x = \frac{M_x}{N_x - N_{x+n}} \tag{53}$$

Example 4   Find the net annual premium for a \$100 000 ten-year term insurance policy issued to a male aged 41 if $j_1 = 4\%$.

Solution

We have
$$P\ddot{a}_{41:\overline{10|}} = 100\ 000A^1_{41:\overline{10|}}$$

$$P\left(\frac{N_{41}-N_{51}}{D_{41}}\right) = 100\ 000\left(\frac{M_{41}-M_{51}}{D_{41}}\right)$$

and $P = 100\ 000\left(\dfrac{M_{41}-M_{51}}{N_{41}-N_{51}}\right) = 100\ 000\left(\dfrac{542\ 803.67-490\ 799.16}{35\ 710\ 416.39-19\ 735\ 276.70}\right) = \$325.53$

In general, the notation for the **net annual premium for a \$1, n-year term insurance policy** is $P^1_{x:\overline{n|}}$ and

$$P^1_{x:\overline{n|}} = \frac{M_x - M_{x+n}}{N_x - N_{x+n}} \tag{54}$$

Example 5   Find the net annual premium for a \$5000 twenty-year endowment insurance policy issued to a female aged 45 if $j_1 = 4\%$.

Solution

We have
$$P\ddot{a}_{45:\overline{20|}} = 5000A_{45:\overline{20|}}$$

$$P\left(\frac{N_{45}-N_{65}}{D_{45}}\right) = 5000\left(\frac{M_{45}-M_{65}+D_{65}}{D_{45}}\right)$$

and $P = 5000\left(\dfrac{M_{45}-M_{65}+D_{65}}{N_{45}-N_{65}}\right) = 5000\left(\dfrac{448\ 564.53-338\ 116.59+674\ 581.66}{31\ 477\ 031.23-8\ 748\ 091.82}\right)$

$= \$172.69$

In general, the notation for the **net annual premium for a \$1, n-year endowment insurance policy** is $P_{x:\overline{n|}}$ and

$$P_{x:\overline{n|}} = \frac{M_x - M_{x+n} + D_{x+n}}{N_x-N_{x+n}} \tag{55}$$

Example 6   Find the net annual premium for a \$10 000 twenty-year endowment insurance policy purchased for a male aged 1 if $j_1 = 4\%$ and premiums are to be paid for only fifteen years.

Solution

We have
$$P\ddot{a}_{1:\overline{15}} = 10\ 000 A_{1:\overline{20}}$$

$$P\left(\frac{N_1 - N_{16}}{D_1}\right) = 10\ 000\left(\frac{M_1 - M_{21} + D_{21}}{D_1}\right)$$

and $P = 10\ 000\left(\dfrac{M_1 - M_{21} + D_{21}}{N_1 - N_{16}}\right) = 10\ 000\left(\dfrac{705\ 565.52 - 623\ 554.38 + 4\ 318\ 944.14}{231\ 087\ 795.39 - 120\ 515\ 183.02}\right)$

$$= \$398.01$$

In general, the notation for the **net annual premium on a \$1, *m*-pay, *n*-year endowment insurance policy** is $_mP_{x:\overline{n}}$ and

$$_mP_{x:\overline{n}} = \frac{M_x - M_{x+n} + D_{x+n}}{N_x - N_{x+m}} \tag{56}$$

Exercise 10.6

Part A

1. What annual premium starting at age 32 and paid to age 59 inclusive is required for a female who wishes to retire on \$10 000 a year, first payment at age 60, if $j_1 = 4\%$?

2. Find the net annual premium for a \$40 000, 5-year term insurance policy issued to a female aged 26 if
   a) $j_1 = 4\%$;
   b) $j_1 = 12\%$.

3. Find the net annual premium for a \$100 000 whole life policy issued to a male aged 34 if $j_1 = 4\%$.

4. Determine the net annual premium for a \$15 000, 20-year endowment insurance policy issued to a male aged 45 if $j_1 = 4\%$ and
   a) premiums are payable for 20 years;
   b) premiums are payable for 10 years.

5. Find the net annual premium for a \$50 000 whole life policy issued to a female aged 31 if $j_1 = 4\%$ and
   a) premiums are payable for 20 years;
   b) premiums are payable to age 65.

6. Compare the net annual premium for a \$50 000 whole life policy issued to a male and a female aged 29 if $j_1 = 4\%$.

7. How much whole life insurance can a male aged 34 purchase with a premium of \$180 a year if $j_1 = 4\%$?

Part B

1. Plot a graph showing the cost of one-year term insurance to a male aged 30, 31, 32,... etc. Compare this to the net annual premium for a whole life insurance policy issued to a male aged 30 given $j_1 = 4\%$ throughout.

2. Given $M_x = (1+i)^{-1}N_x - N_{x+1}$ and $A_x = (1+i)^{-1}\ddot{a}_x - a_x$, prove that
   a) $P_x = \dfrac{1}{\ddot{a}_x} - \dfrac{i}{1+i}$
   b) $P_{x:\overline{n}}^1 = (1+i)^{-1} - \dfrac{a_{x:\overline{n}}}{\ddot{a}_{x:\overline{n}}}$

3. Given $P_x = 0.010\ 809$ and $A_x = 0.185\ 00$, find i.

4. In the past, some insurance companies determined the price for a female insurance contract by using the male premium at a younger issue age. For example, an insurance company using a "3-year setback" would determine the price of a policy for a 30 year-old female by using the price determined for a 27 year-old male. Using the 1969-75 C.I.A. table and a $1000 whole life policy issued to a female aged 35, find the "age setback" that would be required if an insurance company used that method and the male 1969-75 C.I.A. table.

10.7 Review Exercises

1. An insurance policy issued to a male aged 20 can be purchased by paying 20 annual premiums (first one due right now) of $100 each. What net single premium would buy the same policy if $j_1 = 4\%$?
2. Mr. Anderson wants to buy a $25 000 whole life insurance policy at age 32. Find the net annual premium for this policy. What would the annual premium be if he used a 20-pay basis? What is the net single premium for this policy?
3. The XYZ Insurance Company sells a Life-Paid-Up-at-65 policy which offers whole life insurance coverage with premiums payable to age 65. Find the net annual premium for this coverage for $10 000 if $j_1 = 4\%$ to a male aged 38.
4. To what age does a 21 year-old male have a 50% chance of living (based on the C.I.A. Table)?
5. If $\ell_x = \ell_0\left(\dfrac{100-x}{100}\right)$ find
   a) p_{70}
   b) $_3p_{40}$
   c) $_5q_{20}$
6. Complete the following table:

x	ℓ_x	d_x	p_x	q_x
101	320			
102		80		
103	48			$\frac{2}{3}$
104			$\frac{1}{4}$	
105				1

7. Determine the present value to a female at age 28 of a deferred life annuity having 3 payments of $1000 each, the first payment being at age 40 if
   a) $j_1 = 11\%$;
   b) $j_1 = 4\%$.
8. Determine the cost of a life annuity issued to a male aged 98 for $500 a year if
   a) $j_1 = 10\%$;
   b) $j_1 = 4\%$.
9. Write expressions, using commutation symbols, for the present value at age 30 of a whole life annuity of $1 per year with the first payment at age 30; at age 31; at age 65.
10. Write expressions, using commutation symbols, for the net annual premium for a whole life insurance of $1 issued to a 35-year-old with annual premiums payable
    a) for life;
    b) for 20-years;
    c) payable to age 60;
    d) the net single premium.

Appendix 1 – Exponents and Logarithms

1 Exponents

The product a · a · a · a may be abbreviated to a^4, which is known as the fourth power of a. The symbol a is called the **base**, the number 4 which indicates the number of times the base a is to appear as a factor, is the **exponent**.

For a first power we have $a^1 = a$, a second power is called a *square*, a third power is a *cube*.

Example 1
a) $243 = 3 \cdot 3 \cdot 3 \cdot 3 \cdot 3 = 3^5$
b) $(1 + i)^3 = (1 + i)(1 + i)(1 + i)$
c) $625 = 5 \cdot 5 \cdot 5 \cdot 5 = 5^4$

2 Laws of Exponents

If m and n are positive integers and a $\neq$ 0, b $\neq$ 0 we have

  1. $a^m \cdot a^n = a^{m+n}$
  2. $a^m \div a^n = a^{m-n}$
  3. $(a^m)^n = a^{mn}$

4. $(ab)^n = a^n b^n$

5. $\left(\dfrac{a}{b}\right)^n = \dfrac{a^n}{b^n}$

We illustrate law (1) below:

$a^m \cdot a^n = (a \cdot a \ldots$ to m factors$)(a \cdot a \ldots$ to n factors$)$
$= (a \cdot a \ldots$ to $m + n$ factors$) = a^{m+n}$

Example 2

a) $2^3 2^6 = 2^{3+6} = 2^9$

b) $\dfrac{x^5}{x^2} = x^{5-2} = x^3$

c) $(a^3)^2 = a^6$

d) $(2x^3)^4 = 2^4 x^{12} = 16x^{12}$

e) $\left(\dfrac{a^2}{b}\right)^3 = \dfrac{(a^2)^3}{b^3} = \dfrac{a^6}{b^3}$

3 Zero, Negative, and Fractional Exponents

We extend the notion of an exponent to include zero, negative integers, and common fractions by the following definitions:

$$a^0 - 1,\, a \neq 0$$

$$a^{-n} = \frac{1}{a^n},\, n \text{ positive integer}$$

$$a^{\frac{m}{n}} = \sqrt[n]{a^m},\, m \text{ and } n \text{ positive integers.}$$

It can be shown that the laws of exponents (1) − (5) hold when m and n are rational numbers (i.e., zero, positive and negative integers, and common fractions).

Example 3

a) $1 = \dfrac{3^4}{3^4} - 3^{4-4} = 3^0$

b) $4^{-2} = \dfrac{1}{4^2} = \dfrac{1}{16}$

c) $(27)^{1/3} + (25)^{1/2} = \sqrt[3]{27} + \sqrt{25} = 3 + 5 = 8$

d) $(9)^{3/2} = (9^{1/2})^3 = (\sqrt{9})^3 = 3^3 = 27$

e) $\dfrac{a^3}{a^{-2}} = a^3 a^2 = a^5$

f) $\sqrt{\dfrac{x^{-2}}{y^6}} = \left(\dfrac{x^{-2}}{y^6}\right)^{1/2} = \dfrac{x^{-1}}{y^3} = x^{-1}y^{-3}$ or $\dfrac{1}{xy^3}$

Example 4   Using a pocket calculator calculate

a) $\sqrt[5]{3} = 3^{1/5} = 1.2457309$

b) $\sqrt[3]{\dfrac{6034 \times .4185}{1.507}} = \left(\dfrac{6034 \times .4185}{1.507}\right)^{1/3} = 11.877613$

c) $15\,000(1.068)^{-3} = 12\,313.386$

d) $\dfrac{3}{\sqrt[4]{608}} = \dfrac{3}{(608)^{1/4}} = 3(608)^{-1/4} = .60415081$

4 Exponential Equations—Unknown Base

Applying the laws of exponents and definitions of the rational exponents we may solve exponential equations with the unknown in the base using a pocket calculator.

Example 5   Solve the following equations

a) $100(1 + i)^8 = 200$

$$(1 + i)^8 = 2$$
$$1 + i = \sqrt[8]{2}$$
$$1 + i = 2^{1/8}$$
$$i = 2^{1/8} - 1$$
$$i = .09050773$$

b) $8800(1 - d)^{10} = 1500$

$$(1 - d)^{10} = \frac{1500}{8800}$$

$$1 - d = \sqrt[10]{\frac{1500}{8800}}$$

$$1 - d = \left(\frac{1500}{8800}\right)^{1/10}$$

$$d = 1 - \left(\frac{1500}{8800}\right)^{1/10}$$

$$d = .16216045$$

c) $(1 + i)^{12} = (1.055)^4$

$$1 + i = \sqrt[12]{(1.055)^4}$$
$$1 + i = (1.055)^{4/12}$$
$$i = (1.055)^{1/3} - 1$$
$$i = .01800713$$

5 Logarithms

Let N be a positive number, and let b be a positive number different from 1. Then the **logarithm, base b**, of the number N is the exponent L on base b such that $b^L = N$. The statement that L is the logarithm, base b, of N is written briefly as $L = \log_b N$. For example,

$\log_2 16 = 4$ since $2^4 = 16$ and
$\log_5 125 = 3$ since $5^3 = 125$

Logarithms, base 10, are called **common logarithms** and are used as aids in computation. We shall write simply $\log N$ instead of $\log_{10} N$ for the common logarithm of a number N. Hereafter, the word logarithm will refer to a common logarithm. By definition,

$\log 1000 = 3$	since $10^3 = 1000$
$\log 100 = 2$	since $10^2 = 100$
$\log 10 = 1$	since $10^1 = 10$
$\log 1 = 0$	since $10^0 = 1$
$\log 0.1 = -1$	since $10^{-1} = 0.1$
$\log 0.01 = -2$	since $10^{-2} = 0.01$
$\log 0.001 = -3$	since $10^{-3} = 0.001$, etc.

It should be remembered, that $\log N$ is defined for positive numbers N only but $\log N$ may be any real number, that is positive, negative, or zero.

6 Basic Properties of Logarithms

Since logarithms are exponents the rules for exponents will be used to prove the rules for logarithms. Let $A = 10^a$ and $B = 10^b$ so that $\log A = a$ and $\log B = b$. Since

$$A \cdot B = 10^a \cdot 10^b = 10^{a+b}$$

$$\frac{A}{B} = \frac{10^a}{10^b} = 10^{a-b}$$

$$A^k = (10^a)^k = 10^{ka}, \ k \text{ a real number,}$$

it follows that

$$\log A \cdot B = a + b = \log A + \log B$$

$$\log\frac{A}{B} = a - b = \log A - \log B$$

$$\log A^k = ka = k \log A$$

We have shown the three fundamental laws of logarithms.

1. The logarithm of the product of two positive numbers is the sum of the logarithms of the numbers.

$$\log A \cdot B = \log A + \log B$$

2. The logarithm of the quotient of two positive numbers is the logarithm of the numerator minus the logarithm of the denominator.

$$\log\frac{A}{B} = \log A - \log B$$

3. The logarithm of the kth power of a positive number is k times the logarithm of the number.

$$\log A^k = k \log A$$

Example 6   Given $\log 2 = 0.301030$ and $\log 3 = 0.477121$, then
a) $\log 6 = \log(2 \times 3) = \log 2 + \log 3 = 0.301030 + 0.477121 = 0.778151$
b) $\log 1.5 = \log \frac{3}{2} = \log 3 - \log 2 = 0.477121 - 0.301030 = 0.176091$
c) $\log 8 = \log 2^3 = 3 \log 2 = 3(0.301030) = 0.903090$
d) $\log 200 = \log 2 \times 10^2 = \log 2 + \log 10^2 = 0.301030 + 2 = 2.301030$
e) $\log 0.003 = \log 3 \times 10^{-3} = \log 3 + \log 10^{-3} = 0.477121 + (-3) = 0.477121 - 3$
f) $\log \sqrt[3]{2} = \log 2^{\frac{1}{3}} = \frac{1}{3} \log 2 = \frac{1}{3}(0.301030) = 0.100343$

7 Characteristic and Mantissa, Antilogarithms

Every positive number can be written as a so-called **basic number** (number between 1 and 10) multiplied by an integral power of 10. For example:

$$5836 = 5.836 \times 10^3$$
$$0.0032 = 3.2 \times 10^{-3}$$

Taking logarithms of these numbers we obtain

$$\log 5836 = \log 5.836 + 3$$
$$\log 0.0032 = \log 3.2 - 3$$

We notice that the logarithm of a basic number is always between 0 and 1 (since $\log 1 = 0$ and $\log 10 = 1$) and the logarithm of an integral power of 10 is, by definition, an integer. Thus, the logarithm of a positive number may be thought of as consisting of two parts:

(i) an integral part, called the **characteristic**. The characteristic is the logarithm of the integral power of 10 and is solely determined by the position of the decimal point in the number. The characteristic may be any whole number (integer) that is positive, negative, or zero.

(ii) a decimal part, called the **mantissa**. The mantissa is the logarithm of the basic number and is determined by the sequence of digits in the number without regard to the position of the decimal point. The mantissa is always a positive decimal.

Standard textbooks in the mathematics of finance usually contain a table of mantissas (rounded off to six decimal places) of all numbers of four or fewer digits, i.e. all numbers from 1.000 to 9.999. In this textbook we deleted the table of mantissas and we assume that each student has a pocket calculator with a built-in logarithmic function.

When calculators with a built-in logarithmic function are used, then the logarithm of a number N, such that $0 < N < 1$, will be shown on a display of the calculator as a single negative number. For $0 < N < 1$ the negative characteristic is combined with the positive mantissa into a single negative number, representing $\log N$. In this case, the decimal part of the displayed negative number does not represent the mantissa. For example, given

$$\log 2 = 0.301030 \quad \text{then} \quad \log 0.002 = 0.301030 - 3$$

Combining the negative characteristic with the positive mantissa, i.e. subtracting 3 from 0.301030, we obtain log 0.002 = −2.698970. The calculator will display log 0.002 as −2.698970. Note that 0.698970 is not the mantissa of 2.

So far we have discussed the problem of finding the logarithm L of a given positive number N. Another problem when using logarithms in computation is: given the logarithm L of a number N, find the number N. The number that corresponds to a given logarithm is called the **antilogarithm**. We write N = antilog L when log $N = L$. For example

    antilog 1.301030 = 20   since   log 20 = 1.301030
    antilog 0.845098 − 1 = 0.7   since   log 0.7 = 0.845098 − 1

To calculate antilog L on a pocket calculator we use the inverse logarithmic function (INV LOG or 10^x). For details consult the owner's manual of your calculator.

8 Computing with Logarithms

The importance of logarithms in computations has diminished with the development of electronic calculators. Students now can perform quickly operations such as long multiplications or divisions, taking powers or roots, using pocket calculators without aid of logarithms.

In some cases, such as solving exponential equations for an unknown exponent (see section 9 of this appendix), logarithms must still be used, however.

In the following examples we shall illustrate the use of logarithms in situations where they provide an alternate method of solution. We assume the use of calculators with a built-in logarithmic function so that logarithms or antilogarithms can be found quickly without using logarithmic tables. We also show direct solutions without the aid of logarithms.

Example 7   The following equation comes from a compound interest problem. Determine i, which represents the interest rate per interest conversion period if

$$800(1 + i)^{20} = 5000$$

Using logarithms we have

$$\log 800 + 20 \log(1 + i) = \log 5000$$
$$20 \log(1 + i) = \log 5000 - \log 800$$
$$20 \log(1 + i) = 3.69897 - 2.90309$$
$$20 \log(1 + i) = .79588002$$
$$\log(1 + i) = 0.039794$$
$$(1 + i) = 1.0959582$$
$$i = .09595822$$
$$i \doteq 9.60\%$$

Direct solution without the aid of logarithms

$$800(1 + i)^{20} = 5000$$

$$(1 + i)^{20} = \frac{5000}{800}$$

$$1 + i = \left(\frac{5000}{800}\right)^{1/20}$$

$$i = \left(\frac{5000}{800}\right)^{1/20} - 1$$
$$i = 0.09595822$$
$$i \doteq 9.60\%$$

Example 8 The following equation comes from a depreciation problem. Determine d, the annual compounded rate of depreciation if

$$83000(1 - d)^{10} = 10500$$

Using logarithms we have

$$\log 83000 + 10 \log(1 - d) = \log 10500$$
$$10 \log(1 - d) = \log 10500 - \log 83000$$
$$10 \log(1 - d) = 4.0211893 - 4.9190781$$
$$10 \log(1 - d) = -.89788879$$
$$\log(1 - d) = -.08978888$$
$$1 - d = .81322575$$
$$d = 1 - .81322575$$
$$d = .18677425$$
$$d = 18.68\%$$

Direct solution without the aid of logarithms
$$83000(1 - d)^{10} = 10500$$

$$(1 - d)^{10} = \frac{10500}{83000}$$

$$1 - d = \left(\frac{10500}{83000}\right)^{1/10}$$

$$d = 1 - \left(\frac{10500}{83000}\right)^{1/10}$$
$$d = .18677425$$
$$d \doteq 18.68\%$$

9 Exponential Equations—Unknown Exponent

In solving exponential equations for an unknown exponent there is no direct solution available and logarithms provide an efficient method of solution.

Example 9   The following equation comes from a compound interest problem. Determine n, which represents the number of interest conversion periods, if

$$250(1.015)^n = 750$$
$$(1.015)^n = 3$$
$$n \log 1.015 = \log 3$$
$$n = \frac{\log 3}{\log 1.015}$$
$$n = 73.788766$$

Example 10   The following equation comes from an annuity problem. Determine n, which represents the number of payments, if

$$\frac{1-(1.01)^{-n}}{.01} = 5$$

$$1-(1.01)^{-n} = .05$$
$$(1.01)^{-n} = .95$$
$$-n \log 1.01 = \log .95$$
$$n = -\frac{\log .95}{\log 1.01}$$

$$n = 5.1549336$$

Exercises – Appendix 1

1. Simplify
   a) $a^3 \cdot a^6$
   b) $a \cdot a^2 \cdot a^3$
   c) $\dfrac{a^8}{a^4}$
   d) $(a^2)^3$
   e) $\dfrac{(a^3)^2 a}{a^5}$
   f) $(a^2 b^3)^2$
   g) $\left(\dfrac{aa^2}{b^2 b}\right)^3$
   h) $(1.05)^3 (1.05)^{12} (1.05)^4$

2. Simplify
   a) $a^{1/2} a^{1/3}$
   b) $a^{1/2} \div a^{1/3}$
   c) $\dfrac{aa^{-2}}{a^3}$
   d) $(a^{2/3})^{3/2} \cdot a^{-1}$
   e) $25^{-1/2}$
   f) $\left(\dfrac{a^3}{b^2}\right)^{-1/4}$

3. Simplify using rational exponents
   a) $\sqrt{a} \sqrt[3]{a}$
   b) $\dfrac{a \cdot \sqrt[3]{a}}{\sqrt{a^3}}$
   c) $\left(\dfrac{\sqrt{a^4} \sqrt[3]{b^2}}{ab^3}\right)^{-3}$

4. Using a pocket calculator calculate
   a) $\sqrt[3]{.0468}$
   b) $\sqrt[15]{\dfrac{24.60}{396}}$
   c) $\dfrac{37(23.3)^2}{\sqrt[3]{111.3}}$
   d) $\dfrac{(1.065)^{15} - 1}{.065}$
   e) $375(1.03)^{-2/3}$
   f) $\sqrt[4]{\dfrac{21.2}{(.082)^2}}$
   g) $\sqrt{3} \sqrt[3]{5} \sqrt[4]{7}$
   h) $\dfrac{1 - (1.11)^{-13}}{.11}$

5. Solve the following exponential equations
 (i) directly without the aid of logarithms
 (ii) using logarithms

a) $3500(1 + i)^8 = 5000$

b) $823.21(1 + i)^{60} = 15\ 000$

c) $17\ 800(1 - d)^{20} = 500$

d) $8000(1 - d)^{11} = 800$

e) $1000(1 + i)^{-20} = 35$

f) $(1 + i)^{-10} = .9490$

g) $(1 + i)^{1/4} = 1.0113$

h) $(1 + i)^{20} - 1 = 80$

i) $(1 + i)^4 = (1.01)^{12}$

j) $(1 + i)^{12} = (1.05)^2$

6. Solve the following exponential equations

a) $50(1.035)^n = 200$

b) $500 = 20(2.06)^x - 150$

c) $808(1.092)^{-n} = 90$

d) $(1.0463)^{-n} = .3826$

e) $(1.02)^n - 1 = .5314$

f) $3^x = 5(2^x)$

g) $126(.75)^x = 30$

h) $1 + 2^x = 81$

i) $\dfrac{3^x + 1}{2} = 21$

j) $\dfrac{2^x - 1}{3} = 12$

7. Solve the following equations for n and check your answer by substitution

a) $\dfrac{(1.083)^n - 1}{.083} = 21$

b) $\dfrac{(1.11)^n - 1}{.11} = 11$

c) $\dfrac{(1.005)^n - 1}{.005} = 10$

d) $\dfrac{1 - (1.087)^{-n}}{.087} = 4.5$

e) $\dfrac{1 - (1.0975)^{-n}}{.0975} = 6$

f) $\dfrac{1 - (1.025)^{-n}}{.025} = 3$

Appendix 2 – Progressions

1 Arithmetic Progressions

Any sequence of numbers with the property that any two consecutive numbers in the sequence are separated by a common difference is called an **arithmetic progression**. Thus:

$3, 5, 7, 9, \ldots$ is an arithmetic progression with common difference 2.

$20, 17, 14, 11, \ldots$ is an arithmetic progression with common difference -3.

Let us look at the first few terms of an arithmetic progression whose first term is t_1 and whose common difference is d.

1st term: t_1
2nd term: $t_1 + d$
3rd term: $t_1 + 2d$
4th term: $t_1 + 3d$, etc.

We notice that the coefficient of d is always one less than the number of the term. Thus the 40th term would be: $t_1 + 39d$.

In general, the nth term on an arithmetic progression, denoted by t_n, with first term t_1 and common difference d is given by

$$t_n = t_1 + (n - 1)d$$

Given any three of the four parameters, we can solve for the fourth.

Example 1   In an arithmetic progression
a) Given $t_1 = 3$, $t_n = 9$, $n = 7$, find d and t_{10}.
b) Given $t_4 = 12$, $t_8 = -4$, find t_1 and d.

Solution:
a) We have $t_7 = t_1 + 6d = 3 + 6d = 9$ and calculate $d = 1$ and $t_{10} = 3 + 9 = 12$.
b) We have $t_4 = t_1 + 3d = 12$
$$t_8 = t_1 + 7d = -4$$
and solve these equations for t_1 and d. Subtracting $t_8 - t_4$ we get $4d = -16$ and $d = -4$. Substituting for d in the first equation we obtain $t_1 = 12 - 3d = 12 - 3(-4) = 24$.

2 The Sum of an Arithmetic Progression

Let S_n denote the sum of the first n terms of an arithmetic progression. We may write

$$S_n = t_1 + (t_1 + d) + (t_1 + 2d) + \ldots + (t_n - 2d) + (t_n - d) + t_n$$

and

$$S_n = t_n + (t_n - d) + (t_n - 2d) + \ldots + (t_1 + 2d) + (t_1 + d) + t_1$$

Adding the above expressions for S_n, term by term, we obtain

$$2S_n = (t_1 + t_n) + (t_1 + t_n) + (t_1 + t_n) + \ldots$$
$$+ (t_1 + t_n) + (t_1 + t_n) + (t_1 + t_n)$$
$$= n(t_1 + t_n)$$

and

$$S_n = \frac{n}{2}(t_1 + t_n)$$

Thus

$$3 + 5 + 7 + 9 + 11 + 13 = \tfrac{6}{2}(3 + 13) = 48$$

and

$$20 + 17 + 14 + 11 + 8 + 5 + 2 + (-1) + (-4) = \tfrac{9}{2}(20 + (-4)) = 72$$

It is easy to see that the sum of the first n integers is

$$S_n = \frac{n}{2}(1 + n)$$

Thus

$$1 + 2 + \ldots + 100 = \tfrac{100}{2}(1 + 100) = 50(101) = 5050$$

Example 2   A woman borrows $1500, agreeing to pay $100 at the end of each month to reduce the outstanding principal, and to pay the interest due on unpaid balance at rate 12% per annum (i.e., 1% per month). Find the sum of all interest payments.

Solution Interest payments are calculated as 1% of the progression 1500, 1400,... ,100.

The sum of all interest payments is the sum of 15 terms of an arithmetic progression $15, 14, 13,\ldots,1$

$$S_{15} = \tfrac{15}{2}\,(15 + 1) = \$120$$

3 Geometric Progressions

A sequence of numbers with the property that the ratio of any two consecutive numbers in the sequence is constant is called a **geometric progression**. Thus:

$2, 4, 8, 16, 32,\ldots$ is a geometric progression with common ratio 2.
$3, 3x, 3x^2, 3x^3, 3x^4,\ldots$ is a geometric progression with common ratio x.

Let us look at the first few terms of a geometric progression whose first term is t_1 and whose common ratio is r.

1st term: t_1
2nd term: $t_1 r$
3rd term: $t_1 r^2$
4th term: $t_1 r^3$, etc.

We notice that the exponent of r is always one less than the number of the term. Thus, the 20th term would be: $t_1 r^{19}$.

In general, the nth term of a geometric progression, denoted by t_n, with the first term t_1 and common ratio r is given by

$$t_n = t_1 r^{n-1}$$

Given any three of the four parameters, we can solve for the fourth.

Example 3 In a geometric progression if $r = 10$ and the eighth term is 2000, find the first and the fifth term.

Solution We have $t_8 = t_1(10)^7 = 2000$. Thus $t_1 = 2000(10)^{-7} = .0002$ and $t_5 = t_1(10)^4 = .0002(10^4) = 2$

4 The Sum of a Geometric Progression

Let S_n denote the sum of the first n terms of a geometric progression. Thus:

$$S_n = t_1 + t_2 + \ldots + t_n$$
$$= t_1 + t_1 r + t_1 r^2 + \ldots + t_1 r^{n-1}$$

Also

$$r \cdot S_n = t_1 r + t_1 r^2 + \ldots + t_1 r^{n-1} + t_1 r^n$$

Subtracting the above expressions for S_n and rS_n, term by term, we obtain

$$(1 - r)S_n = t_1 - t_1 r^n$$

and

$$S_n = t_1\frac{1 - r^n}{1 - r} \quad \text{or} \quad S_n = t_1\frac{r^n - 1}{r - 1}$$

Thus

$$2 + 4 + 8 + 16 + 32 + 64 = 2\frac{(1 - 2^6)}{1 - 2} = \frac{2(2^6 - 1)}{2 - 1} = 2(2^6 - 1) = 2(63) = 126$$

and

$$3 + 3x + 3x^2 + \ldots + 3x^n \ (n + 1 \text{ terms}) = 3\left(\frac{1 - x^{n+1}}{1 - x}\right) = 3\left(\frac{x^{n+1} - 1}{x - 1}\right)$$

Example 4   A person starts a chain letter and gives it to four friends (step one) who pass it to four friends each (step two) etc. If there are no duplications, how many people will have been contacted after 10 steps?

Solution   We have a geometric progression

$$4, 16, 64, \ldots$$

with $t_1 = 4$, $r = 4$, $n = 10$ and calculate

$$S_{10} = 4\frac{(4^{10}) - 1}{4 - 1} = 1\ 398\ 100$$

After 10 steps 1 398 100 people will have been contacted.

5 Applications of Geometric Progressions to Annuities

In Chapter 3 we used geometric progressions to derive

$$s_{\overline{n}|i} = \frac{(1 + i)^n - 1}{i} \quad \text{and} \quad a_{\overline{n}|i} = \frac{1 - (1 + i)^{-n}}{i}$$

In Chapter 4 we used geometric progressions to solve annuity problems where payments vary. In the exercises of Chapter 4 we encouraged you to use geometric progressions to derive formulas for the accumulated and discounted value of an annuity due and the discounted value of a perpetuity.

In the following examples, we illustrate how geometric progressions can also be used in the ordinary general annuity problems of Chapter 5.

Example 5   Find the accumulated and the discounted value of $1000 paid at the end of each year for 10 years if the interest rate is 10% compounded quarterly.

Solution   From first principles, using geometric progressions, we calculate the accumulated value S

$$S = 1000\left[1 + (1.025)^4 + (1.025)^8 + \ldots 10 \text{ terms}\right]$$
$$= 1000\frac{(1.025)^{40} - 1}{(1.025)^4 - 1} = \$16\ 231.74$$

and the discounted value A

$$A = 1000\left[(1.025)^{-4} + (1.025)^{-8} + (1.025)^{-12} + \ldots \text{ 10 terms}\right]$$
$$= 1000(1.025)^{-4}\frac{1 - (1.025)^{-40}}{1 - (1.025)^{-4}} = \$6045.20$$

6 Infinite Geometric Progressions

Consider the geometric progression

$$1, \frac{1}{2}, \frac{1}{4}, \frac{1}{8}, \frac{1}{16}, \ldots$$

whose first term is $t_1 = 1$ and whose ratio is $r = \frac{1}{2}$.

The sum of the first n terms is

$$S_n = \frac{1 - \left(\frac{1}{2}\right)^n}{1 - \frac{1}{2}} = \frac{1}{1 - \frac{1}{2}} - \frac{\left(\frac{1}{2}\right)^n}{1 - \frac{1}{2}} = 2 - \left(\frac{1}{2}\right)^{n-1}$$

We note, that for any n, the difference $2 - S_n = \left(\frac{1}{2}\right)^{n-1}$ remains   positive

and becomes smaller and smaller as n increases. We say, as n increases without bound (as n becomes infinite), the sum S_n of the first n terms approaches 2 as a limit. We write

$$\lim_{n \to \infty} S_n = 2$$

For the general geometric progression

$$t_1, t_1 r, t_1 r^2, \ldots$$

we can write the sum of the first n terms

$$S_n = t_1 \frac{1 - r^n}{1 - r} = \frac{t_1}{1 - r} - \frac{t_1 r^n}{1 - r}$$

When $-1 < r < 1$, $\lim_{n \to \infty} S_n = \dfrac{t_1}{1 - r}$ and we call $S = \dfrac{t_1}{1 - r}$ the **sum of the infinite geometric progression.**

Example 6   Find the sum of the infinite geometric progression

$$100, 100(1.01)^{-1}, 100(1.01)^{-2}, 100(1.01)^{-3}, \ldots$$

Solution   We have $t_1 = 100$, $r = (1.01)^{-1} < 1$ and calculate

$$S = \frac{100}{1 - (1.01)^{-1}} = \frac{100}{1 - \frac{1}{1.01}} = \frac{101}{.01} = 10\,100$$

Exercises — Appendix 2

1. Determine which of the following progressions are arithmetic, which are geometric, then write the next term of each and find the term and the sum as indicated.

   a) $1, -\dfrac{1}{2}, \dfrac{1}{4}, \ldots$ Find the 8th term and the sum to 10 terms.

   b) $-1, 2, 5, \ldots$ Find the 15th term and the sum to 12 terms.

   c) $19, 31, 43, \ldots$ Find the 9th term and the sum to 10 terms.

   d) $40, \dfrac{120}{7}, \dfrac{360}{49}, \ldots$ Find the 7th term and the sum to 12 terms.

   e) $\dfrac{1}{3}, \dfrac{1}{12}, -\dfrac{1}{6}, \ldots$ Find the 8th term and the sum to 10 terms.

   f) $9.2, 8, 6.8, \ldots$ Find the 10th term and the sum to 15 terms.

2. Find the sum of
   a) the first 300 positive integers;
   b) the first 100 positive even numbers;
   c) all odd integers from 15 to 219 inclusive;
   d) all even integers from 18 to 280 inclusive.

3. Find the 10th term and the sum of the first 10 terms of the progressions
   a) $2, 4, 6, \ldots$
   b) $625, 125, 25, \ldots$
   c) $1, 1.08, (1.08)^2, \ldots$
   d) $(1.05)^{-1}, (1.05)^{-2}, (1.05)^{-3}, \ldots$

4. In an arithmetic progression
   a) Given $t_1 = 2$, $d = 3$, $n = 10$, find t_n and S_n.
   b) Given $t_n = -11$, $d = -4$, $n = 7$, find t_1 and S_n.
   c) Given $t_3 = 18$, $t_6 = 42$, find t_1 and S_6.
   d) Given $t_1 = 7$, $t_n = 77$, $S_n = 420$, find n and d.
   e) Given $t_1 = 13$, $d = -3$, $S_n = 20$, find n and t_n.

5. In a geometric progression
   a) Given $t_1 = 5$, $r = 2$, $n = 12$, find t_n and S_n.

   b) Given $t_1 = 12$, $r = \dfrac{1}{2}$, $t_n = \dfrac{3}{8}$, find n and S_n.

   c) Given $t_5 = \dfrac{1}{20}$, $r = \dfrac{1}{4}$, find t_1 and S_5.

   d) Given $t_2 = \dfrac{7}{4}$, $t_5 = 14$, find t_{10} and S_{10}.

   e) Given $t_1 = 1.03$, $r = 1.03$, find t_{15} and S_{15}.

6. A man borrows $5000, agreeing to reduce the principal by $200 at the end of each month and to pay 15% interest per annum (i.e. $1\frac{1}{4}$% per month) on all unpaid balances. Find the sum of all interest payments.

7. In buying a house a couple agrees to pay $3000 at the end of the first year, $3500 at the end of the second year, $4000 at the end of the third year, and so on. How much do they pay for the house if they make 20 payments in all?

8. In drilling a well, the cost is $5.50 for the first 10 cm, for each succeeding 10 cm, the cost is $1 more than that for the preceding 10 cm. How deep a well may be drilled for $1000?

9. The value of a certain machine at the end of each year is 80% as much as its value at the beginning of the year. If the machine originally costs $10 000, find its value at the end of 10 years.

10. Each stroke of a vacuum pump extracts 5% of the air in a tank. What decimal fraction of the original air remains after 40 strokes?

11. A rubber ball is dropped from a height of 50 metres to the ground. If it always bounces back one-half of the height from which it falls, find
   a) how far it will rise on the 8th rebound;
   b) the total distance it has travelled as it hits the ground the 10th time;
   c) the total distance it has travelled before coming to rest.

12. If a person were offered a job paying 1 cent the first day, 2 cents the second day, 4 cents the third day, and so on, each day's salary being double that for the preceding day, how much would he receive
   a) the 30th day?
   b) for a 30-day working period?
   c) for the each of the three consecutive 10 day working periods?

13. Find the accumulated and the discounted value from first principles, using geometric progressions
   a) of $100 paid at the end of each month for 10 years if the interest rate is 12% compounded semi-annually.
   b) of $500 paid at the end of each half year for 5 years if the interest rate is 12% compounded monthly.

14. Find the sum of the infinite geometric progression
   a) $1, -\dfrac{1}{3}, \dfrac{1}{9}, -\dfrac{1}{27}, \ldots$
   b) $3, 0.3, 0.03, 0.003, \ldots$
   c) $1, .8, (.8)^2, (.8)^3, \ldots$
   d) $(1 + i)^{-1}, (1 + i)^{-2}, (1 + i)^{-3}, (1 + i)^{-4}, \ldots$

Appendix 3 – Linear Interpolation

The first use of linear interpolation in the text is Example 2 of Section 2.5. In this appendix, we expand upon the solution from Section 2.5 to show, in general, how linear interpolation should be applied.

Example 1   How long will it take $500 to accumulate to $850 at $j_{12} = 12\%$ if the practical method of accumulation is in effect?

Solution   As shown in Section 2.5, this reduces to asking: Find n given $(1.01)^n = 1.7$. Solving this equation by logarithms we calculated $n = 53.3277$. Using a calculator, we find:

$$(1.01)^{53} = 1.6945$$
$$(1.01)^n = 1.7000$$
$$(1.01)^{54} = 1.7114$$

This can be shown graphically as follows:

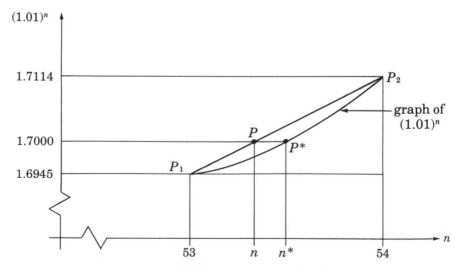

The true value n^* corresponds to the point P^* where the curve gives the value $(1.01)^n = 1.7$. Using logarithms, we can find this exact value of n^*. Otherwise, we are forced to make some approximating assumption.

Under the method of linear interpolation, we assume the graph is linear between the points P_1 and P_2, as indicated by the straight line. The method of interpolation will determine the value n corresponding to the point P on the straight line. Clearly n is an approximate value of n^*.

To find the value n we use the fact that the three points $P_1 = (53, 1.6945)$, $P = (n, 1.7000)$ and $P_2 = (54, 1.7114)$ lie on a straight line, i.e.,

$$\frac{n - 53}{54 - 53} = \frac{1.7000 - 1.6945}{1.7114 - 1.6945}$$

Solving for n we obtain

$$\frac{n - 53}{1} = \frac{.0055}{.0169}$$
$$n = 53.32544379$$
$$n \doteq 53.33$$

This linear approximation, called **linear interpolation**, may be illustrated schematically by the following diagram:

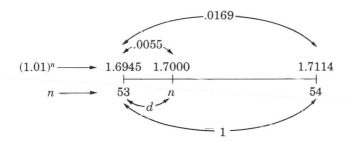

The value n lies the same distance between 53 and 54 as the value 1.7000 between 1.6945 and 1.7114.

Thus

$$\frac{d}{1} = \frac{.0055}{.0169}$$
$$d = .32544379$$
$$\text{and } n \doteq 53.33$$

The data needed for linear interpolation is usually given in tabular form, called an **interpolation table**, shown below.

	(1.01)^n	n		
.0055 {	1.6945	53	} d	
	1.7000	n	} 1
	1.7114	54	

.0169 {   (bracket spanning 1.6945, 1.7000, 1.7114)

$$\frac{d}{1} = \frac{.0055}{.0169}$$
$$d \doteq .33$$
$$\text{and } n = 53 + d = 53.33$$

In Section 3.6 we used linear interpolation to find the interest rate (See Examples 1 and 2 of Section 3.6).

Example 2   Find the interest rate j_4 at which deposits of $250 at the end of every 3 months will accumulate to $5000 in 4 years.

Solution   As shown in Section 3.6, Example 1, this reduces to solving the equation below for unknown rate i

$$s_{\overline{16}|i} = \frac{(1 + i)^{16} - 1}{i} = 20$$

Using a calculator we find

For $j_4 = 11\%$ ($i = .0275$) $s_{\overline{16}|i} = 19.7640$

For $j_4 = 12\%$ ($i = .03$) $s_{\overline{16}|i} = 20.1569$

We want to use a linear approximation to find the value of $j_4 = 4i$ such that $s_{\overline{16}|i} = 20$.

This linear approximation, called linear interpolation, may be illustrated schematically by the following diagram:

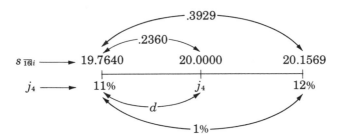

The value j_4 lies the same distance between 11% and 12% as the value 20.0000 does between 19.7640 and 20.1569. Thus

$$\frac{d}{1\%} = \frac{.2360}{.3929} \text{ or } d \doteq .60\%$$
$$\text{and } j_4 = 11.60\%.$$

Usually we arrange our data in an interpolation table:

	$s_{\overline{16}|i}$	j_4
19.7640	11%
20.0000	j_4
20.1569	12%

$$\frac{d}{1\%} = \frac{.2360}{.3929}$$
$$d \doteq .60\%$$
$$\text{and } j_4 = 11.60\%.$$

In Section 7.8, we used linear interpolation to find the yield rate of a bond (see Examples 2 and 3 of Section 7.8).

Example 3   A $500 bond paying interest at $j_2 = 9\frac{1}{2}\%$, redeemable at par on August 15, 1998 is quoted at $109\frac{1}{2}$ on August 15, 1986. Find the yield rate, j_2, to maturity by the method of linear interpolation.

Solution   As shown in Section 7.8, Example 2, this results in linear interpolation between two market prices:

$$Q \text{ (to yield } j_2 = 8\%) = \$557.18$$
$$\text{and } Q \text{ (to yield } j_2 = 9\%) = \$518.12$$

The linear interpolation may be illustrated schematically by the following diagram:

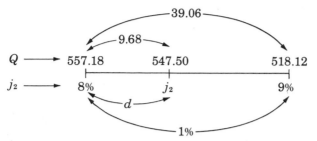

The value j_2 lies the same distance between 8% and 9% as the value 547.50 does between 557.18 and 518.12. Thus

$$\frac{d}{1\%} = \frac{9.68}{39.06} \text{ or } d \doteq .25\% \text{ and } j_2 \doteq 8.25\%.$$

Exercises – Appendix 3

In the following exercises, illustrate linear interpolation schematically on a diagram and also set up the interpolation table.

1. Solve the following equations for n using linear interpolation
   a) $(1.05)^n = 2$
   b) $(1.025)^n = 3.8$
   c) $800(1.03)^n = 1100$
   d) $(1.045)^{-n} = .5$
   e) $(1.0125)^{-n} = \frac{1}{4}$
   f) $1000(1.0225)^{-n} = 700$

2. Solve the following equations for i using linear interpolation
   a) $\frac{(1 + i)^{12} - 1}{i} = 15$
   b) $\frac{(1 + i)^{100} - 1}{i} = 200$
   c) $\frac{1 - (1 + i)^{-20}}{i} = 10$
   d) $100 + 90 \frac{1 - (1 + i)^{-6}}{i} = 600$

3. Find the interest rate j_{12} at which deposits of $100 at the end of each month will accumulate to $4000 in 3 years.

4. An insurance company will pay $100 000 to a beneficiary or monthly payments of $1150 for 15 years. What rate, j_{12}, is the insurance company using?

5. A $1000 bond paying interest at $j_2 = 16\frac{3}{4}\%$ matures at par on August 1, 2005. If this bond is quoted at $105\frac{1}{2}$ on August 1, 1983 find the yield rate, j_2, using the method of interpolation.

6. A $1000 bond that pays interest at $j_2 = 11\%$ matures at par on November 1, 1989. If this bond is sold on May 1, 1984 at a market quotation $78\frac{1}{4}$, find the yield rate, j_2, that the buyer will realize, using the method of linear interpolation.

Appendix 4 – Continuous Compounding

1 Compound Interest at Nominal Rate j Compounded Continuously

In any text on calculus one will find the equation

$$\lim_{m \to \infty} \left(1 + \frac{x}{m}\right)^m = e^x$$

where the number $e \doteq 2.718$ has an infinite expansion and is the base of the natural logarithms.

This equation will be useful in compound interest problems where a nominal rate of interest is compounded continuously.

We have already dealt with problems where the nominal rate j has been compounded as often as daily. For example, consider the nominal rate of interest $j_m = 12\%$ compounded at different frequencies and compare the accumulated value of \$1 over a 1 year period (so-called annual accumulation factors). The results can be summarized in the following table.

$$j_m = 12\%$$

m	Annual accumulation factor
1	$(1.12)^1 = 1.12$
2	$\left(1 + \frac{.12}{2}\right)^2 = 1.1236$
4	$\left(1 + \frac{.12}{4}\right)^4 = 1.1255088$
12	$\left(1 + \frac{.12}{12}\right)^{12} = 1.1268250$
52	$\left(1 + \frac{.12}{52}\right)^{52} = 1.1273410$
365	$\left(1 + \frac{.12}{365}\right)^{365} = 1.1274744$

From the above table we can see that as the frequency m of compounding increases, the annual accumulation factor also increases and approaches an upper bound as m is increased without limit, i.e., $m \to \infty$. To determine this upper bound that represents the annual accumulation factor at nominal rate 12% compounded continuously, shortly $j_\infty = 12\%$, we wish to calculate $\lim\limits_{m \to \infty} \left(1 + \dfrac{.12}{m}\right)^m$

Using the equation $\qquad \lim\limits_{m \to \infty} \left(1 + \dfrac{x}{m}\right) = e^x$

we obtain $\qquad \lim\limits_{m \to \infty} \left(1 + \dfrac{.12}{m}\right)^m = e^{.12} = 1.1274968$

Note   To calculate e^t on a pocket calculator without the function e^x you may use the inverse function $\ln x$. Consult your owner's manual for details.

Example 1   Find the rate j_{12} equivalent to $j_\infty = 15\%$.

Solution   We shall compare the annual accumulation factors at these rates.

$$(1 + i)^{12} = e^{.15}$$
$$i = e^{.15/12} - 1$$
$$i = .01257845$$
$$j_{12} = .1509414$$
$$j_{12} \doteq 15.09\%$$

The accumulated value S of principal P at rate j_m for t years is given by the fundamental compound interest formula (9)

$$S = P(1 + i)^n = P\left(1 + \frac{j_m}{m}\right)^{mt} = P\left[\left(1 + \frac{j_m}{m}\right)^m\right]^t$$

If interest is compounded continuously

$$S = \lim_{m \to \infty} P\left[\left(1 + \frac{j_m}{m}\right)^m\right]^t = P\, e^{j_\infty t}$$

Similarly we can develop the formula for the discounted value P, given S, j_∞, and t.

$$P = S\, e^{-j_\infty t}$$

The following examples illustrate how the formula $S = P\, e^{j_\infty t}$ can be used to find the accumulated value S, the discounted value P, the rate j_∞, the effective rate j, and time in years t.

Example 2   Find the accumulated and the discounted value of $5000 over 15 months at a nominal rate 18% compounded continuously.

Solution   We have $j_\infty = .18$, $t = \frac{15}{12} = 1.25$ and calculate the accumulated value S of $5000

$$S = 5000\, e^{(.18)(1.25)} = \$6261.61$$

and then the discounted value P of $5000

$$P = 5000\, e^{-(.18)(1.25)} = \$3992.58$$

Example 3   A deposit of $1000 accumulated interest of $560 over 30 months. Find
a) the continuous rate of increase;
b) the effective annual rate of increase.

Solution a   We have $P = 1000$, $S = 1560$, $t = \frac{30}{12} = 2.5$ and solve the equation

$$1000\, e^{j_\infty(2.5)} = 1560$$

$$e^{2.5j_\infty} = 1.560$$

$$2.5\, j_\infty = \ell n\ 1.560$$

$$j_\infty = \frac{\ell n\ 1.560}{2.5}$$

$$j_\infty = .17787433$$

$$j_\infty \doteq 17.79\%$$

Solution b   We want to find the equivalent effective rate j for a given rate
$j_\infty = .17787433$ by comparing the accumulated value of $1 at the end of 1 year
$1 at j will accumulate to $1 + j$
$1 at $j_\infty = .17787433$ will accumulate to $e^{.17787433}$

Thus

$$1 + j = e^{.17787433}$$

$$j = e^{.17787433} - 1$$

$$j = .19467517$$

$$j \doteq 19.47\%$$

Note   We can also find j by solving the equation

$$1000(1 + j)^{2.5} = 1560$$

$$(1 + j)^{2.5} = 1.560$$

$$1 + j = (1.560)^{1/2.5}$$

$$j = (1.560)^{1/2.5} - 1$$

$$j = .19467517$$

$$j \doteq 19.47\%$$

Example 4   How long will it take to triple your investment at 15% compounded
continuously?

Solution   We have $P = x$, $S = 3x$, $j_\infty = .15$ and solve the equation below for time t
in years.

$$x\, e^{.15t} = 3x$$

$$e^{.15t} = 3$$

$$.15t = \ell n\ 3$$

$$t = \frac{\ell n 3}{.15}$$

$$t = 7.3240819 \text{ years}$$

$$t \doteq 7 \text{ years } 118 \text{ days}$$

2 Ordinary Annuity of p Payments per Year at j_∞

Ordinary annuities of p payments per year at j_∞ can be treated exactly the
same way as the ordinary general annuities in Chapter 5. This is illustrated in the following examples.

Example 1   Deposits of $100 are made at the end of each month into an account that accumulates interest at 12% compounded continuously. How much money is in the account at the end of 5 years?

Solution   First, find the rate i per month equivalent to $j_\infty = 12\%$, such that
$$(1 + i)^{12} = e^{.12}$$
$$i = e^{.01} - 1$$
$$i = .01005017$$

Second, calculate the accumulated value S of an ordinary simple annuity with $R = 100$, $n = 60$, $i = .01005017$.
$$S = 100s_{\overline{60}|i} = \$8180.15$$

Example 2   A contract calls for payments of $1000 at the end of each half year for 10 years. Find the present value of the contract at 18% compounded
a) semi-annually;
b) continuously.

Solution a   We have $R = 1000$, $n = 20$, $i = .09$ and calculate the discounted value A of the payments.
$$A = 1000\,a_{\overline{20}|.09} = \$9128.55$$

Solution b   First, find the rate i per half-year such that
$$(1 + i)^2 = e^{.18}$$
$$i = e^{.09} - 1$$
$$i = .09417428$$

Second, calculate the discounted value A of an ordinary simple annuity with $R = 1000$, $n = 20$, $i = .09417428$
$$A = 1000\,a_{\overline{20}|i} = \$8863.37$$

Example 3   To prepare for an early retirement, a self-employed businessman makes deposits of $5500 each year for 20 years, starting on his 31st birthday. When he is 51 he wishes to draw 30 equal annual payments. What is the size of each withdrawal if interest is 13% compounded
a) annually;
b) continuously.

Solution   A time diagram is shown below

Deposits:	5500		5500				5500
Age:	30	31	50	51	52		80
Withdrawals:				X	X		X

a) Using 50 as the focal date we write equation of value:
$$5500\,s_{\overline{20}|.13} = X\,a_{\overline{30}|.13}$$
$$X = 5500\frac{s_{\overline{20}|.13}}{a_{\overline{30}|.13}}$$
$$X = \$59\ 395.43$$

b) First, find the rate i per annum such that
$$1 + i = e^{.13}$$
$$i = e^{.13} - 1$$
$$i = .13882838$$

Using 50 as the focal date and $i = .13882838$ we have

$$5500 \, s_{\overline{20}|i} = X \, a_{\overline{30}|i}$$

$$X = \frac{5500 s_{\overline{20}|i}}{a_{\overline{30}|i}}$$

$$X = \$69\ 966.82$$

Exercises — Appendix 4

1. Fifteen hundred dollars is invested for 18 months at a nominal rate 13%. Find the accumulated value if interest is compounded a) annually; b) monthly; c) continuously.

2. A debt of $8000 is due in 5 years. Find the discounted value at a nominal rate 14% compounded a) quarterly; b) daily; c) continuously.

3. At what nominal rate compounded continuously will your investment increase 50% in value in 3 years? Find also the equivalent effective rate.

4. By what date will $80 deposited on February 4, 1984 be worth at least $1200,
   a) at 12% compounded daily;
   b) at 12% compounded continuously.

5. If money doubles at a certain rate of interest compounded continuously in 5 years, how long will it take for the same amount of money to triple in value?

6. Find the accumulated and the discounted value of an annuity of $300 at the end of each quarter for 10 years at 9% compounded a) quarterly; b) continuously.

7. An annuity pays $200 at the end of each month for 5 years and then $300 at the end of each month for the next 5 years. Find the discounted value of these payments at 12% compounded a) monthly; b) continuously.

8. At age 65 Mr. Jones takes his life savings of $100 000 and buys a 15-year annuity certain with monthly payments. Find the size of these payments at 13% compounded a) monthly; b) continuously.

9. How much a month for 3 years at $j_\infty = 11\%$ would you have to save in order to receive $500 a month for 3 years afterward?

10. A deposit of $2000 is made to open an account on April 1, 1982. Quarterly deposits of $300 are then made for 5 years, starting July 1, 1982. Starting October 1, 1988 the first of a sequence of $1000 quarterly withdrawals is made. Assuming interest 10% compounded continuously, find the balance in the account
    a) on October 1, 1985;
    b) on October 1, 1991.

11. Prove that the accumulated value S of an ordinary annuity of n payments of R each, p payments per year over t years is:

$$S = R \, s_{\overline{n}|j_\infty} = R \frac{e^{j_\infty t} - 1}{e^{j_\infty/p} - 1}$$

12. Prove that the discounted value A of an ordinary annuity of n payments of R each, p payments per year over t years, at rate j_∞ is

$$A = R \, a_{\overline{n}|j_\infty} = R \frac{1 - e^{-j_\infty t}}{e^{j_\infty/p} - 1}$$

TABLE I   247

TABLE I

THE NUMBER OF EACH DAY OF THE YEAR

Day of month	Jan.	Feb.	Mar.	April	May	June	July	Aug.	Sept.	Oct.	Nov.	Dec.	Day of month
1	1	32	60	91	121	152	182	213	244	274	305	335	1
2	2	33	61	92	122	153	183	214	245	275	306	336	2
3	3	34	62	93	123	154	184	215	246	276	307	337	3
4	4	35	63	94	124	155	185	216	247	277	308	338	4
5	5	36	64	95	125	156	186	217	248	278	309	339	5
6	6	37	65	96	126	157	187	218	249	279	310	340	6
7	7	38	66	97	127	158	188	219	250	280	311	341	7
8	8	39	67	98	128	159	189	220	251	281	312	342	8
9	9	40	68	99	129	160	190	221	252	282	313	343	9
10	10	41	69	100	130	161	191	222	253	283	314	344	10
11	11	42	70	101	131	162	192	223	254	284	315	345	11
12	12	43	71	102	132	163	193	224	255	285	316	346	12
13	13	44	72	103	133	164	194	225	256	286	317	347	13
14	14	45	73	104	134	165	195	226	257	287	318	348	14
15	15	46	74	105	135	166	196	227	258	288	319	349	15
16	16	47	75	106	136	167	197	228	259	289	320	350	16
17	17	48	76	107	137	168	198	229	260	290	321	351	17
18	18	49	77	108	138	169	199	230	261	291	322	352	18
19	19	50	78	109	139	170	200	231	262	292	323	353	19
20	20	51	79	110	140	171	201	232	263	293	324	354	20
21	21	52	80	111	141	172	202	233	264	294	325	355	21
22	22	53	81	112	142	173	203	234	265	295	326	356	22
23	23	54	82	113	143	174	204	235	266	296	327	357	23
24	24	55	83	114	144	175	205	236	267	297	328	358	24
25	25	56	84	115	145	176	206	237	268	298	329	359	25
26	26	57	85	116	146	177	207	238	269	299	330	360	26
27	27	58	86	117	147	178	208	239	270	300	331	361	27
28	28	59	87	118	148	179	209	240	271	301	332	362	28
29	29		88	119	149	180	210	241	272	302	333	363	29
30	30		89	120	150	181	211	242	273	303	334	364	30
31	31		90		151		212	243		304		365	31

Note: For leap year add 1 to the tabulated number after February 28.

TABLE II

CANADIAN INSTITUTE OF ACTUARIES
1969-75
ULTIMATE FEMALE MORTALITY TABLE
COMMUTATION FUNCTIONS AT 4%

AGE	l_x	d_x	1000 q_x	D_x	N_x	M_x	AGE
0	10000000	16200	1.62	10000000.00	245297221.97	565491.43	0
1	9983800	7787	.78	9599807.69	235297221.97	549914.51	1
2	9976013	4788	.48	9223384.80	225697414.28	542714.99	2
3	9971225	3789	.38	8864382.72	216474029.48	538458.48	3
4	9967436	3090	.31	8520206.07	207609646.76	535219.63	4
5	9964346	2690	.27	8189966.08	199089440.69	532679.88	5
6	9961656	2490	.25	7872841.44	190899474.61	530553.93	6
7	9959166	2390	.24	7568147.65	183026633.17	528661.73	7
8	9956776	2290	.23	7275318.70	175458485.52	526915.38	8
9	9954486	2190	.22	6993889.82	168183166.82	525306.46	9
10	9952296	2090	.21	6723414.58	161189277.00	523826.97	10
11	9950206	1990	.20	6463464.08	154465862.42	522469.35	11
12	9948216	2089	.21	6213626.36	148002398.34	521226.40	12
13	9946127	2387	.24	5973386.13	141788771.98	519971.80	13
14	9943740	2983	.30	5742262.08	135815385.85	518593.37	14
15	9940757	3579	.36	5519749.49	130073123.77	516937.02	15
16	9937178	4372	.44	5305540.58	124553374.28	515026.16	16
17	9932806	4966	.50	5099236.86	119247833.70	512781.69	17
18	9927840	5460	.55	4900661.00	114148596.84	510330.33	18
19	9922380	5656	.57	4709582.50	109247935.84	507738.78	19
20	9916724	5653	.57	4525863.38	104538353.34	505157.46	20
21	9911071	5253	.53	4349310.99	100012489.96	502676.73	21
22	9905818	4953	.50	4179813.26	95663178.97	500460.20	22
23	9900865	4752	.48	4017041.65	91483365.71	498450.64	23
24	9896113	4750	.48	3860686.19	87466324.06	496596.78	24
25	9891363	4946	.50	3710416.46	83605637.87	494814.98	25
26	9886417	5339	.54	3565924.16	79895221.41	493031.01	26
27	9881078	5830	.59	3426921.58	76329297.25	491179.36	27
28	9875248	6123	.62	3293172.73	72902375.67	489235.19	28
29	9869125	6415	.65	3164548.89	69609202.94	487271.84	29
30	9862710	6608	.67	3040857.61	66444654.05	485293.98	30
31	9856102	6899	.70	2921942.54	63403796.44	483334.97	31
32	9849203	7091	.72	2807593.52	60481853.90	481368.36	32
33	9842112	7382	.75	2697665.55	57674260.38	479424.76	33
34	9834730	7868	.80	2591963.64	54976594.83	477479.22	34
35	9826862	8451	.86	2490278.86	52384631.19	475485.35	35
36	9818411	9229	.94	2392439.66	49894352.33	473426.11	36
37	9809182	10103	1.03	2298260.42	47501912.67	471263.78	37
38	9799079	11269	1.15	2207589.73	45203652.25	468987.72	38
39	9787810	12431	1.27	2120241.34	42996062.52	466546.62	39
40	9775379	13783	1.41	2036104.35	40875821.18	463957.38	40
41	9761596	15228	1.56	1955032.22	38839716.83	461196.95	41
42	9746368	16666	1.71	1876906.14	36884684.61	458264.42	42
43	9729702	18097	1.86	1801631.43	35007778.47	455178.41	43
44	9711605	19812	2.04	1729115.81	33206147.04	451956.31	44
45	9691793	21710	2.24	1659219.57	31477031.23	448564.53	45
46	9670083	23982	2.48	1591829.67	29817811.66	444990.76	46
47	9646101	26430	2.74	1526809.52	28225981.99	441194.83	47
48	9619671	28859	3.00	1464063.56	26699172.47	437172.32	48
49	9590812	31170	3.25	1403530.17	25235108.91	432949.06	49

TABLE II   249

50	9559642	33268	3.48	1345162.23	23831578.74	428563.05	50
51	9526374	35152	3.69	1288924.04	22486416.51	424061.87	51
52	9491222	37111	3.91	1234776.88	21197492.47	419488.71	52
53	9454111	39235	4.15	1182643.13	19962715.59	414846.38	53
54	9414876	41802	4.44	1132437.60	18780072.46	410127.13	54
55	9373074	44897	4.79	1084047.68	17647634.86	405292.50	55
56	9328177	48973	5.25	1037360.67	16563587.18	400299.63	56
57	9279204	54098	5.83	992225.50	15526226.51	395062.95	57
58	9225106	60240	6.53	948500.77	14534001.01	389500.74	58
59	9164866	68736	7.50	906064.47	13585500.24	383545.24	59
60	9096130	77499	8.52	864681.77	12679435.77	377011.17	60
61	9018631	85587	9.49	824341.04	11814754.00	369927.43	61
62	8933044	93261	10.44	785113.48	10990412.96	362405.30	62
63	8839783	100066	11.32	747035.48	10205299.48	354523.97	63
64	8739717	105925	12.12	710172.18	9458264.00	346392.80	64
65	8633792	111376	12.90	674581.66	8748091.82	338116.59	65
66	8522416	117098	13.74	640268.79	8073510.16	329749.18	66
67	8405318	123894	14.74	607184.14	7433241.37	321290.24	67
68	8281424	132420	15.99	575225.26	6826057.23	312684.60	68
69	8149004	142689	17.51	544257.12	6250831.97	303840.51	69
70	8006315	154762	19.33	514160.75	5706574.85	294677.11	70
71	7851553	168416	21.45	484828.87	5192414.10	285120.65	71
72	7683137	183166	23.84	456182.00	4707585.23	275121.04	72
73	7499971	198824	26.51	428179.45	4251403.23	264663.94	73
74	7301147	215311	29.49	400796.56	3823223.78	253749.49	74
75	7085836	232770	32.85	374016.40	3422427.22	242384.59	75
76	6853066	251302	36.67	347817.26	3048410.82	230570.69	76
77	6601764	270804	41.02	322175.77	2700683.56	218306.78	77
78	6330960	291034	45.97	297077.05	2378417.79	205599.44	78
79	6039926	311237	51.53	272519.64	2081340.74	192468.07	79
80	5728689	330832	57.75	248535.31	1808821.10	178965.26	80
81	5397857	349079	64.67	225175.37	1560285.79	165164.37	81
82	5048778	364926	72.28	202512.79	1335110.42	151162.38	82
83	4683852	377425	80.58	180649.18	1132597.63	137087.73	83
84	4306427	385597	89.54	159704.29	951948.45	123090.88	84
85	3920830	388633	99.12	139811.91	792244.16	109340.97	85
86	3532197	385963	109.27	121109.37	652432.25	96015.81	86
87	3146234	377296	119.92	103726.69	531322.88	83291.18	87
88	2768938	362703	130.99	87776.73	427596.19	71330.71	88
89	2406235	342744	142.44	73345.06	339819.46	60275.07	89
90	2063491	318252	154.23	60478.64	266474.40	50229.62	90
91	1745239	290338	166.36	49183.68	205995.76	41260.76	91
92	1454901	260165	178.82	39424.50	156812.08	33393.26	92
93	1194736	228923	191.61	31129.45	117387.58	26614.53	93
94	965813	197731	204.73	24196.87	86258.13	20879.24	94
95	768082	168072	218.82	18502.92	62061.26	16115.94	95
96	600010	141080	235.13	13898.18	43558.34	12222.85	96
97	458930	117275	255.54	10221.45	29660.16	9080.67	97
98	341655	96538	282.56	7316.79	19438.71	6569.14	98
99	245117	78278	319.35	5047.46	12121.92	4581.23	99
100	166839	61674	369.66	3303.42	7074.46	3031.32	100
101	105165	46051	437.89	2002.18	3771.04	1857.14	101
102	59114	31276	529.08	1082.16	1768.86	1014.12	102
103	27838	18063	648.86	490.01	686.70	463.59	103
104	9775	7855	803.53	165.44	196.69	157.87	104
105	1920	1920	1000.00	31.25	31.25	30.04	105

TABLE II
CANADIAN INSTITUTE OF ACTUARIES
1969-75
ULTIMATE MALE MORTALITY TABLE
COMMUTATION FUNCTIONS AT 4%

AGE	l_x	d_x	1000 q_x	D_x	N_x	M_x	AGE
0	10000000	22700	2.27	10000000.00	241087795.39	727392.44	0
1	9977300	9279	.93	9593557.69	231087795.39	705565.52	1
2	9968021	5682	.57	9215995.75	221494237.70	696986.56	2
3	9962339	5479	.55	8856483.09	212278241.95	691935.28	3
4	9956860	5078	.51	8511165.66	203421758.86	687251.81	4
5	9951782	4578	.46	8179639.39	194910593.20	683078.06	5
6	9947204	3979	.40	7861419.81	186730953.81	679460.00	6
7	9943225	3778	.38	7556033.80	178869534.00	676436.29	7
8	9939447	3379	.34	7262656.57	171313500.20	673675.74	8
9	9936068	3180	.32	6980949.58	164050843.63	671301.70	9
10	9932888	3179	.32	6710303.23	157069894.05	669153.41	10
11	9929709	2979	.30	6450149.62	150359590.82	667088.39	11
12	9926730	3177	.32	6200206.27	143909441.20	665227.72	12
13	9923553	3473	.35	5959828.77	137709234.93	663319.70	13
14	9920080	4762	.48	5728599.02	131749406.16	661314.13	14
15	9915318	7040	.71	5505624.12	126020807.14	658669.96	15
16	9908278	10206	1.03	5290110.63	120515183.02	654911.25	16
17	9898072	12571	1.27	5081405.35	115225072.39	649671.76	17
18	9885501	14136	1.43	4879761.28	110143667.04	643466.36	18
19	9871365	14807	1.50	4685368.61	105263905.76	636756.81	19
20	9856558	14686	1.49	4498404.41	100578537.15	629999.09	20
21	9841872	14468	1.47	4318944.14	96080132.74	623554.38	21
22	9827404	14151	1.44	4146726.05	91761188.60	617449.53	22
23	9813253	13935	1.42	3981495.16	87614462.55	611708.10	23
24	9799318	13719	1.40	3822924.39	83632967.39	606271.76	24
25	9785599	13406	1.37	3670742.61	79810043.00	601125.53	25
26	9772193	12997	1.33	3524724.80	76139300.39	596290.13	26
27	9759196	12492	1.28	3384650.88	72614575.59	591782.56	27
28	9746704	12086	1.24	3250306.20	69229924.71	587616.76	28
29	9734618	11876	1.22	3121419.03	65979618.51	583741.37	29
30	9722742	11862	1.22	2997702.86	62858199.48	580079.78	30
31	9710880	11944	1.23	2878889.99	59860496.62	576563.17	31
32	9698936	12027	1.24	2764758.72	56981606.63	573158.44	32
33	9686909	12302	1.27	2655125.31	54216847.91	569861.91	33
34	9674607	12674	1.31	2549762.99	51561722.60	566619.69	34
35	9661933	13237	1.37	2448483.30	49011959.71	563407.90	35
36	9648696	13894	1.44	2351085.42	46563476.41	560182.46	36
37	9634802	14741	1.53	2257403.74	44212390.99	556927.14	37
38	9620061	15873	1.65	2167259.59	41954987.25	553606.21	38
39	9604188	17288	1.80	2080465.03	39787727.66	550167.79	39
40	9586900	18790	1.96	1996846.24	37707262.63	546566.89	40
41	9568110	20476	2.14	1916281.24	35710416.39	542803.67	41
42	9547634	22437	2.35	1838634.95	33794135.15	538860.51	42
43	9525197	24575	2.58	1763763.60	31955500.20	534705.89	43
44	9500622	27077	2.85	1691551.05	30191736.60	530330.40	44
45	9473545	29936	3.16	1621855.86	28500185.55	525694.86	45
46	9443609	33336	3.53	1554548.91	26878329.69	520766.98	46
47	9410273	37076	3.94	1489482.06	25323780.78	515490.47	47
48	9373197	41055	4.38	1426551.51	23834298.72	509847.70	48
49	9332142	45168	4.84	1365676.11	22407747.21	503839.67	49

TABLE II 251

50	9286974	49407	5.32	1306794.40	21042071.10	497483.96	50
51	9237567	54225	5.87	1249848.28	19735276.70	490799.16	51
52	9183342	59967	6.53	1194722.70	18485428.42	483744.67	52
53	9123375	66783	7.32	1141270.37	17290705.72	476243.22	53
54	9056592	74355	8.21	1089342.58	16149435.35	468210.45	54
55	8982237	82187	9.15	1038845.23	15060092.77	459610.88	55
56	8900050	89891	10.10	989749.85	14021247.54	450471.09	56
57	8810159	97617	11.08	942070.50	13031497.69	440859.04	57
58	8712542	105073	12.06	895800.30	12089427.19	430822.32	58
59	8607469	112758	13.10	850958.63	11193626.89	420434.51	59
60	8494711	121644	14.32	807510.63	10342668.26	409715.69	60
61	8373067	132378	15.81	765333.76	9535157.63	398596.91	61
62	8240689	145036	17.60	724263.31	8769823.87	386962.38	62
63	8095653	158918	19.63	684150.28	8045560.56	374705.63	63
64	7936735	173180	21.82	644923.44	7361410.28	361792.27	64
65	7763555	186713	24.05	606587.67	6716486.84	348261.25	65
66	7576842	199422	26.32	569230.07	6109899.17	334233.95	66
67	7377420	211289	28.64	532930.75	5540669.10	319828.09	67
68	7166131	222867	31.10	497757.34	5007738.35	305152.02	68
69	6943264	235029	33.85	463727.94	4509981.01	290267.14	69
70	6708235	248003	36.97	430798.83	4046253.07	275173.72	70
71	6460232	261316	40.45	398915.60	3615454.24	259859.68	71
72	6198916	273930	44.19	368057.20	3216538.64	244344.19	72
73	5924986	284873	48.08	338262.27	2848481.44	228705.30	73
74	5640113	293568	52.05	309614.08	2510219.17	213067.19	74
75	5346545	299888	56.09	282210.25	2200605.09	197571.59	75
76	5046657	304616	60.36	256135.63	1918394.84	182351.22	76
77	4742041	309039	65.17	231418.56	1662259.21	167485.51	77
78	4433002	313236	70.66	208016.35	1430840.65	152984.01	78
79	4119766	316439	76.81	185882.60	1222824.30	138850.90	79
80	3803327	317996	83.61	166004.78	1036941.70	125122.41	80
81	3485331	317653	91.14	145393.02	871936.92	111856.00	81
82	3167678	315311	99.54	127059.52	726543.90	99115.52	82
83	2852367	310794	108.96	110011.54	599484.38	86954.45	83
84	2541573	302854	119.16	94254.50	489472.84	75428.62	84
85	2238719	290854	129.92	79829.93	395218.34	64629.22	85
86	1947865	274766	141.06	66786.96	315388.41	54656.63	86
87	1673099	255081	152.46	55159.60	248601.45	45598.00	87
88	1418018	232569	164.01	44951.88	193441.85	37511.80	88
89	1185449	208248	175.67	36133.97	148489.87	30422.81	89
90	977201	183137	187.41	28640.68	112356.00	24319.29	90
91	794064	158217	199.25	22378.02	83715.32	19158.19	91
92	635847	134450	211.45	17230.01	61337.30	14870.87	92
93	501397	112589	224.55	13064.15	44107.29	11367.71	93
94	388808	93057	239.34	9740.95	31043.14	8546.98	94
95	295751	75967	256.86	7124.58	21302.19	6305.26	95
96	219784	61194	278.43	5090.91	14177.61	4545.62	96
97	158590	48468	305.62	3532.17	9086.70	3182.69	97
98	110122	37470	340.26	2358.34	5554.53	2144.71	98
99	72652	27930	384.44	1496.05	3196.19	1373.13	99
100	44722	19700	440.51	885.50	1700.14	820.11	100
101	25022	12789	511.10	476.38	814.64	445.05	101
102	12233	7329	599.08	223.94	338.26	210.93	102
103	4904	3470	707.58	86.32	114.32	81.92	103
104	1434	1205	840.00	24.27	28.00	23.19	104
105	229	229	1000.00	3.73	3.73	3.58	105

Answers to Even-Numbered Problems

Exercise 1.1

2. 16.8% **4.** $131.25, $129.45 **6.** $4880.38 **8.** $1020.76, $1020.48 **10.** $1102.47
12. $97.32 **14.** $22.50 **16.** 22.58% **18.** 56.44%

Exercise 1.2

2. 256 days, 253 days **4.** $284.93, $288.89, $280.55, $284.44 **6.** $62.07

Exercise 1.3

2. a) $529.41 b) $529.81 **4.** $988.31 **6.** $212.99, $158.04 **8.** a) $543.05 b) $541.57

Exercise 1.4

2. a) $414.97 b) $421.48 **4.** a) $332.46 b) $340.13

Exercise 1.5

2. $2197.80 **4.** $11.22, $688.78 **6.** a) $476.19 b) $475 **8.** 13.19% **10.** 17.48%

Exercise 1.6

2. $2040.13 **4.** $1026.15 **6.** $825.65 **8.** $1995.10 **10.** $4697.39

Exercise 2.1

A 2. $625.51, $125.51 **4.** $1695.88, $695.88 **6.** $1687.57, $887.57
8. $1221.37, $221.37 **10.** $2851.52 **12.** $8578.61 **14.** $51.10

B 4. $21 058.48, $22 071.36, $22 620.38, $23 003.87, $23 155.29, $23 194.56

Exercise 2.2

A 2. 16.99% **4.** 12.75% **6.** 5.91% **8.** 9.57% **10.** 7.70% **12.** 6.05% **14.** 9.96%
16. 11.30% **18.** 12.59% **20.** 14.44% **22.** $j_2 = 15.5\%$

B 4. $j_1 = (1+i)^{12} - 1, j_2 = 2[(1+i)^6 - 1], j_4 = 4[(1+i)^3 - 1], j_{52} = 52[(1+i)^{12/52} - 1],$
$j_{365} = 365[(1+i)^{12/365} - 1]$ **6.** 13.04% **8.** 10%

Exercise 2.3

A 2. $42.21 **4.** $192.77 **6.** $414.64 **8.** $978.85 **10.** $1112.44 **12.** $318.14
14. Payments plan better by $505.92 **16.** $3295.42

B 2. $84.43 **4.** Select proposal A with NDV = $41 793.10

Exercise 2.4

A 2. $1956.86, $1957.38 **4.** $198.99, $199.21 **6.** $1757.77 **8.** $520.93

B 4. $2111.09, $1224.25

Exercise 2.5

A **2.** 8.88%   **4.** 13.54%   **6.** 2 years 11 months 23 days
8. 2 years 6 months 12 days   **10.** 10.27%   **12.** 13.52%
14. 6 years 6 months 25 days

B **2.** 9 years 186 days   **4.** 20.780279 years   **6.** $j_1' = (1+j_1)^2 - 1$

Exercise 2.6

A **2.** $809.40   **4.** $2468.20   **6.** $186.14   **8.** $888.02   **10.** $193.61   **12.** Cash option better by $1709.88

B **2.** $3799.09

Exercise 2.7

A **2.** 345   **4.** 6.637 457 3 years   **6.** $1 095 274

B **2.** a) 76 501   b) 0 : 47 A.M.   **4.** 36 886

Exercise 3.2

A **2.** $28 760.36   **4.** a) $677.58   b) $622.78   **6.** a) $47 551.33   b) $195 652.14
8. $3040.04   **10.** $29 477.01

B **2.** $17 790.01   **4.** 14.2, 30   **6.** $\left[(1+i)^{20}s_{\overline{21}|i}-21\right]/i$

Exercise 3.3

A **2.** a) $12 126.49   b) $11 440.85   c) $11 711.81   **4.** $12 091.03   **6.** $5760.04
8. $5735.76   **10.** $955.97

B **4.** 50, 12   **6.** 17.7   **8.** a) $6305.19   b) $1090.21   c) $6878.02   d) $4149.10
10. $(1+i)^{-1} + (1+2i)^{-1} + \ldots + (1+ni)^{-1}$ **14.** NDV of BUY $= -$1 035 649.40,
NDV of LEASE $= -$1 808 658.70, the company should buy the drilling machine
16. NDV of the project $= -$380 547, the company should not proceed

Exercise 3.4

A **2.** $180.76   **4.** $107.46   **6.** $33.94   **8.** a) $1440.20   b) $1217.12   **10.** $278.03

B **2.** $215.98   **4.** $42 102.04   **6.** $103 343.97

Exercise 3.5

A **2.** 185, $382.13, $133.11   **4.** 7, $1410.28   **6.** 32, $345.58
8. 31, $438.06 on July 1, 1991

B **2.** a) 26   b) $795.22   c) $817.09   **4.** $15 115.89

Exercise 3.6

A **2.** 18.40%   **4.** 19.61%, 21.47% **6.** 19.48%

B **2.** 35.07%   **4.** 26.62%, 30.12% **6.** At $j_{12} = 21\%$ it is cheaper to borrow $642 for 3 years and buy a T.V. set

Exercise 4.1

A **2.** $62.86   **4.** $508.79 **6.** $170.51 **8.** $163.51 **10.** $858.06

B **2.** a) $4883.88 b) $5006.92 c) $2203.59

Exercise 4.2

A **2.** $2262.56   **4.** $21 555.41 **6.** $1775.36 **8.** $59.16

B **2.** a) 70, $119.59 b) $741.12

Exercise 4.3

A **2.** a) $4891.64 b) $11 434.77 **4.** 21, $193.63 on January 1, 1996 **6.** 15

B **2.** $13 332.71

Exercise 4.4

A **2.** a) $5000 b) $3205.13 **4.** $31.58 **6.** $8000 **8.** $3147.76 **10.** a) $289.33 b) $3166.40 **12.** 11%

B **4.** $34 457.12 **6.** $44 253.11

Exercise 4.5

A **2.** $571 486.98 **4.** $85 045.11 **6.** $9928.45 **8.** $3934.84

B **4.** $16 090.80 **6.** $\dfrac{1}{i\, s_{\overline{2}|i}}\left(p + \dfrac{q}{s_{\overline{2}|i}}\right)$

Exercise 5.2

A **2.** $3076.01   **4.** a) $81.65 b) $1025 **6.** a) $1043.14 b) $246.95 **8.** $225.23

Exercise 5.3

A **2.** $4909.13 **4.** a) $11 469.92 b) $11 386.59 c) $11 629.86 **6.** 102.2009 m^3 **8.** $638.98   **10.** a) $5889.23   b) $6051.19   c) $6046.96   **12.** $20 034.80 **14.** $8795.06

Exercise 5.4

A **2.** $64.86 **4.** $389.33

B **2.** a) $6759.36 b) $8943.03 **4.** $111 185.28 **6.** $100.98

Exercise 5.5

A **2.** $493.95   **4.** $752.22   **6.** a) $685.36   b) $668.69   c) $661.33   **8.** $214.41
10. Take $70 000 mortgage.

B **2.** 17.52%   **4.** $1307.90

Exercise 6.1

A **2.** a) $68.92   b) $66.27   **4.** $155.30   **6.** $147.29   **8.** Final Payment = $898.57
10. $2163.43   **12.** $173.33   **14.** $733.19, $61.33

B **2.** $146.41   **4.** $1516.06   **6.** 8%   **8.** a) $274.75   b) .00820707   c) 10%
d) $29 738.47   e) 22 years

Exercise 6.2

A **2.** $6315.68   **4.** $128.21   **6.** $1238.33, $81.50   **8.** $25 007.07

B **2.** Pay $95 000 and get a $65 000 mortgage at $j_2 = 15\%$ **4.** 11 years 10 months,
$481.25   **6.** a) 9 years 2 months, $272.58 b) 7 years 3 months, $91.86

Exercise 6.3

A **2.** $10.60   **4.** No   **6.** $41 426.84

B **2.** $125.26   **4.** mortgage B

Exercise 6.4

A **2.** $91.68   **4.** $1309.19   **6.** $6.20   **8.** Yes, $4.36 monthly

B **2.** a) R = $311.63 b) I_{10} = $296.54, P_{10} = $15.09 c) Sum-of-digits: $17 477.61,
Amortization: $16 351.36   d) No

Exercise 6.5

A **2.** $13 977.78   **4.** $262.24, $5541.40   **6.** $140.32, $8447.25   **8.** $113.53

Exercise 6.6

A **2.** $4839.39, $53 589.38   **4.** a) $202 453.74   b) $1 665 536.70   **6.** $1681.45

B **2.** 3 years 7 months, $95.61

Exercise 6.7

A **2.** Sinking-Fund by $1090.80   **4.** 19.56%   **6.** 16.63%

B **2.** 13.05%   **4.** 15.24%

Exercise 7.3

A **2.** $923.14   **4.** $5857.95   **6.** $1873.36   **8.** $5379.48   **10.** $918.18, $1252.31

B **2.** $471.80   **4.** $846.28

Exercise 7.4

A **2.** a) $5881.19   b) $4292.72

B **2.** a) $1107.63   b) $903.75

Exercise 7.5

A **2.** $4761.67   **4.** $995.24   **6.** $10 281.31

B **2.** $10.86   **4.** a) $1051.69   b) $1087.54   **6.** $1081

Exercise 7.6

A **2.** $550.89   **4.** $9662.17   **6.** $1774.41

B **2.** a) $853.71   b) $1165.27

Exercise 7.7

A **2.** $1061.03   **4.** $1161.58   **6.** $116\frac{3}{4}$ **8.** $114\frac{5}{8}$ **10.** a) $849.54   b) $853.79   c) i) $1088.33   ii) $691.34

B **2.** $70.63

Exercise 7.8

A **2.** 11.02%   **4.** 12.82%   **6.** 10.87%   **8.** 13.18%   **10.** a) 9.87%   b) 9.86%   **12.** 10.20%   **14.** 10.66%

B **2.** a) 11.42%   b) 10.98%   c) 10.62%   d) 12.88%   **4.** a) $746.78   b) $1095.02   c) 21.14%   **6.** a) 11.5%   b) $5\frac{1}{2}$ years   **8.** 76%

Exercise 7.9

A **2.** $104 940.53

B **2.** $29 861 132.81

Exercise 8.2

A **2.** $4500   **4.** $D_6 = $8000, $B_6 = $12 000

Exercise 8.3

A **4.** $B_5 = $10 628.82, $R_6 = $1062.88   **6.** 7 years

Exercise 8.4

A 4. $12 500, $7500

Exercise 8.5

A 4. $70 000

Exercise 8.6

A 2. D = $3588.83 **4.** D_6 = $4353.64, B_6 = $15 646.36 **6.** D_6 = $4191.95, B_6 = $15 808.05

Exercise 8.8

A 2. Cement block = $202 696.29 **4.** A = $30 185.77 **6.** $1346.70
8. $194 243.05

B 4. $4290.97

Exercise 9.2

A 2. a) $\dfrac{103}{2704}$ b) $\dfrac{2}{13}$ c) $\dfrac{1}{26}$ d) $\dfrac{1}{26}$ e) $\dfrac{1}{52}$ f) $\dfrac{8}{16\ 575}$ **4.** a) $\dfrac{1}{18}$ b) $\dfrac{1}{9}$ c) $\dfrac{13}{18}$ d) $\dfrac{1}{2}$ e) $\dfrac{5}{12}$
f) $\dfrac{1}{324}$ **6.** a) $\dfrac{3}{8}$ b) $\dfrac{1}{16}$ c) $\dfrac{1}{8}$ d) $\dfrac{1}{8}$ **8.** a) $\dfrac{18}{125}$ b) $\dfrac{54}{125}$ c) $\dfrac{117}{125}$ **10.** a) .225 b) .225

B 2. $\dfrac{1}{6}$

Exercise 9.3

A 2. $4.12 **4.** Yes **6.** 54¢ **8.** $3000

B 2. $\dfrac{1960}{64}$ **4.** 21, $41.04

Exercise 9.4

A 2. a) $1565.22 b) 27.7% **4.** 4.16% **6.** $14 613.24 **8.** $599.69

B 2. 21.38% **4.** 1.18%

Exercise 10.2

A 2. a) .8878 b) .5774 c) .1294 d) .1255 e) .2946 f) .0034 **4.** 627

B 2. a) 1000 b) 409 c) 9 d) .7647 e) .1124 f) .25
4. a) $\dfrac{\ell_0}{100}$ b) $1 - \dfrac{1}{100-x}$ c) $\dfrac{1}{100-x}$

Exercise 10.3

A 2. a) $3062.97 b) $1612.52 **4.** a) $2776.32 b) $2668.58

Exercise 10.4

A 4. $25 616.18 **6.** a) $6652.12 b) $5812.78 **8.** a) $483.82 b) $508.42
10. $419 709.85 **12.** female: $7711.19; male: $9031.32

B 2. $50 730.74

Exercise 10.5

A 2. a) $369.59, b) $312.03 **4.** $4577.57 **6.** $18 136.13

B 4. 6% **6.** .045 128 41

Exercise 10.6

A 2. a) $23.52 b) $21.67 **4.** a) $539.87 b) $875.02 **6.** male: $442.36, female: $350.01

B 4. 5 years

Appendix 1 Exercises

2. a) $a^{5/6}$ b) $a^{1/6}$ c) a^{-4} d) 1 e) 1/5 f) $a^{-3/4}b^{1/2}$

4. a) .360 369 99 b) .830 901 09 c) 4175.8848 d) 24.182 169 e) 367.682 63
f) 7.493 367 6 g) 4.817 537 9 h) 6.749 870 4 **6.** a) 40.297 582 b) 4.816 952 1
c) 24.937 286 d) 21.227 628 e) 21.521 506 f) 3.969 362 3 g) 4.988 439 2
h) 6.321 928 1 i) 3.380 239 j) 5.209 453 4

Appendix 2 Exercises

2. a) 45 150 b) 10 100 c) 12 051 d) 19 668 **4.** a) 29, 155 b) 13, 7 c) 2, 132
d) 10, 70/9 e) 8, −8 **6.** $812.50 **8.** 400 cm **10.** 12.85% **12.** a) $5 368 709.20
b) $10 737 418 c) $10.23, $10 475.52, $10 726 932.25 **14.** a) .75 b) 3.3̇ c) 5
d) $1/i$

Appendix 3 Exercises

2. a) 3.97% b) 1.21% c) 7.77% d) 2.25% **4.** 11.22% **6.** 17.29%

Appendix 4 Exercises

2. a) $4020.53 b) $3973.22 c) $3972.68 **4.** a) June 22, 1987 b) June 22, 1987
6. a) $19 135.85, $7858.06 b) $19 243.26, $7823.72 **8.** a) $1265.24 b) $1269.90
10. a) $7804.35 b) $2058.21

INDEX

Depreciation and Related Topics

30. $R_k = \dfrac{C-S}{n}$

Yearly depreciation, straight-line method

31. $R_k = B_{k-1}d$

Yearly depreciation, constant-percentage method

32. $B_k = C(1-d)^k$

Book value, constant-percentage method

33. $R_k = \dfrac{n-k+1}{s}(C-S)$

Yearly depreciation, sum-of-digits method

34. $D_k = \left(\dfrac{C-S}{s_{\overline{n}|i}}\right)s_{\overline{k}|i}$

Accumulated depreciation, sinking-fund method

35. $K = C + \dfrac{C-S}{i\, s_{\overline{n}|i}} + \dfrac{M}{i}$

Capitalized cost

Contingent Payments

36. $P(E_1 \text{ or } E_2 \text{ or } E_3 \ldots \text{ or } E_n)$
$= P(E_1) + P(E_2) + \ldots + P(E_n)$

Probability of any one of n mutually exclusive events

37. $P(E_1 \text{ and } E_2 \text{ and} \ldots \text{ and } E_n)$
$= P(E_1) \cdot P(E_2) \cdot \ldots \cdot P(E_n)$

Probability of all of a set of n independent events

38. $pS(1+i)^{-n}$

Discounted value of the expectation pS where p is the probability of receiving sum S

Life Annuities and Life Insurance

39. $_np_x = 1 - {}_nq_x = \dfrac{l_{x+n}}{l_x}$

Probability an individual aged x survives n years

40. $_nq_x = 1 - {}_np_x = \dfrac{l_x - l_{x+n}}{l_x}$

Probability an individual aged x dies before $x+n$

41. $_nE_x = (1+i)^{-n}\dfrac{l_{x+n}}{l_x} = (1+i)^{-n}{}_np_x$

n-year pure endowment

42. $_nE_x = \dfrac{D_{x+n}}{D_x}$

n-year pure endowment using commutation symbols

43. $a_x = \dfrac{D_{x+1} + D_{x+2} + \ldots}{D_x} = \dfrac{N_{x+1}}{D_x}$

Discounted value of a \$1 ordinary life annuity

44. $\ddot{a}_x = \dfrac{D_x + D_{x+1} + D_{x+2} + \ldots}{D_x} = \dfrac{N_x}{D_x}$

Discounted value of a \$1 life annuity due

45. $_n|a_x = \dfrac{N_{x+n+1}}{D_x}$

Discounted value of a \$1 ordinary n-year deferred life annuity